SINGING THE PSYCHE–UNITING THOUGHT AND FEELING THROUGH THE VOICE

Voice Movement Therapy in Practice

Edited by

ANNE M. BROWNELL, DEIRDRE A. BROWNELL, AND GINA HOLLOWAY MULDER

Foreword by Shawn McNiff

(With 20 Other Contributors)

CHARLES C THOMAS • PUBLISHER, LTD.
Springfield, Illinois • USA

Published and Distributed Throughout the World by

CHARLES C THOMAS • PUBLISHER, LTD.
2600 South First Street
Springfield, Illinois 62704

ISBN 978-0-398-09424-9 (paper)
ISBN 978-0-398-09425-6 (ebook)

Library of Congress Catalog Card Number: 2023036012 (print)
2023036013 (ebook)

With THOMAS BOOKS *careful attention is given to all details of manufacturing and design. It is the Publisher's desire to present books that are satisfactory as to their physical qualities and artistic possibilities and appropriate for their particular use.* THOMAS BOOKS *will be true to those laws of quality that assure a good name and good will.*

Printed in the United States of America
MX-C-1

Library of Congress Cataloging-in-Publication Data

Names: Brownell, Anne M., editor. | Brownell, Deirdre A., editor. | Mulder, Gina Holloway, editor.
Title: Singing the psyche : uniting thought and feeling through the voice: voice movement therapy in practice / edited by Anne M. Brownell, Deirdre A., Brownell, and Gina Holloway Mulder (with 20 other contributors).
Description: Springfield, Illinois, U.S.A. : Charles C Thomas, Publisher, Ltd., [2024] | Includes bibliographical references and index.
Identifiers: LCCN 2023036012 (print) | LCCN 2023036013 (ebook) | ISBN 9780398094249 (paperback) | ISBN 9780398094256 (ebook)
Subjects: LCSH: Arts--Therapeutic use. | Voice--Therapeutic use. Singing--Therapeutic use. | Movement therapy. | Self-actualization (Psychology) | Communication--Psychological aspects.
Classification: lCC RC489.A72 S56 2024 (print) | LCC RC489.A72 (ebook) DDC 616.89/1656--dc23/eng/20230905
LC record available at https://lccn.loc.gov/2023036012
LC ebook record available at https://lccn.loc.gov/2023036013

CONTRIBUTORS

EDITORS

Anne Brownell, MA, RSA, VMT-R (USA), Director of the Norma Canner Foundation for Voice Movement Therapy

Deirdre Brownell, MA, PhD, VMT-R (USA), with a focus on Hidden Learning Disabilities

Gina Holloway Mulder, MA, BADA (hons.), PGDA, MAP, VMT-R (South Africa) with a focus on Devised Theatre and corporate staff trainings

OTHER

Sebastiana Black, Dip. BACP, MSCT, VMT-R, professional singer/songwriter (UK/ Czechia)

Gertruida Dowse, BA (hons), SW, Dip. Play Therapy, Dip. Marriage Counselling and Preparation, VMT-R, Mediator (South Africa)

Anna Grabner, MA, VMT-R (Portugal/Austria) with a focus on pre-and post-partum birth counseling through the voice

Carol Grimes, VMT-R, professional singer/songwriter (UK), poet, blogger, choir director, teacher, and author of memoir, The Singer's Tale

Eva Haidl, VMT-R, professional singer/songwriter (Austria), singing teacher

Melanie Harrold, VMT-R, professional singer/songwriter, Certified Body-oriented Psychotherapist (UK)

Christine Isherwood, MA, VMT-R, REAT (USA/UK) Director Voice Movement Therapy Training Program and Student Supervisor

Boniswa Kamba, Rev., VMT-R, (South Africa) founder and director Voice Movement Therapy Eastern Cape (VMTEC)

Irene Kessler, MA, PhD VMT-R, opera singer (USA), with a focus on eating disorders

Anne Maarman, VMT-R, Pastoral Counselor, former nurse, (South Africa) with a focus on HIV, long covid, stroke, and abuse

Sophie Martin, MA, VMT-R (Australia) with a focus on indigenous people and those mentally at risk

Nokubonga Cordelia Mathole, VMT-R (South Africa), Founder and Director Voice Movement Therapy South Africa (VMTSA), with a focus on victims of abuse and teenagers with addictions

Julia Norton, professional singer/songwriter, actor, voice-over artist and voice coach (USA/UK)

Veronica Phillips, BACP, VMT-R (London, UK) with a focus on emotional. developmental trauma, attachment needs, and generational and ancestral constellation work

Mali Sastri, VMT-R (USA) professional singer/songwriter and teacher

Tracy Starreveld, VMT-R (UK), theatrical creator and performer, certified proofreader and copyeditor

Ben van Rensburg, VMTR, Certified Addictions Counsellor (South Africa)

Lerina van Rensburg, SDCSA, VMT-R P. (South Africa) postgraduate Education Certificate, Director of Ovie-Vibz Music School, Founder and Director of the Voice Box venue for VMT and related activities

Trish Watts, Dip Music Ed., VMT-R professional singer/songwriter, (Australia) first Director/Member Interplay Australia and the Threshold Choir

Helen White, CPRP, VMT-R (Canada), focusing on mental illness in day treatment clinics

(*Note:* See also Contributor Biographies with contact details at end of book.)

ACKNOWLEDGMENTS

We would like to thank the following people without whom this book would quite likely never have been finished!

Veronica Phillips who kept insisting that it MUST happen.

Nathan Bean who was a very helpful reader in several places and in working on the book.

Alistair Mulder who rescued many photographs

Erika Hahn who researched and checked endnotes and text references and so many other things.

Jo Walters who prepared the text and photos for submission to the Publisher

and A special thanks to Shaun McNiff for his unfailing encouragement, support, and inspiration

FOREWORD

Shaun McNiff

Singing the Psyche elucidates, renews, and advances one of the most important traditions in art healing–spontaneous and full-bodied vocal expression. It is essential reading for those engaging the voice and models how to undertake in-depth and truly art-based exploration of a particular form of creative expression within the larger and interdependent community of art healing.

A Legacy of Artistic Inquiry

In recent years I have been exhorting colleagues to get back to the empirical basis of what we do and focus research and training on how the various kinds of artistic expression further well-being, both examining and perfecting their unique healing qualities while also identifying what they share–all of which is illustrated by this book's presentation of the history and current use of therapeutic voicework together with a comprehensive integration with bodily movement. The fecund terrain generates a wealth of new directions for research and practice.

For example, how does spontaneous, natural, and unscripted vocal expression "vibrate into being" as the authors suggest in the opening page of the preface, and then as posited in their title, bond "thought and feeling?"

Or as Alfred Wolfsohn who originated this vocal discipline, asked–is there a unique connection between the voice and the soul and what does it share with all artistic expression? Is there what Nietzsche called magic in extremes, with vocal expression of the "unbeautiful" enlarging perception of beauty? Does this generate a sense of participation in a *vox humana*–universal human voice, and bonds with all creatures and nature?

And Paul Newham, who connected voicework to professional therapeutic practice, asks whether the vocal tones of our speech are more expressive than words? How can we more completely realize the full range of tonality and what are the impacts? Do these processes relate to other art forms, to movement and the body which is a primary focus of this book and the community of practice the authors have created?

In addition to advancing the depth and power of vocal expression, I greatly respect how the creators of therapeutic voicework developed and furthered understanding of this medium through direct inquiry via their own art. As contrasted to self-absorption, artistic inquiry engages the maker of art as a necessary participant in firsthand exploration of the empirical processes and outcomes of creative expression. Like C. G. Jung (2009), both Wolfsohn and Newham shaped methods through personal vocal experimentation which engaged their conflicts and struggles.

Roy Hart, a student of Wolfsohn, established a theatre group that continued to research and develop his mentor's work with an expanded focus on community, involving people from throughout the world. The Roy Hart Theatre created an environment where actors explored their expression to bring greater "authenticity to the characters they presented." As my experience affirms, community practice and discovery often augment artistic inquiry, further creative energy and depth, and provide a context aligned with the fullness of our lives. I consistently see how effective group environments function as slipstreams of imagination, in which we go farther and deeper together, and where we often vicariously experience as much transformation and healing when witnessing others as through our individual expressions.

Communities of Creation

My personal connection to voice and movement is longstanding and intertwined with many people and processes explored in this book. It might be helpful to briefly describe this history to give a sense of how communities of practice emerge and merge with worldwide continuities to create new forms such as the innovations described here.

Fifty years ago, I established the first graduate program to integrate all forms of artistic expression in therapy. *The Arts and Psychotherapy* (1981) published by Charles C Thomas brought our research and the development of total art expression to an international audience which included Paul Newham. He wrote with appreciation for the inclusion of sound dialogues and enactments, improvisation, therapeutic opera, and other features of vocal and acoustic expression. These processes often emerged from the experimental theatre traditions permeating our Cambridge, Massachusetts community, which at that time differed significantly from more siloed and institutional music therapy. There was an immediate kinship with Paul who went on to write *The Singing Cure* (1993) and *Therapeutic Voicework* (1998), and our close connections are sustained and expanded by this book.

When starting a graduate program in 1974, Norma Canner was the first faculty member I recruited (Brownell & Wilcoxen, 1998). As a mature and respected

New England artist she brought full bodied action—movement, enactment, voice, play—also teaching us how to work in large groups with all of art.

Anne Brownell joined the graduate program toward the end of the first decade and studies with Norma laid the groundwork for her lifework integrating voice and movement—and this book, synchronically published by Charles C. Thomas. It was a time of peak creativity and imagination when many of the processes described here were being investigated. The community was large, heterogeneous, and interdisciplinary with no prevailing doctrines or ideologies other than a shared commitment to a primary emphasis on artistic and imaginative inquiry involving the complete spectrum of art forms including voice and the body (McNiff 2023).

Transcendent and Sacred Dimensions

In addition to closely studying world traditions of art healing, I have always encouraged the creation of personal methods, in keeping with the making of art, and especially eschewing the pre-existing and stock systems so common today. As Norma Canner said to her students, quoted here by Anne—the work is "New, always new."

In my studio groups voice has been the most challenging, new, and transformative mode of expression. Arguably there is nothing more tangible, innate, and visceral in human expression than full-bodied vocalization. We sometimes work exclusively with the voice and often use vocal improvisation together with body movement to respond to paintings, sculpture, and other artworks. There is reliably plenty of resistance and fear, all stoked by past experiences. As demonstrated by the authors, play and various preparatory exercises, alone and with others, are fundamental and a core part of the overall discipline with great significance in themselves.

The work is always focused on presence—supporting, witnessing, holding, and responding to the expressions of each person and moment, all of which reliably evoke a distinct and transcendent sense of the sacred, maybe attributable to the vital energy generated by what Wolfsohn called "dared expression." The welcoming of "unlovely," strange, and thoroughly authentic sounds and bodily movements, often while being encouraged to explore the full range of vocalization in the absence of a planned sequence, is not the norm in our experience and will predictably generate resistance, feelings of vulnerability and incompetence, fear of the unknown, all which become part of the creative mix and a source of expressive energy, making the integration of voice and movement one of the most impactful forms of artistic expression in therapy, and requiring the careful experimentation, study, unconditional support, and supervision documented here.

Forever Unique but Larger than Ourselves

To ease performance pressure and affirm natural expression I emphasize the primacy of breath, slowing down and not doing too much, taking pauses, simplicity, and repetition as the path to depth. Try to put ego aside, or tucked away safely in a pocket as you work, together with all concepts suggesting what to do and not do and focus on letting Psyche sing and move freely through you, and with your responses and sensibilities being necessary partners in expressions made together with so many 'others,' both within you and in your environment. We never create alone.

Among the many admirable features of *Singing the Psyche* is the emphasis placed on studying the community of practice from which the work emanates. The authors describe their unique creations while affirming that we participate in a process larger than ourselves, accessible streams generated by so many more inside and outside the strain of a particular discipline.

I trust that this book by Anne Brownell, Deirdre Brownell, and Gina Holloway Mulder together with their many international contributors, will continue to encourage artistic experimentation realizing the broad range of the "singing body," from the "stirring...guts" to the tender lullabies of these pages. We are invited as Jung said, to imagine the dream further, perfecting the integral relationship of voice and movement as an opening to all of life.

References

Brownell, I., & Wilcoxen, W. (Directors). (1998). *A time to dance: The life and work of Norma Canner* [Motion picture]. USA: Bushy Theater Inc.

Jung, C. G., & Shamdasani, S. (Ed.). (2009). *The red book, Liber novus* (M. Kyburz & J. Peck, Trans.). New York: W W Norton & Co.

McNiff, S. (1981). *The arts and psychotherapy.* Springfield, IL: Charles C Thomas.

McNiff, S. (2023). An integral community of art and healing: Transcending silos in the ecological era. *Journal of Applied Arts and Health,* 14(1), 13-25, https://doi.org/10.1386/jaah_00124_1

Newham, P. (1993) *The singing cure: An introduction to voice movement therapy.* Boston: Shambhala Publications.

Newham, P. (1998). *Therapeutic voicework: Principles and practices for use of singing as a therapy.* London: Jessica Kingsley Publishers.

WHAT OTHERS ARE SAYING ABOUT THIS BOOK

This comprehensive volume will enhance therapists', educators', caregivers', and parents' understanding of the intricacies of using our voices for expression and communication. Through practical guidelines woven together with current interdisciplinary practices, theory and research, Anne Brownell and colleagues creatively decode the language of vocal expression. The importance of embodied expression through "voicedances" which contain the intense feelings within the structure of song ring out through the text. A wide array of vibrant clinical applications with many populations greatly illuminates the voice/movement therapy model. Over and over we learn how the voice and movement are the points of entry for relationships and intervention.

Susan Loman, MA, NCC
KMP Profiler
Former Director Dance Movement Therapy Program
Department of Applied Psychology
Antioch New England Graduate School (USA)

In the beginning was the Voice. *"I have a dream" resounded MLK from the Lincoln Memorial sixty years ago. The ritualized voice can move mountains. As powerful as music and language are in cultural evolution, it is the human voice that sustains connection and authenticity. This book is a true gift to global culture and has the potential to inspire a renaissance of interest and practice in the creative use of expressive voice and movement for therapy, coaching, cultural change and transformative learning. May this book travel far, like a song that heals and blesses, voicing the sacred commitments and compassionate inquiry of its passionate authors!*

Aftab Omer, PhD.
President, Meridian University (USA)

Implicit in Voice Movement Therapy is the notion that wholeness and health are innate. Reclaiming what has been lost through life's vicissitudes is the essence of healing, not repairing what is broken. We reclaim parts of ourselves that could not be experienced, fully owned, or connected to before our loss of innocence. VMT is about reclaiming, integrating, and embodying the self you were before you felt unsafe, inadequate, or unworthy.

Leonard Carr
Clinical Psychologist (South Africa)

As an artist and writer, I and my friends in many different disciplines are well acquainted with creative blocks both in art and in life. When a friend suggested that I may be interested in reviewing a book on Voice Movement Therapy, I said, "Well, OK," expecting to read an informative, but unexciting tome. To my delight, this book clearly explains the basic principles of VMT in the first chapter, then presents five chapters of case studies by VMT practitioners who work with human situations worldwide read like stories. It is a great read and so interesting that I called a musician friend and read one of the stories aloud!

Jo Walters, MA, MFA
University of California, Berkeley
Visual Artist and Writer

PREFACE: TAKING IT TO THE FLOOR

The voice, our original and primary instrument for expression and communication, is the only instrument in which the player and the played upon are contained within the same organic form. The voice box, that tiny structure which houses the vocal cords through which air passes to produce the sounds we utter when we speak or sing is – by its location in the throat – perfectly positioned and – by its ability to express thoughts and feelings at the same time – ably equipped to join head and heart, mind and body, psyche and soma.

However, the words we say and the way we say them often do not match. The message and the messenger may be at cross purposes, the meaning conveyed by the words undercut by the feeling tones in which they are uttered. This can cause misunderstandings both within the self and between the people with whom we wish to communicate. Often it is necessary to go beyond words to achieve a congruence between thought and feeling that will enable us to find the full expression of our wants, needs, and ideas in order to communicate them more effectively to others. One way to do this is to use our actively sounding physical voice and the sensations it produces to literally vibrate into being a bridge between what we are aware of and what we are not, between the conscious and the unconscious mind.

A basic principle of Voice Movement Therapy (VMT), an Expressive Arts Therapy which had its beginnings in the early 1990s with founder Paul Newham's first Professional Practitioner Training in the United Kingdom and the publication of his first book, The Singing Cure, is that when an individual is in deep internal conflict or when a discussion between two people or among a group reaches an impasse, it is taken to the floor to be sounded and moved. Both unplanned vocalization, often beginning without words, and spontaneous movement within a witnessed safe space establish a kind of expressive discharge which can further meaningful contact and break down barriers both within an individual and between people in high states of emotion, frequently concluding with the creation of a song by the person or persons involved which can act as a containing structure. Because VMT begins with the affective tones of the voice rather than its cognitive content and is dedicated to actualizing feeling states through voice and movement, it is to the physicalization of sensation, that place beyond words, that we go.

Conflicts or misunderstandings between individuals or between members of a group, organization or culture often cannot be solved by words alone and the act of "doing" something creatively in voice and movement while up, moving and sounding can be a catalyst for transformation. This kind of work may be intense or it may be gentle, but it always involves action—voicing, moving, sounding, singing. Whether in the context of a therapeutic session or a singing lesson, it is guided by an exploration of the describable qualities of a person's voice in relation to their habitual body movement and posture as a way of breaking down old patterns, both muscular and mental, to open up different perspectives and responses to reveal new ways to enter into the living moment with more freedom. The whole self, body and soul, needs to be engaged, for when talk has broken down – when words are not enough – we know we can "take it to the floor" to be worked out in sound and movement, prioritizing the affective self, the whole feeling body, not just the cognitive mind. Often the right words, the ones that need to be spoken and received, will follow.

The purpose of this book is to provide a basic understanding of Voice Movement Therapy and how it uses both spontaneous vocalization and the creation and performance of song to increase expressive and communicative skills and to strengthen one's sense of self. Chapter One presents an overview of its history and core principles and Chapters Two through Six provide articles by various practitioners to give the reader a sense of how they work, both with clients and students and for themselves, in ways that follow a basic set of principles, yet differ widely in accordance with the nature of the individual or group, the practitioner, and the cultural and socio-economic conditions of each encounter. Some of these articles reaffirm the past work of founder Paul Newham who, taking inspiration from the Alfred Wolfsohn/Roy Hart tradition of extended voicework, established a more specifically psychotherapeutically oriented vocal discipline and worked with individuals with special needs, students of voice, and performers. Other articles show how this work has been extended to new populations: those experiencing mental and physical illness and addiction, displacement and alienation, hidden disabilities, seeking formal mediation and conflict resolution, struggling with fierce emotions, and looking for guidance for transitioning into motherhood pre- and post-partum. Several others illustrate how the therapeutic component of the voice lesson has been broadened and deepened. In all instances, the aim of the editors has been to present a framework within which VMT Practitioners may tell their own stories in their own voices. The final chapter addresses ways in which we see this work going forward.

Anne, Deirdre, and Gina

CONTENTS

Page

Foreword by Shaun McNiff ... xi
Preface ... xvii

Chapter One: The Voice Unchained – Anne Brownell ... 3
Being Present ... 3
Theory into Practice ... 12
The Core Principles of VMT ... 17

Chapter Two: Psychology and Soul Work ... 33
Introduction: The Role of Song in Psychotherapy – Anne Brownell ... 33
VMT and Trauma: Upheaval, Abuse and Alienation. ... 36
The Hidden Voices of Cambodia – Trish Watts ... 36
VMT with the Displaced: Having a Voice when all Else Fails – Sophie Martin ... 45
Healing Hand Project: Kenya 2009 ... 46
Working on Nauru ... 50
Sylvie Sings Her Mouth to Life – Christine Isherwood ... 53
Meanwood: A Group Session: Pyramid of Arts, Leeds, UK – Carol Grimes ... 62
Mr. Handy: A Policeman in Trouble – Boniswa Kamba ... 69
Psychosis, Self-Harm and Addiction: Models of Engagement ... 78
Voice Studio: A Place to Let It Out – Helen White ... 78
Changing Lives: How I Use VMT in Mediation and Conflict – Gertruida Dowse ... 83
A Reflection on a Pilot Study Undertaken on the Efficacy of a Voice Movement Therapy Program with Young Women Aged 18-24 Who Self-Harm – Sophie Martin ... 90
Facilitating Change–Body, Mind and Soul: The Role of VMT in an Addictions Treatment Clinic – Ben Van Rensburg ... 94

Group One: Basic VMT Principles Applied to Working with Addiction 96
Group Two: Body Maps 101
Sounding our Way to Wholeness: Linking the Metaphorical and Physical Voice with Women Experiencing Eating Disorders – Irene Kessler 103

Chapter Three: Channels of the Voice: Affect and the Brain 108
Introduction, My Body, My Enemy: A Life in Recovery – Deirdre Brownell 108
Individuals Experiencing Conditions Present from Birth 113
Dillan: Opening Up Channels of Communication with the Person Trapped Inside – Deirdre Brownell 113
Samuel: A Story of Healing Trauma with VMT – Sebastiana Black 124
Interviews with an Expressive Movement Educator, Three Young Men with Significant Physical and Cognitive Delays, and Their Home Providers – Deirdre Brownell 128
Individuals Experiencing Conditions Brought on by Emotional or Physical Trauma 134
A Case of Selective Mutism and the Work of Tracy Starreveld 134
My Favorite Patient and How I Became the Singing Pastor: A Case Study of a Patient Recovering From a Stroke – Anne Ross Maarman 138
Singing for Joy: Creating Community and Sustaining Function in a Choir with Parkinson's Disease – Carol Grimes 146

Chapter Four: Trusting Our Voice to Support Us in Times of Transition and Stress 151
Introduction – Gina Holloway Mulder 151
Subpersonalities and the Voice – Christine Isherwood 154
Swallowed by Grief, Saved by Voice – Trish Watts 161
Vocal Components Used in Grief Work 163
Key VMT Apporaches 166
Letting the Darkness Sing Itself: Working Creatively with the Shadow to Reveal Buried Rage – Julia Norton 171
Two Case Studies 173
The Voice in Motherhood: How I Use VMT to Support Women in Their Transitional Journey – Anna Grabner 178
Soul Song Deep from the Bone: The Power of Story in VMT – Veronica Phillips 190

Chapter Five: Nurturing the Soul in the Performing Arts ... 201
Introduction – Gina Holloway Mulder ... 201
The Artist-Practitioner: How VMT Informed Me as a Singer, Songwriter and Performer – Mali Sastri ... 203
Singing the Breathing Body: Being Present to Your Own Performance – Melanie Harrold ... 209
Developing the Singer's Vocal Creativity – Lerina Van Rensburg. ... 219
Experiencing the Joy of Singing through the Container of Song – Eva Haidl ... 226
Voice as Archive in Devising Theatre – Gina Holloway Mulder ... 235
Discovering the Roots of Vocal Limitations ... 241
Working with a Dream Image ... 242

Chapter Six: Towards a Living Harmony: Voice Movement Therapy as an Instrument for Social Change in South Africa ... 246
Introduction ... 246
Indaba ... 246
The Reality on the Ground ... 248
Where Our Work is Needed Most ... 249
Steps Toward Change ... 266
A Rainbow Nation Needs Songbirds ... 268

Conclusion: Looking Forward: Growing and Grounding in Uncertain Times – Anne Brownell, Deirdre Brownell, and Gina Holloway Mulder ... 271

Glossary ... 277
Contributors ... 285
Name Index ... 295
Subject Index ... 297

SINGING THE PSYCHE–
UNITING THOUGHT AND
FEELING THROUGH THE VOICE

Chapter One

THE VOICE UNCHAINED[1]

Anne Brownell

BEING PRESENT

"Singers at their moment of greatest affect keep on singing and that is the singing cure." These words were spoken to me by Paul Newham on a transatlantic phone call in 1996 when I was attending my dying mother in hospital on Cape Cod. She was experiencing great pain and fear, and the only thing that seemed to soothe her and alleviate her suffering was my daughter's and my bedside singing, ranging from peaceful to dramatic, depending on what we sensed from her at any given moment and what we knew she loved. Paul, founder of the creative/therapeutic discipline of Voice Movement Therapy, and I, a former student now assisting him, had been scheduled to conduct our first workshops together in the USA over the coming weeks, but that clearly was not going to happen. He had called to see if there was anything he could do and even offered to fly over from London to lend support. I said not to worry because, when I told him how hard it was to carry on singing in this situation, he had in that one sentence given me what I needed: an understanding that what Deirdre and I were doing was a useful and compassionate way to stay fully present with Mother as she went through this process of dying. To be able to express our love for her while sufficiently containing our intense feelings within the structure of song so as not to overwhelm or be overwhelmed–to keep connected in this way–was a great gift and a great learning. There would be time for the unstructured sounds of our own mourning later on.

For me, to this day, the crux of Voice Movement Therapy is contained in that sentence and everything else follows...

Feeling and thought, expression and containment, bringing one's voice into the outside world and experiencing it being heard, if only by one person; the use of breath and sound, melody and rhythm to increase one's sense of self and presence with others, and how to facilitate this process—that is what this book is about. Whether the practitioner is working with clients in therapy needing to express themselves more fully in order to contact and bring forth repressed or hidden memories; with various kinds of performers such as singers, actors, teachers, preachers, or others seeking a more durable, flexible, and versatile instrument to use in their profession; with individuals with language delays or other neurological, mental or physical conditions which are impeding their ability to express themselves and communicate effectively; or simply with those seeking to become more expressive and clear in what they are able to convey through the voice–change of some kind is the order of the day. As Alexander Lowen once notably said, "It is the limitation of our being which makes us sad and angry and constitutes our fear.... If one wishes to change character, it is not enough to talk about feelings; they must be experienced and expressed."[2] Whether one's expressive facility, in singing or speaking, has been hampered by conditions from birth or by physical or emotional trauma experienced later in life, it is the investigation and subsequent embodiment in song of one's issues—with all their shadows and their lights—that we employ to move us toward the fuller expression and depth of communication we desire.

How can this be done through the sounding voice in speech or song? How can I express what I feel and "get it out" in a way that is satisfactory and fulfilling for me? Alternatively, how can I do this so that what I am trying to convey can be not only heard but received? How can I "have my voice" and, at the same time, make contact with another person or persons in the most meaningful way for everyone concerned? In short, when do I simply need to express my feelings and when does that expression need to be, in some way, crafted? To be able to recognize and work with these distinctions is, to me, at the heart of Voice Movement Therapy and what it has to offer. But how did this way of work develop and how does it relate to therapy? For Alfred Wolfsohn, pioneer of a new kind of voicework begun in the aftermath of World War I, it was a means of survival, a redemption of soul.

The Beauty of the Dared Expression and the Right to Make Unlovely Sounds

> The beauty of the dared expression is that only in encountering and overcoming the dark side of oneself can one achieve true artistic expression, uniting all aspects of the self in order to feel whole and encounter others. (Alfred Wolfsohn)[3]

The same could be said of therapy.

Wolfsohn, a German Jew serving in the trenches of World War I, had the experience of hearing severely and mortally wounded soldiers calling, crying, and screaming out their fear and anguish in an incredible array of pitches and sounds. In the thick and deadly muck which was the reality of trench warfare, a tunnel collapsed and Wolfsohn had to choose whether to try to crawl back to rescue a dying comrade—and risk almost certain death himself—or continue his crawl toward the living.

He chose life, but after being sent home from the front, found he could not rid himself of constant auditory hallucinations; he still heard his comrades screaming. Discovering that neither doctors nor therapists nor teachers of singing could relieve him of the voices that were driving him mad, he, like many other pioneers of new forms of alternative therapies, sought to cure himself. While in hospital for what was becoming known as shell shock, he came across the writings of Sigmund Freud and Freud's conviction that the words spoken by the patient to describe deep trauma must be imbued with the feeling and energy of the original event if they are to be effective. Thus began Wolfsohn's quest to find a way, through the quality and intention of the sounding voice, to locate, release, and exorcise the hallucinatory voices that haunted him. After his initial stage of recovery and months of trying to cope with his haunted inner landscape, Wolfsohn had two revelations:

Journeying to Italy for an encounter with nature in a more gentle climate that his doctor hoped would restore him to health, he climbed Mt. Vesuvius where, "He became aware of the intense warmth of the sun, of life singing in him. It was his first real discovery of music within himself and it was life affirming.... In this moment he felt restored, saved, and even more than that, he actually felt happy."[4] For a little while, the accusing voices of those he felt he had abandoned receded and he came to realize that his possibility of recovery ultimately depended on his ability to cure himself.

Wolfsohn knew that he needed to sing, to give voice in an amplified way to the sounds trapped inside him, but the vocal instruction available in his day had no place for the sounds of voices in extremis, only those that were aesthetically pleasing. When one of his teachers, for a few moments, allowed him to shout out the agony and desperation he almost constantly felt inside, he experienced some relief and the realization that "a new way to sing was needed."[5] As he saw it, a voice needed the freedom to express all aspects of the human condition and so must be "unchained" from notions of flawless technique and smooth delivery and allowed not only to express wondrous and pleasant things, but to moan and groan, weep and wail in a manner not found in the churches, concert halls, or salons of his day. The quality and range of sounds must extend, in his words, "from Bel Canto to Hell Canto" if they were to empower a wounded soul and serve as a means of healing.[6] Thus he became acquainted with the notion of *enantiodromia,* the process by which something pushed to its extreme becomes its opposite—for example, "I laughed until I cried—and this opened up for him a whole spectrum of human sound with which to express the totality of the soul. As a result, he developed his concept of the *vox humana*, a universal voice potentially available to anyone, male or female, and capable of astonishing range and multiple timbres with which to express experiences and emotions in sounds both beautiful and unbeautiful, but congruent with the subject matter.

Several years after making a partial recovery and just prior to the beginning of World War II, Wolfsohn fled to England where he was interred as an "enemy alien" and then volunteered for the Pioneer Corps which had a unit for individuals categorized as "aliens and other undesirables" in which he served until 1943 when he was invalided out. The following year, he received permission from the Home Office to give singing lessons in London.

Figure 1. Alfred Wolfsohn teaching Marita Gunther, London, 1952. Roy Hart Theater, Anduze, France.

By this time, he was avidly reading the works of Carl Jung and coming to believe that psychological concepts such as *archetype, shadow, anima* and *animus* were not only distinguishable parts of the human psyche, but could be made audible through the voice. His own struggles to become a singer had led him to conclude that voice problems could not be solved by vocal techniques or medical treatments alone, but needed the perception, engagement and self-understanding of the psyche, or soul. He discovered further that the sounds made by the human voice could give audible form to inner aspects of the mind such as are visually represented in dreams. According to Jung, images represent the way that unconscious mental memories interact with conscious events to influence how we deal with our lives and nothing can be conceived of by the mind without first being represented in an image.[7] Wolfsohn sought to apply this understanding to sound.

Images come in different forms: visual, kinetic, acoustic. From a painting, sculpture, or mosaic we receive physically stationary images, while from dance or film what predominates is an image that moves. Acoustic images are conveyed by sounds that travel through the air, and although fleeting, can be recognized as universal or archetypal: the siren wail of a newborn baby, the evil laughter of a wicked witch, the deep growling signifying danger of an angry dog, a big cat, or a rock-crushing giant; or it may be very personal like the habitual way a particular individual laughs in joy or sobs in grief, or simply says "Good morning." Jung was the first person to document how the speech of people suffering from schizophrenia disintegrates into apparent meaninglessness while still retaining the shape of the speech patterns–the acoustic form or image–but he did not pursue this revelation further, being increasingly attracted to visual exploration. He is thought of by many as the first Art Therapist, although it might be more accurate to recognize him as the first Expressive Arts Therapist, since his process of Active Imagination can be applied to most arts modalities, including singing.

It was Wolfsohn's belief that not only could Jung's ideas on individuation and the fundamental wholeness we possess at birth be heard in the voice, but that these sounds were rooted in an impulse to act. As Wolfsohn said,

> The baby is without any inhibitions, possessed by one drive only: to still [his] hunger. [He] does not actually cry; he cries out... but as he learns to speak and become socialized, he loses much of his natural expression and becomes inhibited... By the time he is an adult, he has forgotten how to scream.[8]

Wolfsohn further believed that by accessing the full range of one's voice, one could not only achieve the natural kind of expressive wholeness found in a healthy baby, but also a return to the totality and wisdom of the soul. If the voice was to be employed as an expression of the true nature of the psyche in its entirety, it would have to connect not only with images of the delightful and comforting aspects of life, but with the shadow and one's most deeply buried images of darkness. It would need to yell, sob, scream, growl, howl, and give expression to all the animalistic, primal, pre-verbal sounds which are an inherent part of every person's evolutionary history as well as their individual developmental progression from child to adult.

Rescued by his discoveries from, as he put it, "the unyielding presence of death" to a "new and intensified life," Wolfsohn determined through his work on himself and with his students that without restoring faith in themselves by correcting their psychic damage, no progress could be made.[9] It was necessary to practice this kind of dared expression, for in so doing, the whole voice, and thus the whole person, could be present. "When I speak of singing," he said, "I do not see it as an artistic exercise, but as a possibility and means to know oneself and to transform that knowledge into conscious life."[10] Offering a service "somewhere between singing lessons and therapy to others who, like himself, sensed that their key to personal liberation and development lay in freeing their voice,[11] he was fascinated by what he described as "The psyche's ability to reveal itself expressively through the form most appropriate to the individual."[12] For him, and for those who found their way to his studio, that form was singing.

Figure 2. Christine Isherwood working with client. VMT Training Center, Martha's Vineyard MA, 2013. Photo by John FX O'Toole

Wolfsohn also believed that the teacher of the "unchained voice" must not only lead students to the spiritual sources of their voice, but to its bodily roots, as well. The voice must be grounded in the body.

Creative Action as an Agent of Transformation

> The most important thing in making art is courage, to take the risk to let surface those parts of you that you'd rather not let people see and to make those parts of you the center of your work.(Richard Foreman)[13]

> I realized that my voice was not embodied... For singing as we practice it is literally the resurrection or redemption of the body. The capacity to hold the voice in identification with the body makes biological reality of the concept 'I am...' Because I had learned to hold myself in sound, I found I was able to hold others as a leader in concentration. Concentration is the summoning of the whole body in one effort. True concentration is prayer.... My life's work has been to give bodily expression to the totality of myself. This means bringing an enormous unconscious territory into consciousness. (Roy Hart)[14]

After Wolfsohn's death in 1962, his student, actor Roy Hart, became the leader of a band of Wolfsohn's most committed followers and took the work into theatre, establishing first a troupe and then a community in Malerargues, France to explore and expand many of Wolfsohn's ideas and techniques, taking them into group work, as well, and creating a tightly bonded community. Whereas Wolfsohn had prioritized a kind of therapeutic voicework, Hart created an intensive program for actors where they practiced how to experience their own emotional truths more deeply in order to add further meaning and authenticity to the characters they presented in performance. As one who had experienced his own tribulations–displacement from his South African homeland, alienation from his peers because of his Jewishness, and a resulting sense of profound aloneness–he sought to combine the personal with the professional so that they might inform and support each other.

Like Wolfsohn, Hart viewed the voice as an expression of the soul and believed that he could, through his own form of discipline and training, teach individuals to persevere in dealing with complex real-life issues. Although he continued to use Wolfsohn's practice of giving individual singing lessons conducted from the piano, group work of a highly movement-oriented, athletically muscular and interpretive nature became increasingly important for his ensemble. Likewise, his own performances were dramatic in their use of the body combined with the voice which he considered to be "the muscle of the soul." Thus, he established his own form of the work which continues to this day as theatre-based personal exploration and application through an artistic process akin to psychotherapy but without a specifically therapeutic framework.

The Singing Cure

> There is, thankfully, a unifying epistemology which underlies all the arts therapies. This is the inherent belief that the necessarily intangible and insensible fabric of the self is represented adequately by the quality and mode of expression ...The orientation of an arts therapist may be perceived as reflecting that particular dimension he or she is most engaged and proficient in accessing and developing... The aim of an arts therapist using voice should, therefore, be to facilitate the amplification of unconscious material and its psychological integration through the sounds of the voice, with due attendance to its physiological as well as its psychological dimensions. (Paul Newham)[15]

In 1962 when Wolfsohn died, Englishman Paul Newham was born, and as one of the first babies conceived by artificial insemination who survived, and discovering in his late teens that the man he thought was his father was not, Newham "adopted" Wolfsohn as his spiritual father and made it his mission to develop his concept of the extended voice further. After studying theatre and psychology at the Jungian-influenced Drama Center in London and then working for a time as an orderly in a hospital, he became a singing teacher and vocal coach, providing workshops in hospitals and schools for people with cognitive and physical disabilities. Subsequently, he trained as a director and performer at Dartington College of the Arts where he was introduced to the work of Wolfsohn by Enrique Pardo, a former student of Hart who had become a key player not only at Malerargues, but in conducting workshops around the world.

Like Wolfsohn, Newham also had a fraught and stormy relationship with the sounding voice. As a child, he was often exposed to fighting between his parents. Escaping upstairs, he and his sister would listen to what he later called "the savage opera" through water glasses held to the wooden floor to try to hear what was happening below. They had to infer this by the sounds, since the words were not audible. So began Newham's fascination with the tones of voice that underlie words and create their own meaning, a fascination which in the kind of voicework he ultimately developed prioritized the tones sounded over the words uttered.

Sensitized like Wolfsohn to vocal extremes and incongruities, Newham became acutely aware of the discrepancy, the disconnection, between what was often happening in real life and how it was more politely expressed in speech and song. Having during his studies come in contact with the work and theories of Antonin Artaud, Peter Brook, Jerzy Grotowski, Hart and other members of a mid-20th century movement seeking to create "theatre without words," Newham noted the contrast with most English and European theatre which prioritized precise diction and formal declamation over more emotionally based components of language. He was also dissatisfied with the way that classical music, and opera especially, took socially reprehensible subjects such as greed, lust and murder and rendered them in exquisite tones and forms according to a carefully established set of rules, many of which he understood to have been developed because of the Early Church's insistence on banishing what it considered to be disharmonious and discordant sounds in music.

In beginning to trace the expressive and healing use of the voice in the West, Newham discovered it had travelled a long way from its cathartic purpose in ancient Greek tragedy and become increasingly more limited than, for example, the extended range and multi-timbered virtuosity of the bel canto singing style developed in Italy in the 17th. century. In the Western world's endeavors to banish so-called "ugly" vocal sounds, it seemed to him that the act of giving voice had been restricted and diminished. The right of an individual, not only to express feelings spontaneously but to tell his own story and sing his own song–including matters society might consider "unspeakable"–had been lost. Becoming ever more interested in the right to give voice in one's own way, he sought further understanding by investigating the role of the voice in psychotherapy.

Early on, Newham had become acquainted, not only with psychotherapeutic and psychoanalytic theory and practice, most notably in the works of Freud, Jung, and Wilhelm Reich, but also with the writings of Dance Movement Therapists Penny Lewis Bernstein, Joan Chodorow and others who described their therapeutic work as employing the same kind of intense physicality he had encountered in his work with Hart's former pupil Pardo and in contact improvisation with Steve Paxton at Dartington College. Coming into contact with more of the Creative Arts Therapies, he became increasingly aware of the way expressive and performance-oriented activities can provide a forum for the manifestation of psychological dynamics.[16] As with the visual arts, performing arts modalities such as dance, drama and music are extremely effective in eliciting and working with unconscious material. The prioritizing of these different expressive arts modalities within an avowedly therapeutic context takes us into a realm of creative action that can move us beyond words to contact what is lost, hidden or repressed which then may be experienced and expressed in creative activity that is often transformational. In an early audio recording project, Newham created what he called "Voicedances" based on the notion of allowing the voice to "dance" in response to spontaneous expressions of the psyche in a way similar to that employed in movement by the Dance Therapists.[17]

For many of us, words–even words physically accompanied by the creation of images, be they visual, kinetic or acoustic–are not sufficient. If we are not talkers by nature, we often have difficulty finding the words to utter what for us may seem "unspeakable." Alternatively, if we are facile with words, they can become our best defense for rationalizing behavior or deflecting the need to express feelings with which we do not wish to engage. We pay a price for this avoidance because such feelings remain locked in our bodies as well as our minds and can provoke physical as well as mental illness.

Working to expand the range and breadth of their voices, Wolfsohn had poked and prodded the bodies of his singing students, seeking to break their muscular rigidity. Beginning first with patients with special needs in hospitals and clinics and then increasingly with others presenting a variety of issues and vocal abilities, Newham developed a kind of bodywork akin to that of Reich, only done while the client is moving and sounding.

As Newham discovered, it was Reich who created the first body-oriented psychotherapy based on his realization that a person who represses memories as a way of dealing with what seem like overwhelming negative feelings renders himself incapable of discharging them because of the way his body muscles have rigidified to hold them in, a process he called *armouring.*[18] Within a combination of specifically devised postures and movements, Reich encouraged his patients to sob, shout, scream and vocally amplify their feelings to help break through these holding patterns in order to release trapped energy in a full body discharge he named *streaming.* His student Alexander Lowen, founder of Bioenergetics, also believed that the energy processes of the body are as important as those of the mind and require physical action to release them, observing further that the qualities heard in a client's speaking voice–the patterns of inflection, tone and rhythm–mirror the nature of that person's underlying emotional dynamics. As Newham later told his students, "Everything we need can be heard in the voice." He combined the very basic kind of hands-on manipulation and compression Wolfsohn had employed with Reich's more evolved methods, but in a way that used massage, manipulation and compression while clients were actively moving and sounding, in order to open up and extend their breathing and help them out of the places where they were "stuck" which, according to Newham, "often manifests itself in a rigidity and singularity of vocal timbre" indicating an over-identification with one aspect of the total self.[18]

THEORY INTO PRACTICE

The past cannot be changed, but by expressing the apparently unlovely material which may emerge from that past through the use of voice, movement and imagery and then giving form to it through the personal creation and witnessed performance of a song, a dance, or an enactment, one's relationship to it can change. In the words of Shaun McNiff, "The principal value of the Creative Arts Therapies is their ability to bring about disciplined and profound therapeutic transformation at the primary level of the senses."[19] This is precisely what Newham sought to do through his emphasis on the practice of repetition and rehearsal of the songs that both clients and students created, in tandem with movement and hands-on bodywork, in order to bring psyche and soma into congruence.

The relatively new discipline of Voice Movement Therapy, dating from Newham's first practitioner training in 1992 and the subsequent publication of his first book, *The Singing Cure: An Introduction to Voice Movement Therapy* in 1993,[20] is, to our knowledge, the first Expressive Therapy which not only prioritizes the voice as its main modality, but has developed a neutral language to use when working with individuals and groups and also when describing and disseminating its core principles, including to people of other cultures. The practice of these principles (described later in this chapter) seeks to bring body and voice into alignment and clarify conflicts within the self by enabling one to become aware of and resolve clashing modes of expression between different aspects of the same person.

Whether or not the kind of mind/body split articulated by René Descartes as early as the 1600s is a product of scientific and cultural misunderstanding of the fundamental unity of the biologically and emotionally entwined psyche and soma—a point of view popularized in the 1980s by Ken Dychtwald in his book *Bodymind*[21] and further examined by Antonio Damasio in a series of works, most notably *Descartes' Error: Emotion, Reason and the Human Brain*[22]—or whether the psyche, like facets of a diamond, is made up of an endless array of subpersonalities which may or may not coalesce around a central one—as investigated by James Hillman and others—it is a concept with which we still grapple. However, there are two areas of note where this concept of a split or separation between mind and body seems quite useful: in traumatized people who "numb out" their bodies with accompanying degrees of mental dissociation in order to survive, and in certain discrepancies between thought and feeling particularly noticeable in speech and song.

The sounding voice can be viewed as having two main channels of communication: the words we say that convey the cognitive meaning, and the tones of voice that convey the affective message which expresses how we feel about what we say or sing. For example, the way one utters a greeting such as "I am delighted to see you" can, by the tone of voice in which it is uttered, be imbued with warmth or dripping with sarcasm. Both Wolfsohn and Hart sought to unite such discrepancies of thought and feeling through the singing voice, to make them congruent, because when the cognitive message and the affective feeling tones and qualities of voice are "in sync," that is when we express ourselves most fully and communicate most effectively. Otherwise, the telling of the most traumatic event or the singing of the most heartfelt song may become detached from the feeling self and incapable of achieving any kind of personal change or catharsis, or of making contact with secrets stored in the unconscious, or moving an audience in performance. The images we use to tell our tales must be imbued with life and passion, so that, in Newham's words, "When we listen to a voice, we are affected by the elusive power of images which seem to stimulate many senses."[23]

From a purely physiological point of view, we are also literally moved by the voice through the action of what are known as the Pacinian corpuscles. Located deep within the skin, these clusters of cells actually move when stimulated by sound, the upper layers whirling around and essentially causing the cells to expand and contract, open and close, sending signals to the brain about changes in the surrounding environment.[24] How does a dog or cat know that a train is coming long before we do? It can feel the vibration of the tracks through these natural biological receptors embedded in the soles of its feet. In the human body, buried deep in mesenteric tissue in the skin (our largest organ) and mostly around the joints, these structures are tuned to react to pressure, touch, and vibration. This includes vibration made by the sound of a human voice so that when we say we are moved by a singer's or a speaker's voice, it is not just a figure of speech; it is the result of an actual physiological process.

How appropriate, both physically and imagistically, that the voice box is located in the throat, in the neck which serves as the bridge between body and brain. By working vocally in conjunction with movement, we can reunite them, or at least alleviate that separation which is becoming quite pronounced in the 21st century due to our increasing reliance on virtual connection through digital media rather than actual face-to-face contact. The difference might be compared to that of an "old-time" film image captured whole on silver paper, in contrast to a digital image which, no matter how precise, is basically an arrangement of electronically generated "dots" on a screen. This is even more abstracted from the living reality it was designed to represent than the image embedded in its entirety on silver paper which, in itself, is a step removed from an in-the-moment enactment in the actual physical world. In similar fashion when capturing the auditory image, analog sound recording is represented in waves, while digital recording is represented by contiguous blocks or columns.

Expressing oneself in song as compared to speaking in abstract symbols such as words takes Freud's observation about the necessity of imbuing one's personal story with the affect of the original occurrence to achieve catharsis, to what might be seen as its logical conclusion. Words may be substituted for deeds, as Freud encouraged his patients to do. However, for many of us, it is the deeds themselves, the expressive and creative actions we undertake when telling our story and singing our song that lead us by a more direct route to the unconscious by engaging our senses as well as our thoughts.

You do not have to be a singer, or even able to carry a tune, to participate in Voice Movement Therapy; you need only be willing to endeavor to give physical voice to the issues that are troubling you within a form that amplifies feeling. Singing requires working with various vocal elements on a continuum: establishing a rhythm, or not, slowing down and sustaining phrases or speeding them up in staccato bursts, making variations in pitch that are low or high or somewhere in between; in short, doing all the things one can do in speech but in a way that amplifies one's affective sensory investment and response, and at the same time clearly illustrates any disconnection between the two main vocal channels and makes them more accessible to engagement through voice, movement, and enactment. It was this need to amplify the tones of voice, to take Freud's "talking cure" further, that led to the experiments of Wolfsohn, and Hart and the other prime movers of Theatre Without Words, and caused Newham to apply it to therapeutic practice.

In response to the interpretative and creative work of the 1940's through 1960's, Newham felt the need to synthesize and create from diverse disciplines a true psychotherapy of singing. In *The Singing Cure*, he traced lines of development in the use of the voice for expression and communication in song and speech, in theatre and music, and in the development of body-centered psychotherapy, noting where the shadow of the unspoken remained unsounded.

As Newham described it, the evolution of human speech from a kind of vocal and gestural song and dance—a proto-language which could not express an event, object, element or feeling without embodying it—became increasingly abstracted in a system in which vocal symbols alone, without the direct sensory engagement of the speaker, could convey a message. This advance created great clarity in the articulation of ideas and the ability to reason and describe; it also created a separation, or disconnection, between the natural world and the sensing and responding bodily self. For example, to say, "A lion is coming" is very different from enacting the lion in sound and movement where, to convey the message effectively, vocalization, movement and gesture must all work together.

In *The Singing Cure* and subsequent writings, Newham further described how this evolutionary process is paralleled by the universal developmental acquisition of speech and language by children who gradually have to give up spontaneous sound-making in which body and voice are synchronous, in order to learn the rules of the abstract code of words needed to function in an increasingly complex society. To do this, they have to let go of the sensuous oral delight of unrestricted sound-making and the compelling power of vocalizing without words to command attention from parents and others. They also become subject to judgment: a word is the right word or it is wrong, its pronunciation is correct or it is not. Many vocal problems have their beginning during this formative time and it plays a part in the dilemma of singers who can vocalize freely but become tense and constricted the moment they must add words. Especially within the fixed structure of a song which not only has to be sung correctly but also has to be conveyed in a way that matches its meaning, this may come too close to the feelings a given performer may not want to express fully for fear of exposure or loss of emotional control.

In the evolution of singing from the primordial voice-dances of our ancestors and the cathartic use of the voice in ancient Greek tragedy to promote healing in both audience and actor, Newham stressed that the voice had lost much of both its curative and its expressive potential. The triumph of an aesthetics of "good" and "bad," acceptable and unacceptable, partially determined by the Christian church's quest for light and more light to banish all shadows, and a classical style of singing that evolved to favor a clear and seamless vocal line produced in one of four basic categories determined by pitch range and certain qualities of sound, were widespread in the Western world.

A problem with banishing shadows in favor of light, of smoothing out ragged edges to make seamlessly beautiful sound, is that it can sometimes impoverish itself and limit the presence of contraries by which to change and grow. As Wolfsohn said, "The psychological concept of the shadow corresponds to the aesthetic concept of ugliness. The beauty of the dared expression is that only in encountering and overcoming the dark side of oneself can one express oneself truly, uniting all aspects of the self in order to feel whole and encounter others."[25] After all, a sunset is not a sunset without its "illumination" by the coming darkness. In the second half of *The Singing Cure*, Newham outlined his system for a true psychotherapy of the voice which could work with extremes on a continuum.

Although I personally mistrust the words "method" and "system," ever mindful of how they can become too rigidly adhered to and cut off new avenues of individual creativity in the process, Newham, to his enduring credit, synthesized many elements of Wolfsohn's therapeutic voicework with aspects of the early psychotherapeutic work of both Freud and Jung, the theater work of Hart, of otolaryngologist Paul Moses in creating categories of auditorily recognizable constituents of vocal sound with which to view both physical and psychological conditions, and with the work of Reich in body-centered psychotherapy, to create what practitioners of VMT believe is the first Expressive Arts Therapy in which the voice is the main modality.

It employs neutral, non-subjective terms for discussing qualities of voice across a broad spectrum and is based not only on creative and therapeutic process, but also upon a knowledge of acoustics and the anatomy and physiology of the vocal system in relation to the rest of the body. So how does it work?

THE CORE PRINCIPLES OF VOICE MOVEMENT THERAPY

> The human voice reflects both physical and psychic states and has the ability to convey cognitive meaning and affective expression simultaneously. It is our primary instrument of communication for both ideas and feelings and can move us with words and beyond words. It is the only instrument wherein player and played upon are contained within the same organic form and therefore can achieve its fullest expression when firmly grounded in the body. It has two main channels of communication: the words we say, the symbols we use to convey our cognitive message, and the way we say them, the tones and qualities of voice which express the affective or feeling message underlying what we speak or sing. It is ideally suited for contacting non-verbal or pre-verbal body memories and calling forth the shadows, even the "unspeakables," through acoustic as well as visual and kinetic imagery.[26]

Due to the dual nature of vocalized language, singing combines both the linear and the spatial–both sides of the brain–and so is uniquely positioned to unearth and work with unconscious material. If you say, for example, "John is going to the store," you are stating a fact, giving us a piece of information: John is planning to go to the store or is on his way. It is the left hemisphere of the brain that organizes these particulars into a clear linear progression, word following word to convey the factual message. If, however, you say, "John IS going to the store," you have added another element, a point of view. It is clear from the way the person says it that it is important for John to go to the store and that the speaker is invested in his doing so. The more forcefully intoned IS has added a feeling element to this statement which is conveyed by the vibrational quality of the way that word is articulated and sounded. It is the right hemisphere that deals with spatial matters; vibration, in spreading into and taking up space, becomes an element of spatial function.

To take this point further: if one has a stroke which affects the speech centers on the left side of the brain, a person can still make a sentence if he is capable of articulating words, and in such a case, the natural prosody of speech can be substituted for the missing sequential capability in order to provide a melodic line, a kind of vibrational scaffolding on which to carry the meaning forward.[27] The tones of voice in whatever the person is able to say—single words, for instance, like go, store, John—are capable of conveying immense feeling. If, however, an individual experiences a right brain stroke, the tonal quality of the voice will be flat, devoid of the contours which are considered to be the melody or prosody of speech in English and in most major Western languages, and a different kind of treatment must be found.

The general significance of this, from a Voice Movement Therapy point of view, is that, in facilitating and reawakening the client's ability to strengthen the relationship between the abstract symbol of the word and the physical reality of the sounding voice, the connection between thought and sensation can be more firmly established. One way to do this is to reactivate the pre-verbal or non-verbal sensate body memory of events through acoustic images.

To this end, the voice in therapy can act as a powerful change agent and VMT operates through specific and demonstrable principles which can be divided into two categories: vocal and non-vocal.

The Vocal Principles

The Metaphor of the Continuous, Flexible Vocal Tube

The first of these is the metaphor of a Vocal Tube imaginatively conceived of as originating at the lips, travelling through the mouth, down the neck into the chest, and descending through the length of the torso to the pelvic floor. Of course, it doesn't really do that, air entering at both the nose and mouth, and food and liquid at the mouth, all travelling down the throat which is composed of the pharynx and the larynx located behind the nose and mouth which leads to just above the vocal box where they split into two tubes, the inspired air travelling through the trachea or windpipe into the bronchial tubes and then the lungs, and the swallowed food entering the esophagus and passing into the stomach. The image is relevant, however, because in order to fill the lungs fully, the viscera drop down to make room for a fuller inflation of the lower parts of the lobes, causing the feeling and appearance of breathing into one's abdomen and even lower down into the pelvic floor. It is useful because it places the relatively small vocal tube, extending in reality from the lips to the trachea, within the context of the whole body and reminds us that events in all parts of the body affect our ability to vocalize. For example, it is not just a sore throat which may make it difficult to speak or sing; a strained shoulder or a stiff hip can pull us out of alignment and restrict our breathing, thereby affecting our ability to produce sound.

The Ten Vocal Components

The second vocal principle is a consideration of the voice in terms of ten identified and named Vocal Components existing on a continuum, or spectrum, of least to most and potentially common to all voices. These are in some cases the same and in some cases different from the terms used in classical singing because what they are meant to indicate and the way they are used may be similar but have a different focus.

The First Eight Vocal Components.

1. **Pitch**, ranging from the lowest to the highest sounds a particular voice can produce;

2. **Pitch Fluctuation**, determined by the amount and consistency of the oscillation of sound around notes (commonly known as *vibrato*), but also relevant to other vocal systems which "slide" or fluctuate or even add different intervals such as quartertones between the notes of the tempered Western scale;

3. **Loudness**, or dynamics, on a spectrum between the quietest to the loudest sounds a particular voice can make;

4. **Nasality, or Violin** (also known as Forward Pharyngeal Resonance) by which we mean, not the sound produced by blocking the nasal passages as when you have a cold, thereby preventing the sound vibrations from reaching the upper sinus cavities, but rather by the concentrated vibration of sound within those cavities which produces a penetrating quality that allows the voice to soar over other competing sounds the way a violin can soar over an orchestra.

5. **Free Air**, sometimes referred to as breathiness, most often associated with sexiness (think of actress Marilyn Monroe) or exhaustion, and also with very old people or children.

6. **Glottal Attack or Engagement**, produced by the vocal cords hitting together, either forcefully as in attempting to sound like a machine gun–ack, ack, ack, ack, ack–or gently in a soft utterance as in the act of gulping.

7. **Disruption**, in which the production of individual notes may be separated by empty space, sometimes over a series of notes, which when properly executed can be done without incurring injury and which is distinct from the term dysphonia used by Speech Language Pathologists to indicate damage to the vocal cords.

8. **Articulation** of speech through the use of vowels and consonants which may, according to its spectrum or continuum, be more or less precisely pronounced.

Vocal Components Nine and Ten. The final two vocal components are placed at the end of this list because they differ the most from classical usage.

9. **Timbre**, or tonal quality, is determined by the size and shape of the vocal tube at any given moment and consists, in this terminology, of Flute (commonly thought of as head voice), Clarinet (commonly thought of as chest voice), and Saxophone (commonly thought of as a deeper version of chest voice and coming more from the abdomen and pelvic floor).

To produce these timbral sounds, particular Facial and Mouth Configurations are used as follows: for Flute, hold your index finger in front of your lips and blow on it as if you are cooling soup; for clarinet, hold the palm of your hand in front of your mouth and blow "hah, hah," as if you are steaming up reading classes to wipe them; for saxophone, open your mouth wide in a deep yawn.

10. **Register** which includes what we call Modal and Falsetto (most commonly used), but which also includes Vocal Fry or Creak which is produced by disrupted sounds made so far at the bottom of our range, the pitch is almost indiscernible—it is most commonly heard in people who are exhausted, ill, or very old—and Whistle which consists of very high sounds such as might be produced classically by a coloratura and are often used by both indigenous and rock and pop singers, for example: the last phrase in each chorus of "Lovin' You" as sung by Minnie Riperton,[28] and a group of male vocalists exploring the whistle register.[29]

It is important to note here that the subcategories of Timbre (Flute, Clarinet, Saxophone) and the two main Registers (Modal and Falsetto) differ from classical usage because, in line with Wolfsohn's concept of the *vox humana*, VMT practitioners believe they can be applied to all voices, rather than viewing high voices as comprised of sopranos singing primarily and tenors frequently in falsetto; and the low voices of baritones and basses singing primarily and contraltos sometimes in modal.

According to the definitions above, any voice may be described using a combination of some of these ingredients which are non-subjective, or neutral, with the exception of the term Falsetto, from false, which harks back to a time when only men were allowed to perform in public which necessitated taking on women's roles and pitching their voices generally higher and in a more stylized manner than normal, or assigning these roles to young boys, or in centuries past, to castrati. Two examples of purely neutral vocal descriptions would be: "She spoke quietly in a low pitch, with a great deal of free air" and "When he sang, his voice had very little pitch fluctuation and was primarily in modal with a predominance of violin."

VMT also employs what is known as "the break," a disruption in the seamless delivery of notes and phrases over the vocal *passagio* (the passage, or break, between two registers which in classical music is referred to as *blending*) in order to create a bridge both to produce a particular auditory effect and to further the expansion of pitch range. Exploring the edge between Modal and

Falsetto by going back and forth between two registers in a manner similar to yodeling has been found to be effective in breaking into new vocal territory by discovering notes not formerly found in the person's range. This kind of deliberate disruption is very different from the unintended absence of pitch, often referred to as "white noise" in speaking or singing that is indicative of some kind of actual physical damage or impediment to the vocal cords.

In addition to these practical components, which have their own psychological uses within the context of other sounds present at a particular time in a particular voice, their relation to both body and psyche in other ways is often addressed through the non-vocal components particular to VMT. In all, especially the first two, they are considered three dimensionally, as is appropriate for VMT voicework and the bodily action of breathing from which they spring.

The Non-Vocal Principles

1. **Convex and Concave**, or the idea that all bodily movement is on a continuum between these two poles, grows out of the positions undergone by the torso in the act of breathing, which can directly affect the voice. To explain: when one breathes in, the chest rises and expands while the lungs inflate and the ribcage expands through the action of the intercostal muscles, while the diaphragm flattens down to make more space for the lungs to fill to their maximum capacity. Conversely, when one breathes out and the lungs deflate to greater or lesser degree, the chest lowers, the ribcage contracts, and the diaphragm rises to help push the air out, taking on the shape of a shallow inverted bowl. Such information is useful, for example, when looking for healthy movement between the two poles and seeing, instead, a client whose chest is rigidly held either in concave or convex, often indicating in the former case anything from a physical weakness to a fear of engaging with the world and in the latter a learned military posture or perhaps a need for protection when confronting the external environment, reflecting the notion that "The best defense is a good offence."

2. **The idea of a Sphere or Globe** in which one can locate oneself kinesthetically, energetically and emotionally, and which is conceived of as an invisible, portable three-dimensional container, a kind of "psychological womb." If asked, people will often determine the dimensions of a sphere, or bubble, around their body by how far they can reach with any part in any direction–up, down, ahead, behind, with arms, legs, chest, back–defining with these gestures what is known as their reach space. You can also create your sphere by amplifying your breath with the motions of your body:

Standing in whatever spot you choose for the center, take in a deep breath and notice that it causes your chest to protrude, becoming convex, and your back to hollow, becoming concave. With your next breath, take a step forward, spread yours arms wide and imagine you are arching forward to meet the inwardly curved surface of your sphere. Then, with your next breath, step back, stretch your arms out and reach them backwards, curving your shoulders and back to meet the opposite inwardly curved surface. Then take another deep breath and notice how your ribcage expands. Focusing your breath on your right side, raise your right arm over your head and allow that outwardly arched side to curve as if to meet the inwardly curving inside of your sphere. Then do the same with your left arm and side. Then do these motions from front to side to back to the other side, describing a circle, breathing as you turn. Explore moving like this on the breath, synchronizing breathing and physically moving in a circle, first one way and then the other. This kind of movement is known in Voice Movement Therapy as the Spiral of Maximum Stretch. It will give you an amazing stretch and open up your body for better breathing if you keep really stretching and don't allow your body to collapse down or in on itself.

The second step is to determine the size of your sphere according to how you are feeling energetically and emotionally. It may at any given time feel as if it extends only inches from your body, or it may feel bigger than the whole room. You may want to be at the front of your sphere, giving out all you have to the world and feeling energetic and strong, or you may feel as if you are teetering on the brink or holding on for dear life; conversely, you may find yourself in the back of your sphere, gathering in all you need while finding safety and a retreat from engagement. You may wish to reach up and out to the stars from the very front, or stay safely back and flat on the ground as if in a sheltering cave. There are so many possibilities.

This may sound complicated, but if you synchronize your movements with deep, slow breaths and notice how breathing into your chest inclines your body forward into convex while your back becomes concave, and breathing out inclines your body back and, while your chest becomes concave, your back is now convex, you will experience how these movements evolve from the act of breathing. If you allow yourself to feel what you are feeling in that moment, you will know how you wish to be in your sphere and at the same time how you want to relate to your external environment, including the people you encounter.

3. **The Human-Primate Interface**, specifically the place where the cognitive and instinctual meet, which marks the first stage in a descent to a more primal or early developmental state of being for the purpose of achieving a more open vocal tube (see number 4 below).

4. **The Animal Postures** designated as Homo Erectus, Primate, and Feline-Canine, encourage on a physical level specific postural and vocal configurations and states of moving and breathing which increase tidal airflow

by expanding the vocal tube, and serve on a psychic level as representatives and vehicles for investigating the shadow: personal, cultural, archetypal. Physically, as one descends from Homo Erectus to Primate to Feline/Canine, the vocal tube both widens and lengthens, producing different Timbres, or qualities of sound.

From the upright, pulled-together stance of Homo Erectus, we relax into Primate, letting the jaw and shoulders drop and the knees loosen to the half-stance of a monkey or ape, beginning to really engage our peripheral as well as our direct vision. From this Primate position, we then drop down onto our hands and knees into Feline/Canine, letting our belly muscles loosen so that we can pant as easily as a dog. This movement progression through what is known as the animal postures takes us from the short, narrow configuration of Homo Erectus, which we also call Flute and which lends itself most easily to articulation; to the wider and longer configuration of Primate which we also identify as Clarinet; to the longest, widest and most open configuration of Feline/Canine, which, in terms of defining the wideness of the tube, we call Saxophone which derives from primal sounds such as yawning, burping, sobbing and screaming. The use of the fourth animal, Bird (also identified as Violin) to rise up from the ground or stoop from the skies, can be applied as a vocal quality to all three timbres to increase the carrying range of your sound and add a more penetrating quality. These changes in the body's relation to gravity help to facilitate the different qualities produced by the timbres identified as Flute, Clarinet, and Saxophone to highlight the major different configurations and timbral changes of which the vocal tube is capable.

The change in how the body feels in assuming the postures, breathing dimensions and other vocal and physical characteristics of these four types of creatures can help us gain access to their use in exploring the Shadow—those parts of ourselves we are unaware of or keep hidden—by drawing on their archetypal relevance and particularizing them for ourselves.

5. **Massage, manipulation, and compression** is a very particular form of hands-on work, the main function of which is to expand respiration and vocalization by increasing the volume of tidal airflow to and from the lungs. First focusing on and particularizing the three primary areas of expansion—clavicular, thoracic and abdominal—to see which areas in a given body are flexible and responsive and which may not be, we work physically with the relevant musculature to create a more open and united breath. This is based on Reichian massage work and Wolfsohn's own explorations, and is unusual in that, following Wolfsohn's practice, it is done primarily while the client is moving and sounding.

Figure 3. Christine Isherwood doing active massage and compression with client, VMT Training Center, Martha's Vineyard, MA, 2013. Photo by John FX O'Toole.

These core principles unite in a single purpose: to facilitate a more embodied and hence a more flexible, durable and versatile voice with which to achieve greater expression and expansion of one's sense of self—one's wants, needs, feelings and ideas—by accessing buried affect and making it conscious through a process which pioneer Dance Movement Therapist and Expressive Arts educator Norma Canner called, "The child's way of knowing: to experience something, to name it through an imaginative creative act, and thus come to know it in a whole different way." (Canner, 1982)[30]. A simple example would be as follows:

A small child sees a dog for the first time. The parents say, "That's a dog," but it does not become really known to that child until he embodies it by saying "Woof, Woof" and wagging an imaginary tail or panting, and then perhaps drawing a picture of a dog. Through such activities the child integrates this new knowledge by putting it in relation to himself, owning it through a sensory-based bodily action which he initiates. He may then name it again for himself as "dog," or "doggie," or "Bow-Wow," the meaning of which he has now made his own through this experience.

In a similar fashion in VMT, just as when working to expand the parameters of the voice we prioritize the sounds rather than the words, when dealing with a client's deep issue or memory we focus on the experience itself. With minimal verbal communication before beginning, we facilitate our client's exploration in voice and movement of that memory or sensation and then encourage its reimagining and reworking into a song or story in a process which is often transformative because what is being investigated becomes known through a direct and holistic encounter on a body level as well as through the mind.

The importance of moving from essentially primitive unverbalized affect to cognition and the ability to name and talk about events, ideas, and emotions that impact one's sense of self is clearly described by Aftab Omer, founder of The Institute for Imaginal Psychology, now Meridian University, in California. As he describes it, if a person finds it necessary to alter his own self-concept in order to fit in and cope with the people and circumstances around him, he forms what has been identified as an "adaptive identity"–what has also been termed an "as if" or false self–which temporarily helps him to adapt and survive in response to adverse life conditions. To move past this type of identity to one that is more true to who the person actually is or wishes to be, we must develop the cognitive understanding necessary to impact it, determining where it came from and if it is still necessary, or if it now can be altered or abandoned.[31]

In an example given by Deirdre Brownell who practices imaginal psychology in tandem with VMT:

> A person with a hidden disability such as dyslexia (an often inherited and invisible learning disability involving problems in acquiring and processing language) may be trying as hard as they can to read, but find their efforts are met with comments such as "You're just lazy" or "How can you be so stupid?" They know they are doing their best and may not feel stupid at all, but it may be easier to pretend they are lazy, to adapt to one of these two points of view in order to fit in with one of the ways other people are perceiving them. After all, in most cases, being considered lazy is preferable to being perceived as stupid and can be seen as a matter of choice. What is happening, however, is that this person is allowing others to co-opt their reality, what they know to be true about themself, in order to protect that self from shame and to find some place in the group to fit in. In so doing, they have lost the right to choose.

D. Brownell continues by applying this concept to her Voice Movement Therapy work:

> VMT is able to help a person change their adaptive identity, to begin this process by contacting and bringing forth relevant material from their unconscious through voice and movement exploration in order to create a bridge between what is trapped in the body, a body memory existing only as sensation or affect, and a conscious understanding by which it can be

> conceptualized, named as a specific emotion, and addressed in treatment. Songs with words come to us through both our feelings and our thoughts, through the affective tones of voice as well as the more consciously chosen words. The process of discovering acoustic images to connect with deeply hidden psychic material and then to write a song from our own revisited experience can take us from a preverbal to a more conscious and aware state.[32]

In forming Voice Movement Therapy, Newham incorporated Wolfsohn's concept of the *vox humana* and its relation to the psyche; refined the notion of vocal components and timbres, reimagining them as wind rather than stringed instruments, as Wolfsohn had; and built upon Wolfsohn's quite basic way of physically manipulating and compressing parts of his student's bodies such as shoulders, ribs, and abdomen which Newham combined with the more sophisticated methods of Reich and his own ideas. Along with many of both Hart's and Pardo's theatre exercises, Newham applied the idea of embodying the voice by retraining the musculature to give the body a new experience of itself. In addition, consideration of the potential emotional/psychological significance of the vocal components, and movement postures such as convex/concave and positioning within one's sphere, were also employed.

Through creative assignments such as the writing of a personal autobiography, its conversion to a fairy tale and then to a ballad; sending people on Voice Movement Journeys in a use of Jung's practice of Active Imagination which prioritizes vocalization; engaging both individuals and groups in spontaneous song-making; and a final crafted personal performance with songs based on ten subpersonalities emerging from their own issues and experiences, Newham invited his trainees to investigate the meeting place between personal expression, performance, and therapeutic process, as VMT students and practitioners continue to do.

Voice Movement Therapy is similar to other performance-based Creative Arts Therapies in its use of both creation and performance to give artistic form and expression to personal trauma and other issues as part of a healing process. This requires actually engaging with one's own material physically and creatively rather than simply talking about it. Just as in Art Therapy, a person would go to their easel or armature to paint or sculpt from the issues that arise, so a person engaging in VMT is encouraged to "take it to the floor" in spontaneous sound and movement, and eventually to form and perform it as an original personal song, much in the way a Dance Movement Therapist would explore and create a dance.

One way VMT it is different from these disciplines is that, as a therapy with voice as its primary focus, it often incorporates a high degree of intervention and direction with a type of massage, manipulation and compression while the client is moving and sounding that is designed to increase tidal airflow while decreasing muscular restriction. This requires that the practitioner not only have a basic knowledge of the anatomy of the vocal apparatus and the breathing mechanism, but also be aware of how hormones work in the body because of the functional connection between the larynx and the thyroid cartilage. To quote Newham:

> In addition to the predominance of muscle tissue throughout the vocal apparatus, the vocal folds also connect to the thyroid cartilage, a dominant station on the endocrine circuit which distributes hormones throughout the body. Because hormonal release is such an integral component to emotional experience, the voice is doubly susceptible to psychophysical events.[33]

In puberty, for example, the healthy development of a boy's larynx is dependent on the release of hormones by the endocrine gland which not only causes physical changes to the larynx, but results in a change of voice quality due to an actual shift in the position of the thyroid cartilage. Hormonal thyroid secretions affect women's voices throughout the lifespan, particularly during menstruation, pregnancy and menopause. As Newham points out, with regard to the effect on the voice of difficult life events or experiences of trauma:

> Because the use of the voice is...so intimately connected to our sense of well-being, our sense of worth and our communicative efficiency, it is probably more prone to accumulation of the muscular ramifications of negative emotionality than any other expressive faculty and these muscular patterns can continue to operate unconsciously long after the specific events which instigated the stress have disappeared.[34]

Within the double container of the practitioner and the song, this discipline is particularly suited to accommodate and work with the highly charged emotions which often emerge when vocal restraints in the expression of feelings are released. A major use of movement, as stated by Newham, is, "To revise unnecessary muscular patterns related to vocalization by giving the body a new sensory experience of itself."[35] This grounds the voice in the reality of the very body which is its instrument. In similar fashion, a major use of image in this work, in sound and movement as well as visually, is to make conscious the places where we are stuck in time, places in our psyche which keep us from being fully present in the living moment, and to help us dispel or transform them. Through enactment in song and story, a client is witnessed by either the therapist alone or in the presence of a group. This process is useful for those for whom vocal expression is blocked, limited, or otherwise difficult as a result of emotional distress, muscular tension, and/or neurological or physical impediment, as well as for those who seek increased personal and/or professional empowerment through the voice.

SUMMARY

Voice Movement Therapy begins not with the spoken word, its cognitive content or articulation, but with the affective aspects of voiced sound. It is, in essence, an exploration of the self and one's ability to communicate non-verbally as well as verbally through the physical voice. It seeks the fullest possible expression of a client's personal and archetypal material through a type of voicework which uses movement and massage, imagery and enactment to plumb the depths of the unconscious and give it expression through spontaneous singing and soundmaking, and then to form it into self-composed and witnessed song.

We, its practitioners, see this work as a multi-modal Expressive Arts Therapy which prioritizes the voice and seeks to increase its flexibility, durability, and versatility through first, an investigation of its organic and developmental relationship to breathing and bodily movement, as well as, second, an exploration of how the components of the voice and related movement patterns reflect different aspects of ourselves and our life stories which, through imagery and enactment, and particularly through Jung's process of Active Imagination, can be used to effect change and growth. The VMT "system" (which we prefer to call core principles and practices) is based on the metaphor of the continuous, flexible Vocal Tube and the identification of 10 Vocal Components potentially common to all voices, in conjunction with the 4 non-vocal principles of Convex/Concave, the Sphere, the Four Animals, and Massage, Manipulation and Compression while the client is moving and sounding.

In essence, the heart of Voice Movement Therapy is the embodied voice. Movement grounds it in the body, it is pursued within the crucible of a committed therapeutic relationship, and actualized in song.

How, then, does this relate to the treatment of major mental or physical illnesses such as psychosis, depression, substance abuse, or stroke; to neurologically or emotionally-based problems such as mutism, behavior disorders, or hidden disabilities such as dyslexia, dyspraxia and ADHD; or to conditions such as displacement and homelessness, overwhelming emotions like intense anger or unremitting grief, or the need for intervention in conflict resolution, performance anxiety, or giving birth? In the following chapters, these and other situations and conditions will be addressed by

VMT practitioners working in their own discipline or adjunctively in ways based on recognizable core principles and practices of this work but that, each time they are employed are, in the words of Norma Canner, "New, always new."

NOTES

1. Wolfsohn often referred to the "unchained voice" to describe the kind of vocal liberation he was seeking. I chose to reverse the word order for the subtitle of the American Training established in 2022, and for this chapter, because I wanted the word "voice" to come first.
2. Alexander Lowen, *Fear of Life* (New York: MacMillan Publishing Company, 1981), pp. 202 and 263.
3. Marita Gunther, unpublished notes on Alfred Wolfsohn, from the Roy Hart Theater Center Archives, Malerargues, France, in Paul Newham*, The Prophet of Song: The Life and Work of Alfred Wolfsohn,* (London: Tiger's Eye Press, 1997).
4. Sheila Braggins, *The Mystery Behind the Voice: A Biography of Alfred Wolfsohn* (Leistershire, UK: Troubador Publishing Co., 2012), p. 26.
5. Noah Pikes, *Dark Voices: The Genesis of the Roy Hart Theatre* (Woodstock, CT: Spring Journal Books, 1999), p. 39.
6. Linda Wise, "Voice and Soul-The Alfred Wolfsohn/Roy Hart Legacy," *The Voice and Speech Review, vol. 5,* issue 1 (2007), p. 2.
7. Carl Jung, "The constituting material of the psyche is made up of images," in Paul Newham, *Therapeutic Voicework: Principles and Practices for Use of Singing as a Therapy* (London, UK: Jessica Kingsley Publishers, Ltd.,1998), p. 89.
8. Pikes, *Dark Voices,* pp. 43-44.
9. Pikes, p. 39.
10. Wise, "Voice and Soul," p. 3.
11. Newham, *The Prophet of Song,* p. 49.
12. Newham, p. 54.
13. Richard Foreman quoted by Ronnie Britton in "The Salary May be Tiny, But It's Priceless Practice," *New York Times,* January 12, 1997.
14. Wise, "Essay: Voice and Soul," p. 3.
15. Paul Newham, "Voice Movement Therapy: Towards an Arts Therapy for Voice," *Dramatherapy, 16,* nos. pp. 2 & 3 (1994): pp. 28- 32.
16. Paul Newham, "Singing and Psyche: Towards Voice Movement Therapy," *Voice: Journal of the British Voice Association, 1* (1992): pp. 75-102.
17. Newham (1992), p. 2.
18. Newham, (1993), p. 17.
19. Shaun McNiff, *Educating the Creative Arts Therapist: A Profile of the Profession* (Springfield, IL, Charles C Thomas, Publisher, 1986), p. 10.

20. Paul Newham, *The Singing Cure: An Introduction to Voice Movement Therapy* (Boston: Shambhala, 1994).
21. Ken Dychtwald, *Bodymind* (New York: Jeremy P. Tarcher Books, 1986).
22. Antonio Damasio, *Descartes' Error: Emotion, Reason, and the Human Brain* (New York: G. B. Putnam's Sons, 1994).
23. Paul Newham, "Voicework as Therapy: The Artistic Use of Singing and Vocal Sound to Heal Mind and Body," *Foundations of Expressive Arts Therapy: Theoretical and Clinical Perspective*, Eds. Levine, E.G. and S.K. Levine (London: Jessica Kingsley Publisher, 1998), p. 91.
24. http://www.soundtherapysantafe.com/blog/archives/06-2019. "In 1734, Johann Wilhelm Albrecht noted the effect of sound on the body as happening quite independently of the ear, though the actual effect described by Albrecht was not discovered until the 19th century. Pacinian corpuscles, named after their discoverer, Italian anatomist Filippo Pacini (1812-1883), are mechanoreceptors located in the skin—the body's largest organ—and are responsible for sensitivity to pressure, touch and vibration. Pacinian corpuscles are composed of concentric rings, somewhat like an onion or a tree, and pressure from vibrations cause the rings to de-form. Outer layers start to spin and sodium channels open, allowing an influx of sodium ions. A build-up of sodium sends signals via nerves that connect to our central nervous system, the nerve bundle deep in the brain called the vagus nerve. The vagus nerve branches to the lungs, heart, upper digestive tract and other organs of the chest and abdomen...and connects with the diaphragm...When you know something in your gut, the vagus nerve is talking to you."
25. Marita Gunther, unpublished notes on Alfred Wolfsohn, from the Roy Hart Theater Center Archives, Malerargues, France, in Paul Newham, *The Prophet of Song: The Life and Work of Alfred Wolfsohn* (London: Tiger's Eye Press, 1997).
26. Anne Brownell, 2004, the website for the International Association for Voice Movement Therapy; iavmt.org
27. S. Sparks, N. Helms and M. Albert, Aphasia rehabilitation resulting from melodic intonation therapy, reprinted from CORTEX, Vol. 10, 1974, pp. 303-316. Varese, Italy: La Tipographica Varese, 1974.
28. Minnie Riperton, "Lovin' You," as sung by, http://www.youtube.com/watch?v=K7MqTrXwojk
29. "Male Singers: Whistle Notes Register," Part 1, http://www.youtube.com/watch?v=KXkz5X7LTDM, last update March 24, 2017.
30. Norma Canner, Class notes, "Movement and Healing," A. Brownell, Lesley College, Cambridge, MA, 1984.
31. Aftab Omer, Class notes in "Imaginal Inquiry," D. Brownell, Meridian University, Petaluma, CA, 2010.
32. Deirdre Brownell, (2020), Commentary based on "Re-Embodying the Voice: Uniting Body and Mind through the Voice to Strengthen the Self."

Unpublished Ph.D Psychology dissertation, Meridian University, Petaluma, CA, 2020.

33. Newham, "Voicework as Therapy," Foundations of Expressive Arts Therapy, eds. Levine and Levine: p. 143.
34. Newham, eds. Levine and Levine: p. 446.
35. Newham, *The Singing Cure: An Introduction to Voice Movement Therapy*, 1983 (Shambhala Publications, Inc.), p. 1.

BIBLIOGRAPHY

Braggins, Sheila. (2012). *The Mystery Behind the Voice: A Biography of Alfred of Wolfsohn.* Leicestershire, UK: Troubadour Publishing Company, 2012.

Brownell, Anne. www.iavmt.org, 2004

Brownell, Deirdre. "Re-Embodying the Voice: Uniting Body and Mind through the Voice to Strengthen the Self." Unpublished PhD Diss., Meridian University, CA, 2020.

Canner, Norma. Class notes, "Movement and Healing." from A. Brownell, Lesley College, Cambridge, MA: 1984.

Damasio, Antonio. *Descartes' Error: Emotion, Reason, and the Human Brain.* New York: G.B. Putnam & Sons, 1994

Foreman, Richard. "The Salary May be Tiny, But It's Priceless Practice," by Ronnie Britton, *New York Times,* Jan. 12, 1997.

Gunther, Marita. Unpublished notes on Alfred Wolfsohn, from the Roy Hart Theatre Centre Archives. Newham, Paul. (1997). *The Prophet of Song: The Life and Work of Alfred Wolfsohn.* London: Tiger's Eye Press.

Jung, Carl. "The constituting material of the psyche is made up of images." Newham, Paul. (1998). *Therapeutic Voicework: Principles and Practices for Use of Singing as a Therapy.* London: Jessica Kingsley Publishers Ltd.

Lowen, Alexander. (1981). *Fear of Life.* New York: MacMillan Publishing Company.

"Male Singers - Whistle Notes Register Part 1" Youtube (website) http://www.youtube.com/watch?v=KXkz5X7LTDM, last update March 24, 2017.

Minnie Riperton. "Lovin' You," Youtube (website) http://www.youtube.com/watch?v=K7MqTrXwojk, last updated May 13, 2023.

Moses, Paul. (1954). *The Voice of Neurosis.* New York: Grune and Stratton.

Newham, Paul (1998). *Therapeutic Voicework: Principles and Practices for the Use of Singing as a Therapy.* London, UK: Jessica Kingsley Publisher.

Newham. (1998), "Voicework as Therapy: The Artistic Use of Singing and Vocal Sound to Heal Mind and Body," *Foundations of Expressive Arts Therapy: Theoretical and Clinical Perspectives,* Eds. Levine, E.G. and S.K. Levine, (London: Jessica Kingsley Publisher, 1998)

Newham. Voice Movement Therapy: "Towards an Arts Therapy for Voice". *Dramatherapy,* Vol. 16:1994.

Newham. (1993). *The Prophet of Song: The Life and Work of Alfred Wolfsohn.* London, UK: Tiger's Eye Press.

Newham. (1993). *The Singing Cure: An Introduction to Voice Movement Therapy.* Cambridge, MA: Shambala Publications Inc.

Omer, Aftab. (2010). Class notes from "Imaginal Inquiry" taken by D. Brownell. Meridian University, Petaluma, CA.

Pikes, Noah. (1999). *Dark Voices: The Genesis of the Roy Hart Theatre.* Woodstock, CT: Spring Journals Books.

Sound Therapy Santa Fe (blog); "The body hears sound through more than just the ears" by Laurie McDonald, posted June 27, 2019. Soundtherapysantafe.

Sparks, S., Helms, N., & Albert, M. (1974). Aphasia rehabilitation resulting from melodic intonation therapy. Reprinted from *CORTEX, 10*: 303-316. La Varese, Italia: La Tipographica Varese.

Wise, Linda. (2007). "Voice and Soul–The Alfred Wolfsohn/Roy Hart Legacy." *Voice and Speak Review.*

Chapter Two

PSYCHOLOGY AND SOUL WORK

INTRODUCTION

Anne Brownell

The word *psychology*, formed by combining the Greek word *psyche* (meaning "breath...life, soul,") with–*logia* (from the Greek *logos*, meaning "speech, word, knowledge") appears in the 17th century in a translation by Nicholas Culpeper of Simeon Partliz's *A New Method of Physick*, in which he declares that "Psychologie is the knowledg(e) of the Soul." Merriam Webster/ dictionary/psychology.

THE ROLE OF SONG IN PSYCHOTHERAPY

This chapter begins by considering the role of song in psychotherapy as a catalyst for change. The value of prioritizing therapeutic work in a medium other than words is that it requires participants to focus on their senses, on what is happening in the body as well as the mind. Our 21st century version of what Descartes referred to in the 1600s as a body/mind split is most evident in the pull between virtual and face-to-face communication. Online communication can be a wonderful thing, connecting people in new ways all over the world; it also can be so omnipresent that it leaves us impoverished and longing for real relationships both with others and with the world around us. For example:

A current TV car commercial begins with two men in an apartment wearing helmets with visors and long snouts staggering around a room in a virtual encompassment which separates them from the reality of their present surroundings. It then progresses to a young woman exiting the building and jumping into her car to take to the road in pursuit of adventure and the great outdoors. The point of the ad, of course, is to sell cars, but the appeal to the viewer is of leaving the virtual world for contact with actual physical reality. One could also, of course, just put down the headset, walk outdoors, breathe in the air and meet a friend for a walk in the park or around the block—anything that might take place in real space and time.

The need to experience life for oneself, even in a world of pandemics and other unseen dangers, can become an urgent necessity. When confronting one's issues, the value of the Creative Arts Therapies is that they give a person a chance to experience them in a different way by re-experiencing and re-creating and then presenting them to another person, or several, in dance, enactment, visual art, instrumental music, poetry, or song, which requires marshalling not just your mind but your body. In short, it requires making a bodily effort. It is not that words are not necessary; they are. We are speaking and verbal people with a need to name, describe, codify, and declare ourselves in speech and writing. We also have a need to experience life through our body, literally to embody our experience.

As discussed in Chapter One, what Voice Movement Therapy has to offer by the use of song as an expressive medium for working through issues is the ability to combine cognitive meaning (the work of the mind) with affective expression (the feeling response of the body) through the act of singing. The two main channels of the voice are the words we say which convey the cognitive message and the way we say them, the tones of voice which reflect the way we feel about what we say or sing. These are often in conflict, and self-composed song—through its amplified dynamics, rhythms, pitches and qualities of sound—makes any clashes between the meaning of the words and the affective or feeling tones of the voice more obvious than in speech and helps us to bring these two channels of meaning and expression into alignment, or congruence.

The articles in this chapter are presented in two parts. Part One: Voice Movement Therapy with Trauma: Upheaval, Alienation and Abuse begins with two practitioners' stories of working with people displaced and uprooted by war and poverty. "The Hidden Voices of Cambodia," by Trish Watts, tells of a project for finding and reclaiming the communal voice of a land still devastated by the aftermath of a brutal dictatorial regime.

"Voice Movement Therapy with the Displaced: Having a Voice When All Else Fails," by Sophie Martin, tells of the importance of finding and expressing oneself through the voice when in desperate circumstances—in a slum in Nairobi and in a refugee camp on the island of Nauru off the coast of Australia—as a way of holding onto one's sense of self.

"Sylvie Sings Her Mouth to Life," by Christine Isherwood, tells about her use of breathing and vocalizing with a survivor of oral sexual abuse, beginning with few or no words which, expanded upon, leads to a reclaimation of self through the creation and power of the personal song, as actualized by this client.

In "Meanwood: A Group Session," Carol Grimes describes how she uses simple songmaking and the teaching of a short children's ditty to brighten the lives of homeless, cognitively and physically delayed individuals left behind and isolated through years of institutionalization and the subsequent loss of the only home they have ever really known.

In "Mr. Handy: A Policeman in Trouble," Boniswa Kamba tells of her work with an individual in a less extreme but still potentially devastating situation and how, when an issue at work has reached an impasse, it can be taken to the floor to be worked on through voice, breath, movement, massage, and the addition of a simple hand drum. In this study, Boniswa tells how she works with this police officer who has been suspended and, in danger of losing both his job and his pension, is very angry.

Part Two: Psychosis, Self-Harm and Addiction: Models of Engagement presents five very different ways of working with individuals at risk in five very different situations. In "Voice Studio: A Place to Let It Out," Helen White recalls how she created a voice and movement "studio" at a day treatment clinic for patients with major mental illness to achieve a more openly creative and spontaneous atmosphere than currently available in their usual therapeutic or recreational groups.

In "Changing Lives: VMT in Mediation and Conflict," Gertruida Dowse describes how she combines the process of formal mediation with VMT concepts and practices to achieve a more affective, and effective, approach.

Sophie Martin's "Voice Movement Therapy in Action: A Reflection on a Pilot Study of Young Women Who Self-Harm" is based on the first formal study using this modality with a specific population in a psychiatric hospital and subsequently published in a journal of art and psychology.

"Facilitating Change–Body, Mind, and Soul–with Clients with Addictions," by Ben van Rensburg, describes two groups based on VMT principles and practices which he created and which became a regular part of the weekly treatment program of a residential clinic for people recovering from substance abuse.

"Sounding Our Way to Wholeness: Linking the Metaphysical and Physical Voice with Women Experiencing Eating Disorders," by Irene Kessler, describes a pilot project for women with eating disorders.

The focus in all of these articles is on describing how giving voice to one's inner turmoil and crafting it, whether in a highly complex form or in the simplest of ways, and sharing it with one or several persons, can be healing by allowing an individual to express, to communicate, and at the same time to contain their strong feelings safely while finding and reclaiming their voice to reaffirm their importance as individual human beings worthy of attention and respect.

I. VMT AND TRAUMA: UPHEAVAL, ABUSE AND ALIENATION

THE HIDDEN VOICES OF CAMBODIA

Trish Watts

Be careful what you commit to over a cup of coffee!

It was a rather ordinary midweek day when my friend Elain asked if we could meet up. I didn't know her very well, so I was surprised when she called. Elain was a member of the Sydney Threshold Choir, a women's chorus that sings at the bedsides of people in hospice receiving palliative care. I was Music Director for the choir at that time. After navigating inner city buses and traffic, I bustled towards an Italian café where I found her sitting in a quiet nook. After a few pleasantries she said, "Trish I've had this 'thing' like a whisper which won't go away." I felt the hairs on my skin stand up; this kind of "whisper language" was very familiar to me and I was all ears!

She continued, "After leaving Australia and going back to Cambodia to live, I noticed the children were not singing enough. Would you be willing to come to Cambodia to help me start some singing and choirs with the children?" I sat there stunned, trying to absorb what she'd just said. Cambodia? I don't know a thing about Cambodia, I don't speak the language, I'm not great with humidity, and besides, I don't work with children! "Why are you asking me and not the local Cambodians to help you with this?" I asked. She said, "There are no kids' choirs and people have forgotten about singing. Parents don't sing to their children. I want the kids to have a chance to experience joy and the love of singing, to help them find their voices and be given a chance to play with them" These words hit me like an arrow of both sunshine and horror, straight into my heart. How could a country not have singing and be denied music? It is our birthright to have a voice, to have the emotional and spiritual language of song. It was unthinkable to me not to have access to singing. I really thought she had not done her research. As it turned out, I had not done mine!

Graphic TV scenes of conflict in Cambodia flashed through my childhood memory bank. The images were raw and violent and I remember my mother turning the TV off every time a scene of war came on. My psyche flicked channels and I saw my older brother, who was conscripted to fight in Vietnam, with his 19-year-old girlfriend running alongside the train as he departed for army training duty, my mother standing sobbing uncontrollably. I was about six years old and confused. I loved my older brother; why was he leaving and why were trains so terrible?

Cambodia was once known as the "Jewel of Asia." Her color, inventiveness, wealth and community life rose from a rich culture of the performing arts. Music, song, dance and visual art were at the heart of Khmer life and present at every ceremony and community gathering. Their musical heritage was unique, artistic and filled with earthy folklore.

Between 1975-1979 the country was gripped by civil war as the Khmer Rouge took control. During these years over two million people lost their lives through slaughter and starvation. The country and its people lived in absolute terror under the leadership of Marxist dictator Pol Pot who attempted to create a "master race" through social engineering. The regime stole the heart and soul of the people, crushing their spirit and trust in each other and silencing their voices. Families were torn apart, labor camps and enforced marriages replaced the sacred ritual practices of treasured family life. Children were separated from their parents and ritually brainwashed with songs of a hateful, cruel regime, turning them against their own kin. Over ninety percent of the artists, musicians, teachers, doctors professionals–the intelligentsia–were killed during those years. It was nothing short of horrific.

As an artist myself, I felt compelled to respond. Could the fragments of melodies that once fed an entire nation be recovered? Could singing together be a medicine of hope and courage for the children and their families?

My experience and training are as a professional singer and Voice Movement Therapy practitioner. I know deep in my bones that the lived experience of communal singing is our birthright and part of our life blood! Our Ancestors and Elders pass down songs and stories because of their love for us, passing on goodness to build resilience and identity, to affirm belonging in our tribe, to enrich our lives with culture, and to instruct us in living and sharing peacefully together. When we are denied access to this lineage, our spirit and soul ache for what is missing, even when we're unaware of the source of this void.

Songs carry the collective memory and medicine of the generations. If they are prohibited, destroyed or forgotten, our lives are weakened and we can become lost, disconnected, grief-stricken and soul-less. When a culture loses its song-lines–songs which recall and pass on important knowledge, cultural values and wisdom deeply tied to the landscape and handed down orally in families as a way of traversing the land–the soul goes underground into hiding. Songs are also containers for emotional psychic energy. They cradle messages of peace, courage, protest, love, beauty and action. Cambodia was, and is, in need of both soul nursing and choruses of self-worth affirmation. Nothing can stir and unite a Nation more powerfully than a rousing anthem of sung goodness.

I felt called! Within six weeks I was on a flight to Phnom Penh. I knew this was going to be a big journey of self-discovery and service, and it was.

I believe passionately that "Every life can SING!" As one who was blessed with a singing father and a vivacious, faith-filled mother, I was pelted into life by the rousing four-part harmony of hymnody. My local rural church choir instilled in me a dream that spirited singing was a way of life and a medicine for all. Singing enabled a freedom that I now never take for granted.

Let me put this in a Voice Movement Therapy perspective: In 2001, I began my training in Voice Movement Therapy (VMT). I'd travelled from the Top End of Australia, the tropical heat of Darwin, to a tiny, snow-coated island called Martha's Vineyard in the USA. I had embarked on a physical journey and a traversing of the soul that would lead me to a totally new and astonishing place of awakening.

VMT works primarily with the belief that each person has not only a right to voice their creative spirit and life force, but that our voices hold a core intelligence that can transform our lives from constriction to freedom, from trauma to compassionate understanding. We are organic social and emotional beings, and having one's voice as an individual is power. Claiming communal voice ensures a future and leaves a legacy. VMT enables safe passage for voicing emotions and thoughts that are hidden, unspoken, denied or swallowed down. It is a therapeutic modality that holds the paradoxes of life with reverence and respect, and in so doing integrates both the shadow and the light within the psyche.

Personally, VMT gave me a way to process and be held in a caring international community of practitioners (International Association for Voice Movement Therapy, or IAVMT) who understand the deeper aspects of trauma and loss of voice. Checking in regularly for supervision and collegial friendship was a life-line. I'm deeply grateful for this training which gave me a lens to respond to this challenging cultural invitation in Cambodia. Without it, I think I would have drowned in the turmoil and suffering I witnessed there.

Karaoke and Soup

Even though I felt a strong YES to working in Cambodia, no one could have prepared me for the total auditory collision my ears would experience. I arrived into an urban reconstruction zone and it was loud! Gone were the peaceful harmonies of choral singing, the grounded rhythm of structured music, and the melodious comfort of birdsong. In its place was dirt, choking dust, and the noisy fractured sounds of construction diggers, with workers hanging off of scaffolding singing off key accompanied by distorted radios!

I was invited to my first ever Karaoke and Soup night by the staff of a local Beauty Spa. It was located in a large restaurant, big enough to hold a wedding reception of 200. Upstairs, a hallway opened out with many doors. It was surprisingly quiet and it felt odd. When I opened the allocated door, a blast of "noise" pelted me. My ears started to pound, as did my adrenals! About 15 people were crammed into this dark tiny room. Big pots of fish soup were simmering and a huge TV screen reflected Khmer pop songs in neon lights. Those holding the microphones were dancing wildly, screaming completely out of tune, and having a fabulous time. What can I say? The Khmer are conditioned to live within extremes and they love to party! After a few songs and saying hello to everyone, I danced my way to the door and squeezed myself out. It was intense!

On reflection, I realize that the first stage of unblocking mutism and punishing silence is to dare to breathe again and let the breath be audible. The second stage, for an individual or culture, is the "primal scream," allowing the wild, untamed voice out! There is a huge need in humanity to be heard, seen, felt and valued.

As children, we need the mirror of our parents to give us the attention required for psychological and spiritual growth. When it is there, the child learns how to modulate and express their emotions safely: how to calm down and communicate what they need, how to regulate the overwhelming energy pumping through their small bodies. The mother's soothing voice and movement, often offered through singing and rocking, helps to quiet the distressed nervous system and reassure the child they are loved and protected. So, too, creating a safe environment to play in where children can squeal with delight as they jump, run, skip and enter the world of wonder is important. I thank the heavens for Karaoke as a safe place where friends can gather in a sound-proofed room to let off steam, take the pressure down, play, and be acknowledged by each other. Maybe if every home and workspace invested in a sound-proofed screaming room, perhaps with the accompaniment and structure of Karaoke, we would all feel more relaxed and more sane. What was Elain looking for in inviting me here?

Elain and I shared a powerful vision and calling: the vision to give Cambodian children and their families a chance to rekindle the love and joy of singing. For me, I had the joy and passion for singing in my DNA from childhood. Elain missed such opportunities. By age ten she was living in a refugee camp on the Thai border. Speaking, let alone singing, was a dangerous thing. I realized as our work expanded into non-government schools in Phnom Penh that Elain was also searching for her voice. She had experienced the power of communal singing and sisterhood while in the Sydney Threshold Choir and couldn't imagine life without singing now that she was back. Could we also start a Threshold Choir in Cambodia, a women's healing choir?

The Threshold Choir concept, originated in the USA by Kate Mulder, is a choir that sings with and for all people with the intention of "kindness being audible." Singing softly for those in need can create healing, connection, belonging, compassion, and blessing. Working with communities where inherited sorrow was a given and raising one's voice in song was both forbidden and unfamiliar, was hugely confronting. The choir concept became a safe container for exercising trust, creating a taste for freedom, and daring to dream again as songs from the past were recalled. Two Sydney Choir members travelled to Phnom Penh to help us start a Threshold Choir. As we sang the first song, we encountered fear in the women: "Is it safe to express?" "I don't know how to sing." "I've never done this before." "How do you do this?" We decided to invite women from the expat community, from other countries but living in Phnom Penh, to join us. Some of these women had sung in choruses before and brought their openness and experience to the group, and it worked. Relationships started to grow and so, too, the ease of singing with others.

I noticed that modulation of the voice was irregular; the volume was either loud or quiet, with little gradation between. Screaming to be heard or silencing to be safe was the norm. In music we call this regulation of volume the ability to play with *dynamics*. *Forte* is the term for loud, *piano* is quiet, *mf* is moderately loud, *mp* is moderately quiet. In VMT one of the vocal components we use is the spectrum from Quietness to Loudness. Knowing that a person has choice around their volume enables the individual to feel in control of their own energy and space. A loud voice takes up space in a room, projecting a sense of command, authority, confidence, or perhaps bullying. A quiet voice brings the listener in close; it is intimate and nurturing if used with this intention. It can also signal timidity or anxiety, which can be read as weakness. To feel one's own power and effect on others is a large part of how we communicate what we value.

Liger Leadership Academy

After six weeks in Phnom Penh, a major breakthrough came when we met up with a dynamic entrepreneur and fellow Australian, Dom Sharpe. He co-founded Liger Leadership Academy, a project-based school which supports young Cambodians to become change agents for their country. It is one of the best schools in Cambodia and a home to over 100 students aged between 10-15 years. These students are hand-picked from all over the Khmer provinces for their high capacity to engage in teamwork, leadership and entrepreneurial thinking.

We set up two choirs of 25 students each and sang with each one for an hour a week. I had no Khmer language and the students had limited English. The singing was loud, rough, wild, out of tune, out of sync, and out of control. There was no modulation in volume or tone. It was like herding brumbies (Australian wild horses), not sheep. These kids were smart, willful, highly motivated, free thinking and embodied.

Using the lens of Voice Movement Therapy, I was listening for the intention behind the sounds. How do we craft the use of quietness and loudness to express emotional connection and authenticity so that people "feel" it? In Cambodia it has not been safe to feel. Showing and expressing how you feel is not esteemed and is done with a high risk of being misunderstood. Revealing too much emotion can trigger fear, judgement and silencing. Over time, what was incredible was experiencing these young students as they came into tune, into sync, as a unified body. The group body became a living collective, a culture of "soundhealth."

Acapella Group

As we sang, I heard the strong voices of three girls who became the core for what was to come. The girls requested a special study group on acapela singing. They wanted to sing like the girls from the movie *Perfect Pitch* who sang using harmonies. YAY! I went home and watched the movie to get up to speed!

What does harmony sound and feel like in the body and in the group body? Sung harmony was completely foreign to these girls. The concept of singing and holding different notes separately, yet in harmony with the main melody, was an enigma to them. The main voice in the sound track of their parents' generation was one of a harsh bellowing Dictator; there was no room for a voice that was different.

Traditional Khmer music, to my ear, is very angular. It uses patterns of melody that are hard to remember tonally, let alone repeat, and are sung solo with Khmer string, hammered and blown instruments. The remnants of Khmer folk songs are far more singable, yet do not carry harmony parts. Sung harmony is strange to their ears, hard to comprehend and hold.

These 11-year-old girls were so enthusiastic, emotionally open, innocent and unselfconscious, completely unafraid to express themselves with full volume. I felt their strength and power as young emerging women–like they could conquer the world. These girls were straight from village life and normally would not have had the opportunity for education like this. There was in them pure health, a natural resource of goodness and unhindered vibrancy. They also carried a hunger to be led and mentored with no pretense. I was hearing a direct connection with the life-force; it was pumping through their veins, coming out their mouths and filling the whole room. They were like warriors, singing with their whole bodies!

As an 11-year-old myself, I had nothing of the confidence these girls had. I remember rehearsing music as a Westerner with the insidious edge of perfectionism that was expected. Perfectionism can be crippling and a killer of creativity. It can haunt the progress of self-expression like no other. The outer and inner critic can be so strong, it can shut down a spark of talent before it gets started. Perfectionism and having to "get it right" can create terror. How much better it is to create a safe emotional container which allows learning through a willingness to experiment and improvise.

When Liger Learning Academy had Open Days, the 50-voice choir sang for the parents and visitors. They began to have an auditory identity which lifted the profile of the school with pride, dignity and joy! They were ready for the next step.

By now I had a curiosity for finding local Khmer songs that would resonate with the children and their families. When I asked people to share a song from their culture, it was like speaking into a vacant car park. People simply couldn't remember any, nor would they have had the confidence to sing them if they had. Who held the songs? Where were they? What if we could seek out the old songs of Cambodia, the lost hidden songs held in the collective memory of the elders who were still alive? What if we could unite two generations, the old and the young, through the connecting link of traditional folk songs before they disappeared forever?

The idea was hatched to create a Hidden Voice Project as part of the student 6-week Experiential Learning Curriculum. Thirteen students were sent home on their holiday break with MP3 recorders and asked to interview anyone with grey hair in their village to see if they could find old songs. I invited an Australian film documentary producer, Belinda Mason, to assist in training the students. The first two weeks were focused on intensive skills development: learning the art of interviewing, recording songs, translating, writing scripts, and basic film production. We then hit the road in a bus!

Voices from the Village People of Mondil Kiri and Kampong Speu

After a restless night sleeping in a hammock, fleeing from scorpions and monsoonal rain, 13 teenagers, three facilitators and I piled onto a bus to head into the forests of Mondil Kiri and the indigenous lands of this country. We were on a mission: to find the hidden voices of Cambodia!

Flying through crowded city streets, dodging dogs on crusty fractured roads and passing through thick forests, our bus finally came to a halt. Our masterful driver grinned widely. Surrounded by the lush tropical forests of Mondil Kiri, we had arrived in the indigenous lands of Cambodia. Tribal elders warmly greeted us and led us slowly into a hut where a ceremony of Calling the Ancestors began. Huge gongs and chanting took over as smoke filled the hut. I felt like I was being transported back to a place where the dreamtime was more important than conscious time. It was mesmerizing.

This was the start of bringing together the younger generation with the older to search for the endangered hidden songs of Cambodia, to record and document them. Our hope was that the students would pick up some of these songs for their own repertoire, experience the stories, and keep them alive by performing them.

Figure 4. Liger Leadership Academy students singing with village elders. Taken while recording and filming *Hidden Voices of Cambodia* for Cambodia Sings, Kampong Speu Provence, Cambodia August 2015.

Figure 5. Trish Watts staff and students, Empowering Youth Cambodia (EYC) from Lakeside School, Phnom Penh, Cambodia – 2015.

Over six days, we travelled through several provinces and slept within the heart of village life. The students interviewed senior song keepers in markets, around campfires and under trees. What emerged were songs filled with joy, fragility, longing and sadness. It was incredibly moving to witness. To see the eyes of our Liger children light up as they interviewed grandparents, uncles and aunts, to experience them singing along with these village elders left me with a heart soaked in goodness and hope. The elders were very shy to sing and they often covered their mouths, gazing down so as to have no eye contact.

Prompted by the curiosity of the children, fragments of songs started to emerge. We became "dream catchers," as threads of melody and words were remembered. An elder would start to sing a melody and then forget and giggle while another would hide behind and sing into the back of her head. Gradually the community of elders started to bounce back and forth remembered songs from a previous life where there had been childhood happiness. There was embarrassment which gave way to toothless smiles, tears, sadness, warmth and joy. Yes, joy! The children said, "They are so happy we came! They said they would have forgotten their songs if we hadn't come."

What power there is in the human voice to connect heart to heart, to communicate that we hear you, acknowledge you and that we care. In time we were able to weave together the phrases of many Khmer songs from the countryside which have now become part of the children's repertoire and are sung with deep feeling and pride in their cultural identity.

Some titles of the Khmer Folk Songs that emerged are: Derm Traeng Yool (The River Reed in the Wind), Rolork Kanhjrol Root Torng Gech Knea (Rhythm of the Waves), Soun Sne Pkar Brei Jorm Pei Jorm Paa (In the Wild Love Forest Flower, Magnolia), and Sang Sne Oudom Groeusna Rajana Ahnagoot tmei (We Build Love with Superiority, Design a New Future—edging towards the replacement songs reflecting Pol Pot's dictatorial policy).

The land still weeps today; it still bleeds for the generations lost, caught in a time warp of survival and the ghosts of those who suffered. The sacred dreaming, the rituals that held the medicine for community life were severely fractured, almost severed. Into this wild environment I had the privilege to step and meet a warm-blooded people hungering for understanding and teachers who could walk with them and believe in their worth and goodness.

Today, Renewed Hope

The number of young adults under the age of 30 is exploding in Cambodia, making up eighty percent of the population. Motos (motorbikes) roar up and down the streets carrying young families, sometimes up to five on a bike! A young spirit fills the air. It's exciting, exposing, and with an element of genuine danger. This energy is ripe for new life.

What if Khmer youth could reclaim their birthright to have a voice, to have their song, to sing again? What if community singing could open a doorway of trust and joy? What if songs could ignite imagination and the capacity to dream again?

Safety is not a given in our times; we have to intentionally create, build and sustain it, and rebuilding a country takes deep intentional work. Cambodia Sings created opportunities for over one thousand children to sing weekly with beautiful singing leaders in Phnom Penh. In slums, on the streets, in factories and in villages, the voice of the youth is rising again, seeking to heal generational wounds and reclaim for Cambodia its soul and place as a treasured jewel of Asia, one humble note at a time.

VOICE MOVEMENT THERAPY WITH THE DISPLACED: HAVING A VOICE WHEN ALL ELSE FAILS

Sophie Martin

Voices are glorious, unique, and absolutely vital to both the one voicing and the one listening. In populations where war and violent conflict have resulted in trauma, displacement and the seeking of refuge, working with the body and the voice becomes a way to understand, heal and express life stories. For Refugees and internationally displaced people, having a voice translates into having power back over their lives, expressing themselves beyond the bureaucratic story they have had to tell, and truly being heard. However, there is no single refugee voice. The experiences and journeys of displaced populations are as diverse and unique as their individual voices. Voice Movement Therapy provides an opportunity for the safe exploration and expression of these unique voices and, importantly, a space for all people to be heard.

This article focuses on my experience as a Voice Movement Therapy Practitioner with two different populations of displaced people: those living in the slums around Nairobi, Kenya in 2009, and Refugees and Asylum Seekers in offshore detention on Nauru in 2018. It is important to note that the case studies presented here are factual; however, they are written from my own perspective and in my own voice. Stating this at the outset is imperative in order not to reinforce some of the ethical issues and power imbalances inherent in working with marginalized populations and voicing for them.

In the past decade more than 100 million people were forced to flee their homes and seek refuge in and outside their own countries (UNHCR, 2020). This staggering number is hard to imagine and overwhelming to try to solve. Within this number are a 100 million stories and a 100 million unique voices. I have been privileged to work with some incredible people, hearing their stories of struggle and strength. It has inspired my work and challenged my notions of resilience. This article shares four individual stories of some I have worked with. It focuses on healing trauma through breath, song and storytelling using the vocal and non-vocal components of Voice Movement Therapy.

II. HEALING HAND PROJECT: KENYA 2009

The Healing Hand project was dreamed up by Charlotte Campbell-Stephen, an Australian woman whose personal experience in Kenya led her to work with Kenyan women. I was part of a team of complimentary health practitioners who travelled there to work within slums and internally displaced person camps (IDPs) that had increased significantly due to post-election violence in that country in 2008. The people living within these camps were experiencing profound poverty, sexual violence, lack of adequate drinking water and food, and had both recent and generational trauma. The Healing Hand Project aimed to provide healing for individuals experiencing trauma through complimentary medicine and creative arts therapies, and also to add to the education and training of those already living and working with traumatized individuals.

Voice Movement Therapy (VMT) played a unique role within the Healing Hand Project, as songs and singing are a part of the fabric of life in Kenya and could be heard everywhere we travelled. VMT makes room for the expression of all kinds of music and focuses on the unique voice of each client and their experience. Working within a culture that weaves song and movement into everyday life ensured that the experiences of the clients during a Voice Movement Therapy session were able to be accessed through voice, song and movement very naturally. These sessions, whilst first giving the client a safe space to explore the trauma they had experienced, also tapped into a cultural heritage of using song and movement to express their lives. In this way the work I did with VMT during my time in Kenya—or the clients I worked with, for the other practitioners in the Healing Hand project, and for myself—was incredibly moving, healing, and life-changing.

MY DIARY from the Kibera Slum
The following is an excerpt from my diary in 2009 written while working in Kenya:

All I can see are roofs shackled together as we launch off through the paddock of plastic bags, stepping over the stagnant shit-filled water holes. The smell assaults me as much as the vision does. We are told not to touch our faces once we enter the slum. Charlotte has her head down and her demeanor has shifted to, "Don't fuck with me." She moves fast, purposefully, stepping over piles of gunk and occasionally stepping into them. I can see the soles of her shoes starting to get caked with brown sticky effluent. At first, I can't look up, can't take it all in. The size of the homes that we whizz past are smaller than I imagined and my stomach churns with anxiety and the stench that is seeping into my nostrils. Dogs with patchy fur scavenge the path and women sit, blank, hardly looking up when we speak the "Habari" greeting as we pass.

The noise of children abounds. "How are you?" they say in their singsong way to exactly the same tune every time; they want to shake my hand. Their skin is rough and I feel dirty and ashamed and overwhelmed. But I must keep trudging through, following Charlotte's footsteps as she cuts around corners and steps over plastic bag upon plastic bag. How can human beings live this way? Everything is brown–the houses, the ground, the skin around me–and everything is so crowded together. As we march through, my head starts, finally, to lift and I take in my surroundings bit by bit. People stare off into the distance from doorways and there are just endless piles of shit, mud and thongs discarded amongst shirts that have been trampled into the sludge. How will I be of use? How can I connect?

Breath: "Janice"

One of the key things I noticed while working with clients in Kenya was an uneven breathing pattern as a result of traumatic experiences to body and mind. Many of the women in Kenya whom I worked with exhibited a "freeze" response in the body. They described not feeling connected to their bodies anymore except for feeling pain such as stomach cramps or neck ache. Connecting with each other through the breath can be a gentle, safe and emotional experience that assists clients in re-connecting to themselves and beginning their healing journey.

Janice is a Kenyan woman who is in charge of a women's self-defense and assertiveness training group set up to support rape survivors and prevent rape in the Korogotcho slum in Nairobi. She has a lot of stress due to funding issues and straightaway she tells me she has a terrible voice. I invite her to start breathing and I can see that, as she breathes into her belly, she does so in reverse, breathing in and pulling her belly in and then breathing out and pushing her belly out. We begin to work on this and I ask her to relax and let her belly go as she breathes in, letting the air fill it. As she does this, she relaxes and begins to cry.

I ask her to continue breathing. It is very hard work for her to concentrate on filling her belly with air and then letting the air out and I ask her if she would like to add a little sound to the outbreath. She still has tears and begins a low moaning sound that I encourage her to start to let out even more. The moaning turns into a long low note and then comes back to the breath which has returned to a natural pattern; the tears have also come to an end. She seems relaxed and says that she hasn't heard herself make that kind of sound before.

Over the time we worked together she practiced this exercise and her breath moved more and more into her belly. She described the breath as helping her feel stronger and giving herself time to relax. This seemingly simple exercise allowed Janice the time she needed to re-connect to herself and notice her feelings for a moment.

Song: "Anton"

Voice Movement Therapy encourages clients to write songs based on their experiences. The composed song can become a container for intense emotions and tell personal stories. It can also assist the client in starting to recover from traumatic events through retelling the story in a creative and safe environment.

Anton is a boy of 11 years whom I treated at the Kabira Slum Mosque. I had worked with a couple of children before him when he gravitated toward me. When he caught my eye, it was because I was working with his friend. They performed a rap together that they often did in the streets. It was full of energy and the chorus was sung by both of them with the words, "Come down and join us, come down to our place, come on down, come on down." They both obviously loved rapping together and they both had sudden smiles on their faces. The joy was contagious and people all around were clapping and laughing. I encouraged them to keep rapping together and to make up raps about their lives.

Later in the day I sat down next to Anton to talk with him about his rapping and we chatted about how it made him feel good. Whilst doing that, I listened to his voice which was really quite raspy and had a lot of disruption. I asked him if I could check out his breathing as I had done with some of the other boys. He said this would be ok and I put my hands at his chest and his back. His breathing was also uneven and raspy and when I asked him about this, he spoke about smoking bhang (marijuana) to help him forget. The story he told me then was very sad and I felt privileged that he felt safe enough to talk to me about it. During the violence, he had watched his sister and his mother raped and then killed by soldiers and then watched his brother try to fight them and also be killed. After the soldiers took the bodies outside, they came back and raped his grandmother, as well. He was hiding in the kitchen and he said that he had to stay very quiet so they couldn't find him. After that, he went down to the river and his friend offered him some bhang. When I asked him what he wanted to forget, he said that he often gets nightmares about what happened to his mother, brother and sister and only remembers bad things.

At this stage, he was very close to his emotions and trying quite bravely to keep himself strong which I have noticed a lot of young boys in Kenya seem to want to be. So I asked him if, when he remembers his mother and brother and sister, whether there are any good things that he can remember. He talked about his mother singing while she did the washing and his brother teaching him how to fight and rap.

Then I asked him whether he would like to make up a rap about his mother, brother and sister, to which he nodded and stood up to work with me. Quite suddenly he launched into his own rap about how much he needed his mother and brother in his life. The chorus was, "Mother, come to me, hold me and sing to me" which we sang together, and then I kept the beat to give him some support while he made up the words to his rap about his mother and how much he missed her and needed her in his life. Then we sang to his sister, "Sister, come to me, come to me and laugh with me," and her rap was all about living in the slums and how she was missing out not being there. Then a little boy of two or three came over to us and Anton rapped to this little boy, "You look like my brother, be safe, rap with me, I can teach you"; the chorus was "Brother come to me, come to me and rap with me." All the way through this experience Anton kept checking in with me through eye contact that it was ok to keep going and he seemed very close to his memories and his feelings. During the final part of the rap quite a few people joined in with us to sing the chorus which had gone back to, "Mother come to me, come to me and sing with me."

Both of these experiences were incredibly moving, with emotions just under the surface. Working with people in intense situations opens and sharpens your senses, and both of these sessions had a profound impact on the way I view trauma when working with the voice.

Figure 6. Sophie Martin talking with a group of children in the streets of Nairobi, Kenya - 2009. Photo by Charlotte Campbell-Stephen

III. WORKING ON NAURU

From 2016 to 2019 I worked on Nauru in an offshore detention facility created to detain refugees and asylum seekers who had claimed asylum in Australia. For the majority of my time there, I worked with children and families from countries such as Iran, Iraq, Sri Lanka, and Myanmar, to name just a few. The people I met and worked with had experienced multiple layers of trauma in their home countries where violence and persecution had forced them to flee and seek safety elsewhere. Additionally, Australia's harsh detention policies had brought further trauma to the refugees and asylum seekers in Nauru where living conditions were challenging and indefinite detention had left many people in a liminal state unable to make decisions about their lives. Depression and mental health issues were common and in the time that I was there many grownups and children resorted to desperate measures in order to receive assistance from the Australian Government.

MY DIARY from Regional Processing Centre 1 on Nauru
An excerpt in 2016 written while working there:

The plane soars over the bluest of blue oceans and the clouds part to reveal a tiny picturesque island. With spears of rocks jutting up between the waves, the colors on the island are bright, the blue ocean against the green in the center. The beauty hides the harsh conditions of life on Nauru: the steamy weather that brings a lethargy and the phosphate dust that covers everything. Those flying in to work at the detention center brace themselves for landing. They steel themselves for the weeks ahead, knowing there will be challenges. When I arrive, I walk into Regional Processing Centre 3. RPC is where the refugee families live and I am suddenly surrounded by children. They sing and laugh, knowing I will play and dance with them. Even the adults welcome me back again, knowing that I have no power over the government's decisions about their lives, knowing that I will be with them, good times and bad, for the next few weeks.

Play: "Aran"

Voice Movement Therapy encourages play as a form of expression: playing with sound, playing with movement, and using play as a way to connect to others. When working with traumatized children, using play can be a way to understand the trauma the child has experienced. It can also be a safe way for children to communicate what has happened to them and what they are experiencing in the world. Using voice and song can also be a way to encourage play with children and can bring joy and fun to the therapy room.

Aran was a little Tamil boy of four years living in the family camp in Nauru. His mother and father were concerned about his memories of the trauma he had witnessed and also the effect that their current situation in Nauru was having on him. He wouldn't play with the other children very often, and when he did, would end up having arguments with them and come back to his mother for comfort.

The first time I met Aran was in one of the activity tents set up for a women's sewing group. He was running around pulling things off the table and attempting to get his mother's attention while she sat chatting with the other women. He seemed agitated and upset that she wouldn't play with him. I approached him gently and sat down on the floor next to where he was playing. At first, he didn't look at me, but there were boxes on the ground which I started to play with, making sounds as if they were singing or talking to each other. He found this very interesting and came a little closer to me and eventually took a box and started to make engine noises toward my boxes.

This game continued for several minutes before he started arranging the boxes in a square around me, telling me it was his bus. When I asked if I was sitting on the bus, he told me to get off, stating that he was the bus driver and he would tell me if I could get on. He pretended to drive around the room, seeming deliberately to avoid me before pulling up next to me saying, "ID card." When I fumbled around in my pockets looking for something to use, he said, "No ID, No Bus" and drove off again. He approached me a second time and I showed him some paper I had folded up to look like an ID card, but he said, "No, no ID, no bus" and drove off again. This happened several more times before I said, "I'm sorry I don't have an ID card, but I need to catch the bus" and he said, "Ok, sit up the back and BE QUIET! And no crying!" and off we drove together in the imaginary bus around the room. At one stage I started to sing "The wheels on the bus go round and round" and he marched up to me to say loudly, "Be quiet! You don't sing, I sing" and he started to sing which made the women in the room laugh and he started to smile.

This became the game we played for several days, or similar games where he was in control of the situation and re-enacting what he was experiencing in his everyday life on Nauru. Slowly he started to play games with the other children and was able to laugh in the family camp where they lived.

Song and Politics: "Maryam"

Working with the voice is empowering, as clients make sounds they may not be allowed to make in their everyday lives. Songs can also allow people to say the words they want to say to others but may not have been given the opportunity to do. Sometimes just singing these words can be enough for the client to begin to heal those feelings and sometimes it is important for the client to sing to the people they want to send a message to. When working with refugees and asylum seekers on Nauru, I encountered many examples of highly politically charged vocal expression. Children would shout, "Fuck ABF (Australian Border Force)" as they ran by those in uniform. Adults would chant and protest at the gates of the regional processing centers. This last case study expresses the story of a young woman who sang the words she wanted to say to the politicians.

Maryam is a young Iranian woman who had been gifted a keyboard by a social worker on Nauru and was secretly practicing and singing in her room. She dreamed of being in a thrash metal band and when I first met her, she wanted to learn about how to use her voice to scream into the microphone using the thrash singing style. We worked for several weeks opening up this part of her voice and she began to use this singing style to sing thrash songs with her own local band.

One day, however, when I entered the room, she was practicing a different style of song. The song was "Bird Set Free" by Sia Furler. She excitedly told me she had been asked to sing at an event where Nauruan politicians and Australian officials would attend and she wanted to sing this song.

As she sang the song her voice got stronger. However, when she reached the line, "But there's a scream inside that we all try to hide, we hold on so tight, we cannot deny," her voice cracked and she started to cry. I encouraged her to keep breathing and keep singing and slowly the tears stopped and were replaced by a strong clear voice singing the song to the end. Afterwards, she spoke about feeling very connected to this line, feeling the injustice of being in detention and wanting to scream at everyone. We sang the song quite a few times and each time her voice had a directness to it like she was piercing a hole in the wall of the tent with the sound of her voice.

This song gave Maryam the opportunity to sing something she wanted to say but didn't feel she had the words. Unfortunately, the event was cancelled, but she often sang this song in session to express her feelings of being strong and fighting against her situation.

MY DIARY in 2018:

RPC3 is silent, it's eerie. No one lingers in this dusty, moldy place any longer than they have to. I see the mothers taking food for their sick children; they look up but don't speak. Their children are protesting in ways never seen, ways that should never be seen, starving themselves to skeletons, cutting themselves to show that they bleed like everyone else. They fly to Australia family by family and it's my last trip here. I smell the memories, the voices, the songs, the lives.

Each of these case studies demonstrates the efficacy of Voice Movement Therapy as a part of the healing journey of a client who has experienced the trauma of displacement. The opportunity that VMT provides to connect voice, body and mind, offering a safe container for the client to retell the story of their trauma and connect to others, can contribute to the healing of trauma.

I would like to acknowledge the bravery and strength of the people whom I worked with in Kenya and Nauru. The experiences that I shared, the laughter, the tears, the voices I witnessed, and the songs that were sung and created have a power beyond words.

SYLVIE SINGS HER MOUTH TO LIFE

Christine Isherwood

Who is this person? Why did she come?

It was waking up in the bed of someone she had no recollection of meeting after another night of intoxication which brought Sylvie to work with me. She had been given my number by a colleague some time prior at a work social and this day she decided to use it.

"Sylvie" (pseudonym) was in her mid-40s when she came to VMT. Her body was contracted, arms clasped close to her sides, concave chest shrinking into itself, and she described herself as having an anxious disposition. Her breath was fast and shallow, her movements speedy and jerky, her voice a high-pitched flute with the speech fast, short, sharp, and clipped. Her mouth performed a dance of constant movement, pressing her lips shut into a thin line which became almost a grimace, and then pursing them.

Sylvie had grown up with her mother, father, two older brothers and her uncle (her father's brother). Her mother worked in a department store, her father and uncle on building sites. It was not a harmonious household; the father had a bad temper and a keen drinking habit in which his brother and wife joined. Sylvie, withdrawn and silent, discovered at an early age, encouraged by laughing drunk adults, that drinking allowed her to be someone different from the sad and largely forgotten child she felt herself to be. She quickly came to appreciate the freedom drinking accorded her and said that when she had a few drinks her mouth would fly with a freedom she found hard to imagine when sober and talking with others came easily. She acknowledged, however, that her drinking had progressed and now she drank a lot. Of late, she had often found herself feeling that she needed a drink in order to be able to cope at all, not just when she was with people.

Sylvie lived alone and had an administrative job in a large organization. Although she played the part of being happy enough at work, she felt that her life was one of pretense: no one really knew her or how she felt; she did not really care about anyone, nor did anyone care for her. She said she was always trying to please others, often felt manipulated, and could not stand up for herself. No one had ever stood up for her.

Touch had been a dangerous thing for her growing up; physical and emotional abuse was rife within the family and she had been orally sexually abused by the uncle at a young age; he had died of alcoholism some years prior to this time. Describing herself as naturally clumsy, she frequently dropped things or bumped into them and seemed to have little awareness of her body in time and space.

Hungry for physical connection, sex had never happened within the context of an intimate relationship. Although alcohol allowed her freedom to be with people physically, she would find herself having sex with people whom she would not have chosen were she not drunk. Intellectually, she proclaimed her right to have sex with whomsoever she wanted, but at a feeling level she wanted to care and be cared for, to love and be loved, to matter as a person rather than merely as a body that would suffice. Of late, she felt as if she were missing in action. Nights with others had become times of blackout; she'd been present but knew nothing of the experiences and the days following were drowned in waves of loss, shame, and regret.

Talking about herself in front of another person was a new experience for Sylvie. She had a strong streak of self-censorship which would swiftly enter to contradict what she had said or to call herself a liar. Words would come out, then would be snatched back.

A heavy drinker, Sylvie had also smoked like a chimney since adolescence. Her hunger she described as endless and voracious. She stated that the tactics with which she had once soothed herself no longer worked; previously she had felt her pain and past less when drunk, full with food, or high. Now, regardless of what she consumed, it no longer adequately relieved her of feelings, although she still felt compelled to stuff herself and then would despair when the act was done. Having reached the conclusion that she needed help, she was desperate to stop filling herself up with things she did not want and longed to be able to learn to trust herself–her words, body, actions–rather than being compelled by behaviors that brought only distress.

The first step in our work was to create safety and containment, a space for her to begin the process of coming to her body and voice, so that she could have a physical sense of herself *within* a body in order for her to feel and know herself and start to have an awareness of her own boundaries. Key to Sylvie's reclaiming of herself would be the need to take ownership of her mouth and her relationship to what was in it.

Sylvie's breath was short and narrow, the outbreath a tiny stream emerging through pursed lips. The idea of breathing brought fear. In order for Sylvie to access more breath and bypass the fear, I employed creative images which allowed her to expand breath without suggesting that her current supply was in any way inadequate: drinking nectar which slowly trickled down into her throat and soothed it; sipping breath from Cupid's cup; breathing in the sky with sunlight seeping in; a bird being tenderly fed by its mother.

When working with a pattern that has been held for decades, the fact that the body attitude and behaviors adopted are there for a reason needs to be taken into account. The body did what it needed to do in order to protect itself. It will not serve to try and take away patterns that the wounded self came up with in order to defend against external insults. Working by amplifying these patterns in an expressive creative way allowed them to be brought to consciousness, while breathing through an artistic prism enabled her gradually to allow the breath to become fuller and slower, introducing her to the spaces in her body. Trauma had impacted her relationship with breath; holding her breath as abuse was occurring allowed her to remove herself from reality, to dissociate from her body and move into her head as a means of protecting herself.

Extending the breath enabled Sylvie to extend her vocalizing. Letting breath in allowed sound to be carried out on waves of air and enabled her to access a greater range and variety of expressive non-articulated sounds, letting herself be taken by surprise by her own voice and by feelings that had not previously been accessible to her. Thus, she began to bring sensation back to that which had been numbed.

Once trust had been established in the working relationship, we focused on bringing awareness to her mouth. Unconscious initially of the movements of her lips, she spent some time touching, feeling, and moving them, bringing back sensation and life. In slowing down their sequence, she started to become conscious of some of the feelings and stories lurking within. She noted that cigarettes fitted neatly into the small space created by her pursued lips and filled the gap as if the cigarettes were a stopper. In one session as Sylvie sounded 'Oooh' in a contained way through those pursed lips, I suggested she let the sound lead her and follow what it wanted to do. As she did so, the amplification began to tell its own story and she began to feel the tension in her face which had been keeping everything in place. Her face trembled into tears; liquid fell from her eyes as sound fell from her mouth, and her mouth began to open wider, which was confusing for her. She expressed that she felt scared of losing control; normally, she said, her mouth was never so wide open without being filled with matter. As she explored and voiced with a wider oral space, her mouth spasmed several times as she became aware of sensations and vibrations. Her lips began a noticeable sucking motion as if sucking on an object her mouth stretched to accommodate, something bigger than her oral space could comfortably fit around. I suspected that the contortions and tics of her mouth had formed themselves around a much larger story.

As Sylvie expressed some of what she had been obliged to keep contained, her voice descended into her body, the pitch dropped and widened, and feelings were carried on waves of sound, seeming to shake loose old material. She wandered into unfamiliar vocal territory, passing through aural landscapes, her voice claiming and exclaiming tremulousness, high-pitched whimpers of fear. Sounds pained, discarded, silenced, and unheard became howls of outrage anchored in wild and abandoned parts of herself. I encouraged her to linger in areas that felt good to her, replaying melodies or rhythms.

As her mouth, voice, body and ears began to recognize melodies which she could depart from and to which she could return, she found signposts to hold onto, repetitions upon which she could elaborate vocally and melodically. Making artistic choices as to what to express, she no longer had to live in the raw grief and anger of what had befallen her. In that way, some sounds were familiar, and expanding upon those initial sounds enabled her to begin the process of trusting herself, giving shape and form to what was intangible and making something that was hers. She began to develop a sense of direction, of destination, building new melodic memories and discarding what she chose. Her confidence in her voice and ability grew as she learned she could depend upon herself and the tales her body conveyed. Her melodic structures began to shape into words as a song arrived on rivers of vocalizing and tears and marked a major transitional moment in terms of dealing with the issue of her mouth:

> My mouth
> it's my mouth
> not your mouth
> leave me alone.
> Get out of my mouth
> get out of me
> leave me alone.
> My mouth
> my mouth
> not your mouth,
> it's my mouth.
> It's only my mouth,
> get out of my mouth,
> do not come near me
> This is mine.

When she first began discovering the words of this song, she would collapse into tears and whimper that she couldn't and it hurt. I encouraged her to stay with it, to let this energy have its voice. With support, she was able to harness her power and she rose to a crescendo, screaming,

> Because this is mine
> this is mine
> never yours,
> always mine.
> You took my mouth from me
> you took me from me
> but now I'm back,
> now I'm back,
> now I'm back
> you are gone.

She saw this song as a liberation, a rejection of the intruding person, a claiming of herself in ways she had not previously been able to do. Improvising enabled Sylvie to start to trust sensations in her body, her oral cavity, her feelings and impulses. As her self was changing and developing, sounding the inner landscape enabled her to self-create, making something which came from her and was hers. The many creative vocal possibilities enabled her to sound her feelings about what she had endured—expressing, changing, shaping, transforming. In the site of abuse and memory she was able to find new experiences, to give her mouth agency, and to express what had been inexpressible. In finding relationship with her mouth, Sylvie's vocal and imagistic explorations expanded, translating sensations into images, amplifying her intrinsic melodies and letting song lyrics develop from her vocalized expression and words.

In one session, with nasality her dominant sound, I asked her to imagine she had the power to shape her life how she wanted it. Widening her mouth and face, she began to turn in different directions, casting arcs with her body in semi-spherical shapes. Her arms followed suit and she began to cast a spell, saying she needed this much space and this much space, de-marking space with her arms. She said, "This is my space, this is my face, and I will take all the space that I want; you may not step inside this space unless I allow you." With her arms she instigated up and down movements, as if flapping her wings, and declared herself a firebird who would burn anyone who touched her without her express permission; this included even looking at her the wrong way.

Come to me my firebird
hold my tender heart
coat my lips with maple love
I swear I won't break you.

Now I am the firebird,
and don't you even dare
to write my name upon your lips,
for it will cost you dear.

I pulled that ragged child
from her ancient hiding place
I held her to my arms
and breathed love into her heart.

My breath burns with fire
a ferocity lives inside
it saves me from the worst of you
and warms my blood at night.

I am a firebird,
I dazzle and I dance,
safe to move,
safe to be.
I am all of me,

brilliant,
ferocious,
dancing,
here
and singing me.
I am me.

Her movements fluid, Sylvie sang her improvised firebird song, owning her voice, mouth, body, and the space. She said she was fiery yet tender, tough yet gentle, protective and all-encompassing. She said she was free to move, to sing, to drip tears which would feed, nourish and heal her. She said she was powerful and no one could mess with her; she would beat them off with her wings, and if she wished, she could fly away. The firebird image stayed with her and she would bring it to mind in difficult circumstances or when she felt the need of additional strength. I later discovered that the firebird is synonymous with the phoenix, that Sylvie was rising from her own ashes.

The first year of life is predicated upon oral experience. The mouth is the site of nurture and connection with another, as babies explore and discover pleasure and its lack. It is where they start to understand themselves and their world, navigating eating, drinking, sucking, breathing, and sounding; where power and ownership are experienced, as control over what comes in and what leaves is exercised. Here relationships are being forged with the inner world of the self–including expression, self-soothing and self-regulation–and with others in the outside world. They are being formed, as well, between tongue, cheeks, jaw and teeth. The ability to digest matter, experiences, and ideas, and to be stimulated and gratified are also being discovered.

The mouth is one of the primary ways of discovering identity. Sylvie's relationship between nurture and abuse was disrupted, and this disrupted the development of self and identity. The transgressions against appropriate oral development meant that she was forced to take in that which was not wanted, but upon which her survival may have depended, as the oral abuse was perpetrated by a family member. Ownership of the self through determining what we take in is basic; if one's orifices are not one's own, then the signals of appropriate boundaries and determinations as to what belongs where, what may be allowed entry and what refused, can become confused. Her mouth and self had been forged around the desires of another. This early violation meant Sylvie had to hold secrets inside her mouth, body and psyche. Her sense of self was predicated upon believing she needed to hide her essential self, that she was unacceptable, unlovable, and undeserving, that there was something inside her which was too terrible to imagine, yet also too terrible to let out.

Sylvie came to the realization that her mouth was confused in its desires;

she did not know what she wanted, needed, or craved at any time. In the interests of survival, barriers are often constructed around the wounds we have experienced, repressing and consigning them to the unconscious in an attempt to prevent them from emerging. She described the senses of her mouth as being in chaos and said she often filled the hole full to shut up its clamor. In the body's attempt to incorporate the trauma, the memory of it had become part of Sylvie's somatic patterning. She had developed many ways of reacting subconsciously to the fear of oral penetration by clamping her mouth tightly shut and using addictions, including eating disorders, drinking and avoidance of intimacy and relationships. All of these were rooted in an unconscious endeavor to keep the child that had endured such treatment silent and, indeed, allowed her for periods of time to escape from her feelings. Although I had made some inferences based on her oral cavity behavior, it was important for Sylvie that her mouth was allowed to reveal for itself what it was declaring with its actions.

The work of coming to the body takes time. Sylvie had felt that her body was unsafe for her since being a small child and had continued a negligent relationship with it into adulthood. It was necessary for her to come into relationship with her body, to listen to what had happened to and in it, and how it had affected who she had become. Her personal story needed to be heard so that what she had endured could be received and understood and her experience witnessed.

Sylvie was initially very judgmental of any sound she made and often wanted to withdraw and judge it. She felt that her voice had been silenced for years, her words forbidden, and that led to feeling her self was forbidden. Freedom came in multiple ways. She was no longer swallowing down or subduing her experiences; instead, she was starting to heal the ambivalence around her mouth by expressing herself and starting only to swallow what she desired. It was a clear and tender rewriting of her somatic reality in a combination of gentle, slow, deep expressive and agonized voice and movement work.

Writing new stories from early difficulties takes a lot of work. The ambiguity of the site of feeding and nurture being also the site of wounding is a huge injury. This related in no small way to the lack of trust Sylvie felt in herself and her rejection of her own words. Her journey began by a new knowing through the means of the internal realm of breath, body and voice. Initially, it was sounds unfettered by language which enabled her to express her feelings. Listening to her body's cries and creatively shaping her material allowed her to use her voice to forge a new reality from her emotional and physical experiences, incorporating her understanding, compassion and knowledge to bring together different elements into a new relationship which enabled her to know it in a whole other way, thus finding agency over her life. Voicing enabled her to express and break down material that she had never been able to digest or countenance. As she was able to express some of the feelings which had been silenced for so long, Sylvie's voice became stronger, able to say 'No!' and stand up for her, to declare the oral space hers and nobody else's, and to claim and comfort that small child who still dwelt inside.

The rebuilding of Sylvie's relationship with her oral cavity allowed her mouth to explore in safety, tuning in to rather than suppressing sensations and feelings while attempting to untangle some of the strands which brought confusion as she began to rearrange the structures of herself. Forging new patterns of vibration provided alternatives to the oral chaos; in expressing and removing old patterns she was able to change them by making new rhythms. She began to feel deeply the transformative and liberating effects of owning her voice. Releasing the breath enabled greater freedom of voice and movement, as well, and the freedom to engage in certain actions that might hold within them the shadow of the initial action that originated the trauma.

Being present with and psychologically holding Sylvie as her story unfolded was crucial to creating safety for her ability to listen to and acknowledge it for herself, enabling her to remain conscious and not fall into an inability to differentiate what was occurring in her mouth. She described it as inhabiting a previously unknown landscape. The ability to be honest with herself in the presence of another for the first time in her life allowed her to start to acknowledge some of the trauma she had lived through, to witness and have empathy for herself rather than constantly berating herself for who she had become and her unwanted behaviors. Through understanding that it was possible to be who she really was, Sylvie was able to become conscious of feelings that were occurring and to find relationship with her body and within herself.

Through the musicalization of the trauma, Sylvie was able to unshackle from some of that which had kept her bound. Her mouth became the instrument of change and also, down the line, of love and acceptance, allowing her oral cavity to fill with the sound of herself and forging a conscious relationship with her mouth. Over time, she was able to use her voice to comfort or express herself when times were hard, spontaneously composing songs and beginning to notice that when she wanted to silence sensations in her body, she was able to make different choices rather than drinking or eating herself into oblivion. No longer helpless in the face of an old energy, she could start to bring some of her self-determination and agency into her mouth and own it. Through being able to feel her body, she was able to establish boundaries of what was acceptable to her and to find a greater degree of safety in her body.

Sylvie was able to reassess what she wanted and described herself as learning how to be kind to herself. She became more empowered, able to make and deepen friendships, and create relationship not only with herself but also with another person. She continues to sing and to use her voice to self-soothe and to declare herself.

MEANWOOD: A GROUP SESSION: PYRAMID OF ARTS, LEEDS, UK

Carol Grimes

He sat on a hard-backed chair, a frail and elderly man, head bowed, eyes downcast, his thin and gnarled hands clasping and unclasping on his lap, his two bony legs clamped together at the knees. As I sang my song, squatting down in front of him, he replied almost inaudibly and with a slight stammer, his modest and timid demeanor giving the impression of a person being told to agree with authority. This was "Fred," aged approximately 73 years, with "Clare" sitting next to him, her large body almost overflowing her wheelchair, wearing a blue and white floral print dress, her face startling for its open, expectant and beautiful innocence.

Fred and Clare were two members of a group of people, sixteen in all, known as the Swarthmore group. The common thread that bound them was the long-stay institution in Yorkshire known as Meanwood Park Hospital. The group had all been residents who had within the last three years been rehoused in group homes or care centers out in the community. They ranged in age from 40 to 85 years old and had high support needs; including being wheelchair bound and having so-called "challenging behaviors." Several were also blind, one profoundly deaf and two partially so.

I had been invited by Jane, a co-worker with the group and someone with whom I had worked in November 1999 when I was facilitating a group, alongside other artists, for Welfare State International in Ulverstone, Cumbria. I had worked for this company before and the content was always rich and exploratory. The work this week was based on Rites of Passage, this particular one being Death and the rituals of the Funeral. Jane had invited me to take part in the performance piece that she had devised over the five-day course.

Her subject matter had touched me. It concerned the death of a man named John, a previous resident of Meanwood. She had met John on her first visit to the Hospital. It was the experience of that meeting and the recognition of the inhumane and harsh conditions endured by such people as Fred and Clare, often from early infancy or childhood through to old age—a lifetime—that inspired the work that Jane is involved with today. Two sentences from her work in Ulverstone still echo inside my head: "Watch with care. Catch the glance-dance offering of friendship." Over meals and during one evening we had spoken about Arts and Therapy and their use in long-stay institutions. Jane had presented a grim and depressing picture of the "music therapy" she had witnessed at Meanwood in those early days: broken tambourines and songs which held no meaning for the people present"—dull, lifeless and devoid of inspiration or connection. The week in Ulverstone had proved it to be a supportive and creative place for her to work through the anger and despair that her previous work over the years had, understandably, aroused in her.

As I sang my first song in front of this group of people in a large and cheerless room in central Leeds, I felt my throat tighten, hot tears pricking my eyes, and I was uncertain, indeed nervous and concerned, as to whether I would be capable of engaging with this group and how I would even begin to find a way of communicating and involving them in any sort of cohesive interplay. How would I connect?

I wanted them to have the joy of song and the pleasure of dance. I was overcome with the need to please these people, more than any I had ever sung for in my life. And yet all I felt inside me was a sense of helplessness and inadequacy. I was faced with twisted and misshapen bodies; voices that could produce little more than strangled and inarticulate sounds; mouths that discharged saliva and moans, displaying decayed teeth and lolling tongues. A tiny birdlike woman, sitting twisted in her wheelchair, blood still fresh on her hands and face, an outsized plaster stuck onto her forehead—the results of daily self-harm.

Jane had asked me to sing a few songs, to perform a concert for the group and then begin to work, encouraging everyone to sing and to move. As the group contained people with hearing difficulties, I realized that my ability to sing with a big voice was going to prove an asset in this situation, my early days as a busker (unlicensed street singer) coming home to roost. Singing a repetitive phrase, a riff, I clapped out a rhythm, encouraging people—volunteers, co-workers and the group—to sing along with me while I attempted to relate to and integrate everybody in the room. Once I felt a sense of sound and involvement, I began my first song, singing over the sounds the group was making.

Beginning with difficulty, struggling to find focus and to control my own emotions, moving around the group making sure that I found each pair of eyes, and in the case of the two blind people present, that I approached them gently, not too abruptly or too loudly, I tried to sing with clearly articulated words, using my face, my mouth, to create a revealing picture of my songs and making full use of my arms and hands. Clear signals. I felt an acute lack of a language: signing! After the session, a young volunteer informed me that the system called Makaton was simple and effective.

I had chosen some songs old and new. Jane had told me that some of the younger ones loved to hear the Beatles songs from 1950s radio days. Thank goodness for the songs and the memory of a shared music culture. May, aged sixty-five, wheelchair-bound and with speech that was extremely difficult to understand, began to move around in her chair almost immediately, her face animated and full of laughter, emoting shrieks and grunts. Jane grabbed the chair and they whirled around the floor, as if dancing in an old-style School Dance, May howling and leaping with pleasure—if such a thing is possible in a wheelchair, and I witnessed it, so I know that it is. Jane told me that May has a wicked sense of humor and I could see this so clearly as the bizarre and wonderful dance took place.

Rose, capable of slow and careful independent movement, slipped out of her chair and made a steady and rhythmic circuit of the room within the circle of the group, a dance of intensity and focus, her knees bent and awkward, adopting a shuffling motion whilst her arms were engaged in delicate and fluid movements with obvious connection to the rhythms of my song. The first song was barely out of my mouth and already I had some dancers on the floor. Those dancers gave me such palpable feelings of relief; I cannot hope to reach everybody, but if some enjoy this day, then I will feel I have been of use.

As I sang, I became aware of a voice both mirthful and maniacal. I found myself momentarily distracted, forgot my lyrics, lost the sense of where I was and why and with whom. All the pressures of a performer's life, striving for perfection, pleasing the audience, wanting to impress and prove myself to others, flooded into my mind: an attack of self-doubt, of being judged and found wanting. I momentarily disappeared inside myself. With some effort I reconnected with what was happening, the theatre taking place. I was a part of it. The reality of the situation became clear. Struggling with my own idea of a good performance here and now was not important. Connecting with the present, being with the people in this room, allowing my instincts as a performer, true to myself—this is all I can expect of me in this moment.

"Whoosh! Whoosh!" A man called James, aged 47, his means of expressing excitement drawn from a limited vocabulary that included "Aba, aba" which indicated "Me, me," his forefinger jabbing at his chest, and "No, No." He rushed around the room, his ability to sit and focus quite limited. On occasion he would sit with the group, appearing to take in what was happening, staring at me. His face was craggy, lined and intense with a large and jutting jaw, his eyes in turn anxious, elated or angry. Then after a while he would take off, running wildly around the room as if unable to cope with all the energy that his body contained. He would come to a halt, standing by a wall, one hand down his trousers, his sweatshirt up around his chest, beating his stomach incessantly or rubbing his penis with tensile strength as if beating frantic, urgent time on a drum.

I introduced a rhythmic pattern, asking the members of the group. in turn, to tell me the name of their favorite food. Bob, a man who was partially deaf, said "Banana," so we all sang Banana, a perfect three-syllable word to sing percussively. Banana was followed by Fish and Chips, and Bread and Butter (Fred's food), then Plums and Sandwiches. I clapped the rhythms of their chosen foods and we all sang our words as if we were a percussion orchestra. We ended up with nine or so participants, some singing food names, others sounds of their own making, winding and weaving in an eerie and unique vocal patchwork across the pulse of the group sound.

Bugger rang out loud and clear. "Bugger! Bugger!" This was interjected by hysterical and shrieking laughter from Joan, one of the younger members of the group. I stomped my feet to the beat of "Bugger! Bugger!" with Joan until she began to dance in time with her voice, stamping her feet. With "Bugger" and "Whoosh," "Bananas," "Fish and Chips" and several "Bread and Butters," "Plums" and "Sandwiches," we created a rhythmic and colorful piece of music.

The pace I normally worked at and any expectations I may have had as to what I could achieve from a musical perspective had to be totally relinquished. Some people were unreachable, locked away in another reality. I had to be careful, patient and prepared to change tack at any moment, to accept failure and that some ideas might not work, necessitating a quick shift into another idea, revaluating preconceived thoughts about what music is. What is perfection?

I remembered a song I had learned many years ago in childhood and had sung to my own children: "There's a worm at the bottom of the garden and his name is Wiggly Woo." A simple melody, an old song, and two or three people seemed familiar with it. We were off and I, for one, thoroughly enjoyed it. We sang this several times, and once again, any preconceptions of what and how I might normally work had to be abandoned. I worked slowly and with clarity, giving people time to absorb, to remember and to understand. As the session progressed, I observed that one or two people were holding a melody and I decided to add some simple harmony: 3rds and 5ths and the octaves above and below. The volunteers were wonderful and seemed to be enjoying the singing as much as anyone in the room. That was the moment I felt it all fall into place. It is not them and us; it is us. It is we. In that moment I felt as if I was part of that community.

Feeling the need for the group to catch its collective breath, I sang the John Lennon song, "Imagine" which pleased the Beatles fans, bringing James back into the circle once more. Encouraging the group to sing the first two lines over and over, some singing the lyrics, I asked two of the volunteers to sing the melody along with Fred and Clare. When I felt we had established a fairly solid base, I began singing harmonies and giving harmonies to those I felt could hold them, one or two members of the Swarthmore group now more confident than the young volunteers. Then I gave out some rhythm parts to others who had enjoyed the food song. As the harmony and pulse emerged, I noticed Pat, partially deaf and totally blind, sitting on the lap of Steve, a core worker, lying comfortably back on his chest, her head on one of his shoulders, moving from side to side as he sang. During the feedback process which concluded the session, Steve said that Pat had indeed responded strongly to his harmony work. She was hearing Steve's voice, feeling the vibrations inside his chest and possibly the voices in harmony closest to them. I felt that this was the only moment during the afternoon that she entered into the music.

Adam in his wheelchair, his body locked and twisted, had very little clarity in his speech. His voice held extreme tension and rigidity. I was told that Adam was a Leap Year baby. As a result of this accident of birth, he insists that he is in fact only thirteen years old, another example of the humor and fun hidden for most of their lives. As the afternoon unfolded, Adam became increasingly vocal, his face alight with expansive smiles, his chin and chest wet with saliva. He attempted to clap his hands and seemed to want to communicate, to sing and to move, his voice wild and raw, his misshapen hands clawing the air trying to find the Rhythm.

Another wonderful bit of history concerned Mick who, at over 80 years old, was one of the elder members of the group and the first to arrive that morning. After being relocated outside the community, he had become very ill and was sent back to Meanwood Hospital, "To die," as Jane put it bluntly.

He survived and to this day likes to "pretend shoot," fingers held in that classic cowboy-with-pistol position, well loved by little boys when I was a child. "Ambulance Men," he sneers, his finger pistol at the ready. He sits in his wheelchair as a result of operations on his knees and feet and says he loves to paint and draw. Mick launched into song each time I sang, not necessarily the song I was singing at the time, but he was singing when he wasn't shooting "Ambulance Men."

To the sophisticated musical ear, the singing may have held dysphonic, raucous and clamorous sounds, unsettling and angry sounds, piercing and penetrating sounds. Some of the people attending this session were certainly doing all this and more. To my ear the sounds were indeed often disturbing, but a wholly authentic articulation of the human being vocalizing spontaneous and immediate feelings.

As to how I feel I could work with a person who has had constricted and inarticulate speech for so many years, I imagine it would have to be the result of a long process. Building a trusting relationship with whomever one is working with, a gentle exploration of what is possible, working with care, expanding the realm of potential within the voice, listening and observing. What is it that constricts the voice within? In the physical manifestation of the individual's voice, where is the tension? Using rhythm and vibration, melody and harmony, in some cases massage and movement, one could, at the very least, bring the joy of a voice in song into the hearts and minds of a population who for years, indeed often for a lifetime, have had their truthful voice denied to them, locked away.

I had taken for granted these gifts of freedom, the right to speak and sing. I had made it my life. Singing for my children. Singing for their supper—and mine, too.

The core workers had brought with them a huge pile of scrapbooks overflowing with color. These were the diaries, the books of life, of personal history, and a previous project. I was given the honor of handing these out at the end of the session. I felt a sense of the ritual and importance attached to this procedure. I felt as if I was handing out the Oscars!

James (Whoosh!) grabbed my hand. "Aba, Aba," he said, jabbing my finger onto a photo of himself inside his book. "Me! Me!" The photo was of several people, James in the near distance, full length, hardly recognizable, but it was he, captured on camera and a tangible proof of his existence. Watching him rush around the room, his diary spilling from his arms, "Aba, Aba," I thought about my own life rich in its documentation. My children's every mood and moment caught lovingly on my camera. The locks of baby hair, first baby tooth, first shoes, the identity tags from their tiny wrists at birth, the bears and train sets, the books and childhood paintings lovingly preserved, all kept safely for those moments when they might want these treasures and memories from their childhood, their lives the most important part of my own.

My heart felt as if it might break. I suddenly wanted to leave. The group was gradually dispersing, the room being cleared, the tea urn emptied. Whoosh. I needed to cry. On the train travelling back to my home in London later that day, I thought about what could have enhanced my work, what resources would I need to work with a group such as the Swarthmore? Songs Ancient and Modern. Enlarging my repertoire to encompass a broader range of songs from different genres. Music Hall and Vaudeville, Folksongs, Pop songs, songs from the war years, Hymns, and me not a practicing Christian, but in so many cases if a song fits, then I will sing it, singing the songs which may hold meaning for the people I am singing with.

A Follow-up Session

I returned to Leeds where I met up with Jane and the group for a second time. The group was all involved in a project around the song, "There's a worm at the bottom of the garden." All manner of paintings and creations had emerged, in Jane's own words, "In some cases dark and others playful."

The song had apparently been a great success! So, the only childhood song that had come to my mind had proved fruitful and served to remind me that it is often the simplest things that will resonate and connect with others, an element which in the performing community often lies forgotten in the search for originality. Art inspired by singers such as the Swarthmore group, my Sing for Joy choirs begun almost ten years ago by and with people with Parkinson's disease and other neurological diseases, my experience in Musical Theatre working with people with real stories about real lives lived on the very edge of danger and death... How that manifests itself into art that is never comfortable but often beautiful. In my own way, I am humbled by all of this and privileged to work so closely with art expression and voice, inspired by all whose lives I come in contact with.

From my experience working with people and using the principles of Voice Movement Therapy, I believe that singing for the heart in torment, vocalizing as a means of communicating the very innermost tenebrous feelings—emotions that cannot be spoken of in a common language, words often being inadequate—can in many cases assist with long held trauma, depression and/or simply a desire to be able to speak up, sing out, and find a sound and confident voice as a means of self-expression. The movement of a body in the throes of a dance, in tune with the impulses of the soul, the heart, the breath, is an exhilarating experience for those who have perhaps never managed to use their voice and body in such a free and uninhibited way. Singing, screaming, crying, laughing, shrieking, moaning, shouting—all this is the expression of the inner life, of the memories that lie imprinted in the body within the map of a human life history.

Our very skin and bones are steeped with the unfolding development of our own lives. Unravelling the past, making sense of hitherto unfathomable feelings and voicing them can be a rigorous, even brutal undertaking in one unused to voicing the unspeakable. To face the darkest corners and look at the most feared memories is a daunting procedure. To vocalize those shadows, to find the voice that can convey what is within, is to assist an individual in releasing long-held and often deeply buried trauma. This is where the interface between art and therapy begins: in the act of creation. In the artistic expression of truth and of innate feelings in poetry and prose; with painting and image; masks and dance; and especially, in this instance, in the singing of the song, the soul song pouring out from within, the song that sings in response to profound and heartfelt emotions, letting it flow... This is art as solace for the soul.

MR. HANDY: A POLICEMAN IN TROUBLE

Boniswa Kamba

I would like to present to you this case study and I will call him "Handy," a pseudonym. Handy grew up in the rural areas of King William's Town. He is a married man with three children. He has a very good relationship with his wife and his children, as well. His children have grown up. They are adults who are working for themselves. Handy did not know me. He was referred to me by the Wellness Manager from the Traffic Department who knew that I am an Educator in HIV/AIDS and a Counselling Officer and that I have been working with them for a long time.

Handy is an educated traffic officer. He graduated with a BA Degree from the Faculty of Science at the University of Fort Hare. He has worked for the Traffic Department for almost 27 years. He is the Supervisor in the District and has recently been given authority to work with others as a Senior Officer. Due to a dispute and poor working relations with one of his colleagues, he was suspended one month without pay. He was then instructed to undergo counselling and anger management sessions and I received a letter from the department requesting me to work with him.

1st Session

As I was requested by the department to conduct these sessions at the Traffic Department building, I had to make an appointment as to when to meet with Handy, and the date was set. I was then given a special office where I would be together alone with Handy. As he entered this office, which was an office with enough space to move and make sound in, he found me already there. He greeted me with a hard voice but was humble and looking very sad. I allowed him to sit a little closer in front of me. I wanted him to share more of his background.

He mentioned that he was married with three children. Handy does not normally visit the Doctor unless there is something serious at the moment. Otherwise, he seldom goes. Handy was never a singer before. His last singing was at school, but when he joined College, he never sang. Handy shared a lot about his work and his relations with the Senior Officers. He mentioned that they were doing a roadblock in one of the areas in Cacadu District. There was a time when he was found sitting in the car by one of his colleagues and would not get out of the car to guard the roadblock, even when told he must do that by his fellow officer. As a result, at the end of the month, he was told that he was not going to get his salary because of what happened that day. As he was sharing the story, his eyes turned red. I could see he was not happy at all. I then introduced myself and what I do and checked for another date to meet with him. He said he is in need of counselling very much.

2nd Session

In this session, I shared with him that I am going to use principles of Voice Movement Therapy which is about liberating the voice, breathing in and out, loosening your muscles and singing freely according to how you fell physically, emotionally, socially, mentally and spirit-wise. I then requested him to get to the floor and begin to shake, shake his body. We were wheeling our hands around as if we'd just finished washing them. All parts of his body were shaking. At first, he seemed as if he was not going to follow my instructions, but as we went on he tried to do what I was doing. We did that for a while and then we stopped for sharing. How did he feel about it? I felt that my work was very good and that in the next session, we will work together harmoniously.

3rd Session

I said we are going to make a follow-up of what happened in the previous session and continue with something else. I asked if he had ever done deep breathing and he said, "When I visited Doctor." I said we are going to do such breathing today. I told him the importance of breathing, breathing through the mouth right to the stomach, and how by that way you get more oxygen into the lungs. We did breathing right through. We did it standing, we did it sitting down. We did this for some time until he felt tired.

Then we went on with him lying on his side. I then requested him to make any kind sound he could do coming from the mouth. He did that with a low medium sound in a grinding, disrupted and reluctant voice. His voice is big like a donkey. After a while we went back to the floor. I wanted him to share how he felt after that. He could not explain it clearly, but he said he is so angry, he cannot feel a thing. I encouraged him to come again because that was not going to take just one day to get healed.

4th Session

Handy and I began walking around in a circle. We tried to swing our arms around, front and backwards while doing deep breathing and sounding. He was a big heavy man and it was hard for him to bend. We held our hands up above the head, then lifted our shoulders slowly and I asked him to let his hands come down to his shoulders and then let them drop while he bent over in concave letting his hands go down passing his waist, hips and legs toward the toes. Because he had a big waist, I asked him to let the muscles go as much as possible while trying to do this. We did it for a while. When we came back into a sitting position, he shared that it was not easy, though he managed to do it as mandated. For me, working with this man alone was not easy. This was in a closed space and no one could see what was going on there and I knew he was an angry man, so I was not comfortable. Whilst he was tense with me, on the other hand I was tense with him, but I carried on.

After that session, I went to two of my colleagues, one of them a Human Resource and Development Officer. I told them that sessions are going on and the man is getting more upset and I am afraid of working alone with him. My colleague MacLoud, the Human Resource and Development Officer, volunteered himself to be in these sessions with me as a witness and it happened that the man was very happy to have another man present. MacLoud attended all the sessions from then on.

5th Session

At this session we went back to the floor. I let him do the breathing with his eyes closed. I let him do the sounding, and he followed me as I was doing it. As we were breathing and sounding, I let him come up with something else. We had a little bit of pause. He decided that we would do some drawings because he likes to do that. He did a picture of a crying woman. When we were sharing, he mentioned that he had to draw this because as we do these exercises his wife is at home waiting for him to bring money, but he can't get it because his employers are not concerned that if he can't work, he can't get the salary to support his wife. He is very angry about the whole thing.

6th Session

I went alongside Handy doing the breathing, as it is always the first thing to do when we meet in the morning. I asked him to create a sound as he breathes. He did it beautifully. His voice was low, most likely his natural voice. I noticed that his voice is very limited as if it is blocked somewhere. He frequently did coughing and began afresh. When I noticed that he wants to come higher in pitch with his voice but is blocked on the way, I came nearer to him and asked if he wanted me to give some help and he said yes. But then he said, "Mama, it is not me, I am angry–how can I do these things being angry as I am now? Do you want my voice to appear nice here, yet I am dead inside?" That gave me another chance of thinking about this afresh.

The fact here is that this man is suspended without pay. When sharing this to me he said. "Why?" From a constitutional point of view, procedures were not followed at all. But how can I intervene? No, I must just do what I was requested to do. The session ended.

7th Session

In this session we did sounds differently. By that time were walking right around the circle. His voice was louder today and he was able to take it to a higher pitch and he did it as if it is a sound of the pig, with pitch fluctuation which helped loosen his voice more. I realized later on that he is very fond of dogs. He asked me if he cannot do the sound of a dog? I let him do that and his voice came out better. He could walk around doing this voice of a dog, and he ran around the circle as if he is running after his dog. I said "Okay, can you take your dog up and down?" He did it exactly as I said, in pitches. He was stretching with his dog. He was walking around the circle with his dog. He was fully engaged, and that was what I wanted.

8th Session

In this session I asked him to slightly turn and rise up, trying to keep that deep breathing while we moved around the room stretching arms, voicing and sounding. We held our arms as if we are holding a ball in front. I let him make his own space. As he was making this big "O!" he was feeling his own space with his arms, holding and moving them in front of himself. I walked slowly towards him and sensed that he did not want me to come closer, so I asked him if he could tell me if I was too close. He said, "Yes, you are too close" It was very important for him that he could say that.

We continued with the opening and closing with the arms and moving our bodies backwards and forwards in convex and concave. We did that for a while, dancing around the circle, bending and stretching from side to side, forward and back and in other different positions. After that, I could see that he was exhausted. I was tired, too.

9th Session

This time when we were getting to the floor, I gave this man a paper again for him to write down his imaginings after he went through the stages of breathing and sounding. He drew the picture of a vulture. He commented saying he likes vultures because vultures have strong good eyes. When the vulture sees the victim, he doesn't care whether it is underwater or down amongst the trees. He just goes for it.

10th Session

In this session we began walking around. I was wanting to engage him both physically and vocally. I wanted him to feel his voice and the importance of having such a voice. When he was voicing out, I could feel that his voice is coming alright, but that he needed some massage for it to come out clearly. Difficult as it was for me, I asked him if I could be at his back and assist him in breathing and in getting out his voice. He accepted. I began by stretching his right arm, starting from the neck. At this time, he was sitting on the floor. From the neck I went down to the ribcage. I did it repeatedly, stretching his neck back and forwards. I could sense that he is getting a little bit more comfortable. At that time his voice was going its own way, from lower to upper higher pitch, from a shallow to a more full sound. As I was doing that, he just said, "Okay, it's enough." He commented and wished that if these sessions could be done with his wife included, he was sure that all could be right. Unfortunately, we were not able to do that. He commented about the message on his back. He just said, about those muscles, that maybe by the time he finished these sessions they would be ok.

11th Session

We worked hard on vocal sounds. On this day he brought me a hand drum. He wanted to sing with the drum. He said in the beginning of our sessions that he is not a good singer. At this time when he was beating the drum, I saw a talented man who can do more than he thinks he can. Then we worked on his voice, imitating different kinds of animals. He became a lion. His eyes could take in the whole space using both his peripheral and his central vision. He became tired. He requested water to drink. I gave it to him.

After a while, I let him walk slowly to calm down and then we discussed his feeling about his journey with the drum and making his voice with different sounds. On the feedback, he commented that he could easily find himself looking upwards and not at the drum that he was beating. He said also he noticed that he was losing weight and told me that he often finds himself at home doing these exercises. He was happy with that. Thirdly, he finds he is able to handle the anger, even though he has not yet finished these sessions. I was happy because, me, too, I was motivated by the way he reacted towards all the sessions. I had wondered how his behavior would be because I did not get to even ask him if he would be my client, I just worked on him because the letter that was sent to me mandated it. It is different when a person comes to you voluntarily and when it is mandated that they must work with you. I was pleased that his man's mandated situation was working so well.

12th Session

In this session I invited him for a small walk on the floor. We did that right round the circle. I wanted him, as an official, to master the way of walking when you get to your office. Sophisticated people don't just walk. Their walk is different. It was difficult for him to do that. His comment was that he is coming from a rural area and had never been exposed to smart walking, even at school. There were no rules taught about that. But he was very willing to try to do that walking and breathing and voicing as if it were out of the top of his head. I felt it was very important for him to be able to leave the past dispute behind and his feelings of anger and shame. Therefore, if they allowed him to go back to his work, I felt that his walking with dignity would help him to prove that he had changed. I think that was a very good idea and I myself gained a lot from it.

13th Session

At this session we did stretching of muscles and getting more relaxed, and I reminded him to continue with VMT breathing through the mouth into the abdomen. Here I thought of acting like an animal. We then started with the ape, or primate, style and that helped to break some tension because it was a more relaxed way to be. I can see that the ape is loose and I wanted him to be able to be less tense.

We started walking all over the hall as little apes talking to each other just like they do. We were both tired by then. We shared our experiences and then the session ended.

14th Session

We started here with a circle. At such times my colleague MacLoud, who usually just observed, would ask if he could join us in the circle of walking, and that made us all very comfortable. The man liked it when MacLoud joined us and it gave him an opportunity to experience a bit what the work felt like. We then went back to the breathing exercises which was our priority to do when beginning our sessions each day. I explained to Handy that he must never forget the VMT areas of breathing—Chest, Ribcage, and Abdomen (see page 23)—because it would help him if he was shocked or angry to recognize how he was depriving himself of the air and be able to take a full breath to calm himself. Then he could handle that situation better and not get into such problems again.

We did the exercise when you rub your hands together to make heat and run them down the sides of your face to loosen the jaw muscles because I had noticed that Handy frequently rubbed his face up and downwards to loosen the tension there. He began to loosen up his shoulders, also, stretching his legs and moving his feet and toes on the floor. I noticed that he likes it and I let him do that repeatedly. Most of the time was spent on the breathing areas. Breathing was the only place where he felt very comfortable when he finished and then his voice came out the way he liked it. Though he was not familiar with this in the beginning, as we went on he became geared to it. I was pleased that he got used to it because I know that it will help him.

15th Session

I showed Handy a drawing from Paul Newham's book *The Singing Cure* that I always show my clients when I facilitate these sessions: how one must imagine going into his abdomen/her abdomen so that they don't have to lift up their shoulders. They must imagine their abdomen being a balloon, expanding when inhaling and deflating when exhaling. I also explained that the abdominal muscles must help them to exhale by contracting or pulling them in. And then I invited him again to the floor. We did the breathing using all the three parts of the body. Handy was enjoying every little bit of the action that took place then. I felt good, as I was getting to the end of the sessions and I could see Handy is feeling better now than before.

16th Session

At this time, I wanted to check to see if he was understanding that he could make his space-what I call it because many people I work with do not understand the concept of a sphere. I drew an imaginary line in the corner of the hall and asked him to stand behind it because I wanted him to feel how limited his voice was and that he could extend it further.

He began to breathe shallowly and gradually, but then was able to project his voice in front of him across the line so that it reached further, and he was so comfortable with that! He did it for a while. Then we did feedback. He mentioned that he is still struggling with his muscles, as they are not used to such actions. He realized it when he woke up in the morning. I asked him to do more of the massaging with his wife at home and that was the assignment for the next session.

17th Session

When we met in this session I invited Handy to come for the massage, starting from the breathing areas. At this time, I did tapping and maneuvering the muscles of his back, and I think he was overworked by stress because he said he could not make sounds, like something painful is coming on his back. This was a process which took us time to get over. He started vomiting and I was running up and down trying to give him help, but eventually all went back to normal. The pain in his back and the stress it called up caused that to happen.

18th Session

At this point, I asked Handy if he would accept it if I asked his District Manager to come and observe what we had gone through, as he was the person who said I must work with him and he wanted to know what was happening. Handy said that was no problem. I then phoned the District Manager to come and be part of us, as we were about to do the final session. He accepted the call.

19th Session

Today Handy was expected to perform in front of the District Manager. Before we did that, the three of us talked together. Then Handy started with breathing and he did that very well. He went on to beat the drum and the manager could not believe that because he did not know that he had that skill. Handy's song was just an ordinary rural area song that says, "Go, we will meet there." It was well done. And the District Manager had never seen him so calm. He said to Handy there and then, "Please report back to work the following Wednesday." It was amazing.

20th Session

Handy and I discussed the work that we did. He said it was a good job done. At the beginning of this he had asked himself, "What is it all about, this breathing?" but later he realized that the breathing is worth something. He looked also at the amount of kilos he lost. And finally, he said, "This is a course to be attended."

21st Session

We needed one more session to finish. The challenge was to bring a written paper where he wrote all the things he came across, especially this last episode. He said, "I worked for this department for almost the whole of my life and now when I am about to take my pension, there are some issues that crop up leading me not getting what I deserve." That paper was burnt up, with curses. He said, "I feel good and the anxiety and sadness I had at the beginning of these sessions (the anger and depression) is all gone." Afterwards, I get together and share some talks with other department members about VMT. Everybody finds Voice Movement Therapy worthwhile. We depart.

Transference & Counter Transference

When this man first came to work with me, I asked him to take off his shoes and put them by the door. This happens to be something that is done in our culture when one goes to a local healer. He asked me if I was a witch doctor. He didn't know what to expect of me, but it made him uneasy. So, for him, I appeared like a strange and scary witch doctor.

In the story of my life, I have a reason to be afraid of large violent men and this man reminded me of them. Carefully I had to manage my sphere which I did in the first session where this came up by holding my ground and continuing to work with this man. Then, because I was still afraid to work with him alone in the room with nobody around, for good reason I spoke to my colleagues about my concerns. When my male colleague volunteered to witness the sessions and be present with me, I accepted for him to come. This guaranteed safety for both myself and my client and did not interfere with his healing process, but actually by protecting myself, I acted in the best interest of both my client and me.

Summary

After I went through all these processes of Voice Movement Therapy with my client, I felt that I was not only equipping him to experience VMT, but I was getting an opportunity to stand firm for what is right for me. VMT has no limit, you go on and on. Maya Angelo, in her book, *I Know Why the Caged Bird Sings,* says, "A bird does not sing because it has an answer, it sings because it has a song."

I want to say that when hurtful and difficult situations happen in our life and drive us back into isolation, making us feel as if we are nothing, there is an answer in VMT: You just let your voice become unchained by expressing and sharing your feelings with other people. In this way, you can claim your own voice and speak only the truth as you know it and it makes you feel better about yourself I will go on with VMT as long as I am alive. (16th Sept 2013)

II. PSYCHOSIS, SELF-HARM AND ADDICTION: MODELS OF ENGAGEMENT

The articles in this section present four very different ways of engaging individuals at risk in very different situations. "Voice Studio: A Place to Let It Out," by Helen White, recalls how she created a voice and movement "studio" at a day clinic for patients with major mental illnesses to achieve a more openly creative and spontaneous atmosphere than currently available in their usual therapeutic or recreational groups. In "Changing Lives: VMT in Mediation and Conflict," Gertruida Dowse describes how she combines the process of formal mediation with VMT concepts and practices to achieve a more affective, and effective, approach. Sophie Martin's "Reflections on a Program using Voice Movement Therapy with Young People Who Self-Harm" is based on the first formal study using this modality with a specific population in a psychiatric hospital and subsequently published in a journal of art and psychology. "Facilitating Change–Body, Mind, and Soul–with Clients with Addictions," by Ben van Rensburg, describes two groups based on VMT principles and practices which he created and which became a regular part of the weekly treatment program of a residential clinic for people recovering from substance abuse. "Sounding Our Way to Wholeness," by Irene Kessler, describes a pilot project for women with eating disorders.

VOICE STUDIO: A PLACE TO LET IT OUT

Helen White

There was a piano in the psych ward, so it made sense to find someone who could play it and initiate a good old singsong. There was unbounded revelry until I tried to get an elderly lady out of her "geri" chair so that she could join in. I noticed she was feeling the beat of the music, so I dashed to help her. My creative antics came to an abrupt halt with a banging on the plexiglass window of the nurses' station and the Head Nurse yelling for me to "Put her back in her chair." I quickly decided I should remain quiet in case this behavior could prolong my discharge.

My love of song and dance goes way back to childhood when I performed in a Girl Guide production of "Oliver;" then bought my first LP, "South Pacific" learning all of the songs; and then had a chorus part in a high school production of the "Pirates of Penzance." Auditioning and getting a part in the choir was also a high spot during high school. As youngsters, my brother and sister and I, together with neighborhood kids, would put on shows in a neighbor's garage, charging admission and using blankets for stage curtains.

Imagine how I delight in my work today, running a weekly Voice Studio class for clients of the Carlington Assertive Community Treatment team (ACT) who come to sound, sing, laugh, recite poetry and do the most amazing improvisations. I never dreamt that I would be enticing folks to sing, dance, move, groove, and getting paid to do it!

ACT services are for people with "severe and persistent mental illness" who have had 50 days' hospitalization, homelessness or jail time in the previous two years before entering the service. The ACT model provides psychiatric treatment and rehabilitation-intensive services 24/7 in the community. We go out to wherever clients are, whether they are living independently, or are in boarding homes or shelters. We are a multidisciplinary team made up of a psychiatrist, three psychiatric nurses, an addictions counsellor and two other mental health counsellors besides myself and our manager who is also a nurse. I am also one of two peer specialists on the team with lived experience of mental illness. For the past eighteen years I have been employed in the mental health system: five years addressing systemic advocacy in a provincial psychiatric hospital and the last thirteen years doing clinical work on a psychiatric treatment and rehabilitation team as a Mental Health Counsellor/ Peer Specialist.

In the course of my work at ACT, I started to notice clients who, like me, had been interested in music, singing, dancing and the performing arts at some time in their life and, because of illness or lack of opportunity, never been able to explore their talents. At 51, I signed up for "Life Song," a course in singing and songwriting given by Barclay McMillan who had worked with the founder of Voice Movement Therapy (VMT), Paul Newham, assisted by Anne Brownell at her studio in Somerville, Massachusetts. It was Barclay who encouraged me to go to Martha's Vineyard to participate in the VMT training. The ACT team's program director completely supported my involvement from the very first day. She encouraged me to take the leave to do the training, saying she hoped I would be able to provide some activities in this field when I got back.

On my return, I wanted to provide a space for people to sound, move, sing, express themselves and perform: an opportunity for them to find their voice through breathwork, imagery and movement; a way to enhance their vocal abilities and to increase self-esteem and confidence through participation in activities and social interaction with others. I chose the name Voice Studio because it suggested a place where anything to do with the voice might happen and didn't sound too intimidating. I wanted to avoid using the word "group" because it could sound institutional since our clients had already been offered so many groups at various times. The word "Group" could suggest prescribed forms of behavior, or "therapy." I was aiming for something different, more open, and I wanted the participants to be able to be as loud as they wished!

We sent out fliers and all members of the ACT team heartily promoted Voice Studio to our clients. They brought in people I hadn't even thought would be interested. The success of this venture is due in large part to their dedication in providing top service and their interest in the VMT work and willingness to try new approaches.

Voice Studio is located in an old Catholic high school in downtown Ottawa, only a ten-minute drive from our community health center. The building is now home to many non-profit organizations, including some psychiatric self-help agencies. It was chosen because it was spacious, had high ceilings and lots of windows, and because being loud was allowed. There is a piano for us to use and one young man, who has never had a lesson, plays beautiful music on it. After class, I encourage people to go up to one of the agencies to use the computers or just have coffee.

The first class started in September 2008. I was very nervous but kept telling myself I knew everyone and was well prepared. About five minutes into the first class, I realized that I was not going to be able to do anything from my plan. The voice students were bursting full of ideas and just wanted to sing. We did 15 classes and then broke for the Christmas holidays. Then our city had a bus strike for six weeks, so we had to break until the strike was over and we have been going every week since then.

Barriers to people attending include transportation, sedating effects of psychiatric medication, low motivation to leave the house, and high levels of anxiety. About half of the participants get there by disability transportation and some are picked up and driven by ACT staff. We are fortunate to have been able to hire someone to assist with the classes. He is someone with lived experience of mental illness and not only sings himself but can encourage the others by singing with them.

Average attendance is four to five singers and the classes are open. There is a core group and others come and go depending on their schedules or circumstances. At the beginning of each class, we start off with some Sphere work (see page 21), then go into slow, gentle exercises and stretches. Sometimes we do relaxation and visualization work on the floor for those who can manage it, although many of the participants have physical disabilities; some are confined to a wheelchair and others prefer to sit in a chair. We do lots of jaw and face stretching and sounding which comes very easily from this group. Belly breathing is always focused upon. I try to insert different vocal and non-vocal techniques each week, but usually the group is so eager to start singing that they race quickly through the warm-ups, getting way ahead of me. People then have a chance to do individual work which is usually a song that has meaning for them and we often have exercises designed to get some of the shyer singers involved. Recently, we have been finishing off with a couple of favorites of the entire group: "Born to Be Wild" by Steppenwolf and "We Are the Champions" by Queen. We end by slowing down, getting back into our Spheres, and grounding.

Each class is completely different and depends quite a bit on who is attending. They have done some wonderful improvisations. Pretending to hold babies, rocking them to sleep, and making up their own lullabies was one they particularly enjoyed. I have a little recording device now to capture this so I can play their songs back to them.

"Fred" told us that when he becomes loud and exuberant, the nurse in charge of his retirement residence tells him, "Wait until Voice Studio and then you can let it out." Lately, a young man joined us at Voice Studio and he had the idea to plug the speakers into his MP3 player. He sang and moved and took up lots of space. It was delightful to see and hear him, as I had only previously known him to be quiet and shy. He stole the show singing Willie Nelson's, "Maria, Shut Up and Kiss Me."

In April of this year, Voice Studio participants were invited to perform at the Carlington Community Health Service's Volunteer Recognition luncheon. They were offered financial compensation and invited to stay for lunch. Five students agreed to participate and we enjoyed all the planning and rehearsing. The last rehearsal day came along and Emily said she had decided not to sing her Beatles song, but had written a poem she wanted to recite, instead. She kindly gave permission to share it here:

Getting There, by Emily Jane Nunn
(About getting over my mental illness)

The universe is brimming with troubled souls like me
We want our pathway open and our footing free
Ahead I see the tantalizing glitter of an easy goal
My vision is to unify the humble and the pure.

My task is to be patient and to conquer idle doubt
To grasp the valuable truth beyond the moon
I know a woman who would be understood
She lives in fear, but yet chastises terror

Together we enlist our scant vocabulary
To conquer loneliness and alienation.

We tread the boards of our dormitory
With friendly words and gestures full of pain.
What will come with spring, so keenly sought?
And weather mild, so dearly bought?
I can but tread on solitary ground, with tact,
And listen, full of eagerness, for a familiar sound.

The group of singers did an excellent job and I hope that other opportunities like this will come along for them. They were delighted with the three-course lunch, the gift bags, and the pay (I think in that order).

After 15 weeks, the participants were asked to fill out evaluation forms if they had attended two or more times. A total of 16 people had attended at least once. We received 7 responses. Everyone answered that they enjoyed the classes. Responses to the question, "In which of the following areas have you experienced a positive change as a result of participating in Voice Studio?" were:

–Ability to use singing voice	7
–Confidence	3
–Self-expression/self-awareness	5
–Improved relaxation	1
–Physical activity	5
–Relationship with ACT Team workers	4
–Self-esteem	3
–Social contact	5
–Knowledge of community resources	3
–Other	0

Two comments were received about what they would change: "No primal screaming, it leads to chaos" and "It needs to be on Fridays."

At the time of writing this, I received two requests from men asking if they could bring their guitars to Voice Studio. One is asking for guitar lessons and I hope to find someone who will come to our center and give lessons outside of the scheduled class.

This is, without a doubt, the most marvelous work I have ever been involved in. The amazing Voice Studio singers are starting to choose songs/poems/plays for their performance at the Carlington ACT annual party in November and we are all raring to go!

CHANGING LIVES: HOW I USE VOICE MOVEMENT THERAPY IN MEDIATION AND CONFLICT

Gertruida Dowse

> As soon as our feelings have a voice, they no longer seek revenge for having been ostracized by eating away at our unseen and unheard heart.[1]
>
> Paul Newham

With the process of mediation, I help people to stop looking for revenge, stop looking at the wrong someone else has done them, and to realize what the actual situation is. I help them to look both within and away from themselves to consider the actual problem and how to solve it. This is not a situation of, "You are wrong and I am right," but an effort to seek a mutual agreement that suits both parties. To do this with success, each one has to be able to look at and beyond their own anger.

As a therapist, I want to help people to change their lives by changing their mindset, to look at things and people differently, connecting with their own body and healing from the inside out. By bringing such a change, I can add value to lives.

II. EXPLAINING MEDIATION

Mediation is an alternative method for resolving conflict between two independent parties who do not want to go through a costly court process to settle their dispute. Usually, a person who is in need of mediation believes that their opponent has incompatible goals and has interfered with them in a way that has put a strain on their limited resources.

Mediation is a modality that is voluntary, confidential and self-determined. It works according to a structure provided by the mediator to enable each party to feel heard and respected, so that they may reach a mutual agreement. It is a structural process to find a solution, not a therapeutic one.

What is Missing?

I use Voice Movement Therapy to help individuals focus on what they are feeling and experiencing inside their bodies. It helps them to open up and focus on the overall situation and not just themselves. This larger view helps them to give up their preconceptions and negativity about the person they are in conflict with and can bring healing. I find it useful to bring in Voice Movement Therapy with its expressive techniques to keep the process in the here and now, focusing on what is really going on, the problem, by finding a way for them to give voice to their own feelings and thoughts so that they can both feel heard and hear others.

The missing link, for me, is thus the therapeutic part of healing and changing which VMT can provide.

The Actual Structure

In a mediation process, there are usually four sessions, or four parts of one session, depending on how complicated the situation is.

Session 1 is a combined session with both parties, to listen to both sides and to give each party an opportunity to hear the other person, each one making a statement. In this way we all know the issue from each client's point of view and can begin where they are.

Sessions 2 and 3 are individual sessions to find out the needs of each party and discuss a possible solution, focusing on the here and now through the client's self-reflection in which they can look at the assumptions they have made. They need to understand that feelings like anger, fear, disappointment, frustration, and pride stand in the way of reaching a mutual agreement. It is usually in sessions 2 and 3 where the switching of individual's points of view happens.

Session 4 is a combined session to summarize the issue and check with each party to see if it was a correct summary. This is the time to bring in the changes in thinking and feeling each has experienced in the individual sessions and how that can create satisfying movement, clarity, and a sense of relief for both of them. Now we can discuss possible solutions and make a contract for what actions each will follow.

I use Voice Movement Therapy in Sessions Two and Three to help clients reflect on themselves and their own feelings and interpretations, and then to focus on the feelings and needs of the other party. Through simple structures, Voice Movement Therapy helps clients to "get out of their own way."

Conflict and confrontation usually occur when there are opposite positions and goals and no clear understanding of the situation or problem to be solved. By bringing Voice Movement Therapy into the existing mediational structure, I can help the clients to look at the situation differently and act on what author Jim Rohm recommends for dealing with human conflict: "If you don't like how things are, change it. You are not a tree." Below I wish to present three case studies. The names are not real names, but the situations are, and the individuals involved gave consent for me to use their situations in this article.

II. THREE CASE STUDIES

Conflict in Needs

In this study, both clients are white and English speaking, but have different needs because of the generation gap between them and being in very different life-stages. "Joe," a young man in his late twenties, is in the beginning of his adulthood, establishing his life with his wife and children in their new home, and very excited. They have just bought a house in an area where most of the residents are older and have lived there a long time. These two are just beginning a life together. Joe filed for a mediation process after his much older neighbor hammered on his door early on a Saturday morning, accusing him of ruining his garden. Joe, at that moment, did not know who was banging on his door or why.

Marne, on the edge of life and who has lost interest in it since his wife died a year ago, is alone with nothing that excites him anymore. He is a man in his late sixties who has lived in the same neighborhood for 40 years. In losing his wife, he lost interest in a lot of things, even his garden which was always their pride. That Saturday morning, he saw a change in his garden and he was furious.

During our first joint session, Joe explains in a submissive, high-pitched voice that he and his family are new in the neighborhood and had planned a housewarming-party for their friends. His wife asked him to clean up the mess between their house and their neighbor's, so he mowed the grass and got rid of the weeds. There is no fencing between the two houses to make a boundary and he did not understand why the cleaning up upset his neighbor so much, because now it looks much neater.

Marne explains, in a hard-harsh voice, that Joe ruined his garden, that he lost his wife a couple of months before, and in the area that was cleared was a rosebush his grandchildren had given him. The loss of this bush is what upset him the most. Unfortunately, all that Joe and his wife had seen was an untidy, overgrown lawn and bushes.

In this case, I use the VMT concept of the sphere (see page 21) in the individual sessions, without explaining it to them, just having them experience it. I ask both of them to take deep breaths, calm down and focus on themselves and what it is like for them right now. Bringing in the sphere helps them to focus on the here and now. In the combined session, all the focus was on their negative feelings toward the other, or offending, party and that blocked their thinking. To use their minds to concentrate on the problem in a different way might change some of the negativity and help them see themselves and each other in a different light. While sitting with closed eyes, I ask them to think of a color that can represent, can "explain" what they are experiencing at this moment. Bringing in the sphere helps each one to look inward; and then

I ask each to imagine an opposing sphere of a different color and see how the two spheres might interact.

Joe experiences shades of blue. He is sad. He thought he had done a good deed by cleaning the garden and is very disappointed. He wanted to help his neighbor by cleaning his garden and mowing the grass, and also please his wife at the same time. At first he could not understand Marne's rage, but then he realized that he was supposed to introduce himself and ask permission to clean Marne's garden. He was in a hurry because they were running out of time before their party. What can he do now? He wants to have a good relationship with his neighbor.

Marne saw red and black. He was angry about the rosebush to which he was emotionally attached and that made him experience the pain of his loneliness and losses even more. He thought that if his neighbor had asked him to tidy the area between the two houses, he would have found someone to do it for him. He realizes that this situation has forced him to look at the reality that he neglects his garden and now he feels ashamed of his outburst towards his young neighbor.

In summary, both Joe and Marne asked forgiveness of each other because they realized that they were each too hasty and made the wrong assumptions: Marne, that he reacted out of pain and shame and now promises to get garden services to keep his garden tidy; and Joe, that he needed to ask permission to tidy Marne's garden. He offers to buy another rosebush, which Marne refuses, because it would not be the same. Joe understands. They promise to pay each other the necessary respect in the future and agree that they need each other and would like to be friends.

Power Struggle with Ego and Pride

This mediation was requested through the hospital's management because the conflict between two strong leaders was also influencing relationships between and among other people.

In this study we find a power struggle. Both clients are Afrikaans speaking, but they are from different ethnic groups and in different life-stages. There is both a generation gap and issues of superiority involved. These create conflict, not only between the two who are directly involved, but are also affecting both the staff and the local community.

Sue, a Sister (nurse) in a rural hospital, is a colored lady who has spent her whole working-life in the hospital of this small town. She is in her sixties and near retirement. For years, she was head of both the trauma department and the maternity ward. She did all the planning and knows that she runs the ward very efficiently. The community knows and trusts her; they appreciate how she does things and they accept it. All this has changed since a new and unknown doctor was appointed as the head of the hospital.

Pete, a young doctor in his early thirties, is a white man who recently joined the team from a big city. He saw some loopholes in the running of the wards and was concerned about the role of the community, members of whom were trying to dictate how rules could be bent to accommodate all of them according to their points of view.

Sue has been in control of the trauma department and maternity ward for such a long time that the community sees Pete as an "incomer." He put new rules in action and made some minor changes, he ignored her expertise, and the community did not understand the changes. According to Sue, he made too many mistakes. Pete, about twenty years younger than Sue, claims that he made the changes because they were more reasonable and would help all those working in the ward to work more efficiently. He experiences that the Sister does not value his knowledge and still wants to be in control. She wants to please the community and that brings more conflict; the community complains to her and she blames it all on the doctor.

In the individual sessions I make use of active imagination. Each is asked to breathe, and while breathing, imagine that a bright light is shining from above their heads, showing them their inner selves. They are asked to walk around in this light and experience what they can learn from it.

Sue experiences fear, fear of losing her job and her position as the head of her two hospital units. She is financially and emotionally not ready for retirement. She also fears the reaction of the community, that they will not listen to her anymore and that she will become just another member of that community. She is angry that the doctor was allowed to make changes in her ward without consulting her. She knows that some of the changes do bring a better work flow and more control. She still thinks she has the same knowledge as he does because of her experience over the years.

Pete is angry because the Sister does not acknowledge his knowledge and expertise and will not try to understand why he made the changes. He comes from a much bigger hospital in a city and knows his work. He has appreciation for Sue's dedication and knowledge and does not want to "work her out." He only wants to do what is best for the hospital. There are certain rules that he needed to put in place for everyone to do their duties the best they can. He realizes that he maybe jumped to the conclusion that Sue tried to "work him out" and be again the sole manager.

In the joint session, both Sue and Pete explain that they do not want to work in this hostile environment, that they will appreciate each other more, not jump to assumptions, communicate their feelings and ideas more clearly to each other, without fearing for their own jobs. They both acknowledge that they value the other's expertise and knowledge. They know that they could work well together, to the benefit of the patients, community and hospital.

Divorce Mediation/Broken Relationships

Solly filed for the mediation sessions after his wife indicated that she wants a divorce and has asked for a lot of things which she never had while they were married for 40 years. He does not have the financial means to provide them and also cannot afford a lawyer to do the dividing of possessions.

In the first session I am introduced to San and Solly, both white people in their late sixties and Afrikaans speaking, have been married for more than 40 years. San wants a divorce after she finds out that Solly is having a sexual relationship with one of his workers, a colored lady in her late twenties. He denies it, but she also has accused him of supporting the woman. She got affirmation of this after hearing that he was at the christening of her baby and people told her the child had the same looks as Solly.

San and Solly have lived on a farm in separate areas of the house for about the past five years. After the rumors of the affair became known to the community and to her children, she moved out and went to live with her daughter. People advised her to get the most from her husband when she divorces him because he cheats on her, and that with a colored person. Solly does not have much financial means, but San wants a car, even though she does not have a driver's license.

In Sessions 2 and 3 I ask each member of the couple what they need and want out of the sessions. To help them focus on themselves, I ask them to walk around in the room and just utter the words that come to their mind while walking and focusing on their inner self. I hope that the movement will "unstick" the emotions in their bodies.

San shouts, "How could he?" several times and also, "What will people say?" and "My poor children!" She realizes that she has not cared about her husband for a long time. She needs him in order to have a place to live and also someone to take her to town when she needs to go there. She is satisfied to be on her own and keeps herself busy with preserving fruit and cooking jam. She does not cook meals for her husband anymore and he is responsible for washing his own clothes and tidying his own space. She also realizes that she does not need much. She would like to have some of the things in the house, especially those that belonged to her mother, but actually she is satisfied with what she has. She does not need a vehicle because she cannot drive one and also does not want to go through the process of getting a license at her age.

She does want revenge and has tried to make Solly suffer because he has humiliated her and hurt her feelings. She does not want him to go to jail for not providing her with the things she has claimed. All their children are already out of home and can provide well for themselves. They do not need financial support. She does now have a house to stay in, with her daughter, and does not need a vehicle she can't use.

Solly only shouts, "Why, why, why?!" He mentions that he and his wife did suffer financially all these years. The last years she did not care for him and also does not bother about what is happening in his part of the house. He cannot understand why she now makes such a big deal about it. The lady that she is accusing him of having an affair with does all his cooking, washing and cleaning. He cannot understand that it is suddenly a big issue for San if he is involved with someone else. He admits that he supports the other lady because she cares for him and also needs the things he can afford to give her.

He always wants the best for his wife but cannot afford the things she is now claiming. When she needs to go to town, he always makes a plan to take her and he will do so in the future. She has survived all these years without the luxuries she now claims.

In Session 4–The couple agreed to share the household items and furniture according to what was originally theirs and what each now needs. San will mostly take the ornaments and personal items, and her pots to do the preserving and cooking of jam. The stove, one bed and washing machine can stay in the house for the use of Solly. If they are not living under the same roof anymore, San doesn't care what Solly is doing. There is no pension fund or other financial means to divide. Solly will help San when and where he can if San needs it.

They are willing to settle the agreement and go their separate ways without mocking each other anymore. The Mediator will draw up the divorce agreement and send it to the lawyer to complete the divorce proceedings.

Summary and Conclusion

Mediation as an alternative process to resolving conflict between parties does help them to reach agreement; but with Voice Movement Therapy to support the process, it also brings healing and change, helping people to see the situation differently and to move on in a positive way.

This combination helps individuals to stop looking for revenge and focus on solving the actual problem that must be solved. It helps them to give up preconceptions and negativity. Voice Movement Therapy helps to separate the person from the problem and to realize that the person is not the problem; the problem is the problem.

Voice Movement Therapy also provides a narrative that flows and helps individuals to understand themselves and each other better. It also softens the cold structure of the mediation process and helps people relate to each other better, in a less adversarial way. As Mediator, I need to help clients focus on themselves, their own feelings, needs and experiences, and not on the other person because, after all, you only have control over your own feelings and experiences.

This proves the saying of Mahatma Ghandi: "If you want to see change, you have to change." These are a few examples of many mediation sessions and outcomes which have included child maintenance cases and family plans, and workplace mediation where whole companies were involved.

NOTES

1. Paul Newham, *The Healing Voice: How to Use the Power of Your Voice to Bring Harmony into Your Life* (Shaftsbury, Dorset, UK: Element Books Ltd., 1999), p. 178.

A REFLECTION ON A PILOT STUDY UNDERTAKEN ON THE EFFICACY OF A VOICE MOVEMENT THERAPY PROGRAM WITH YOUNG WOMEN AGED 18-24 WHO SELF-HARM

Sophie Martin

> During VMT I found my real voice. It probably sounds weird to say that, because I have always had a voice, but now I feel that I understand more about it and its importance in my life.
>
> "Trudy," VMT pilot study participant

Around the world, Nonsuicidal Self-Injury (NSSI), otherwise known as self-harm, has become a trend for young people, in particular, to try to cope with life stresses by expressing their emotions in the only way they can seem to find. In Australia, according to data collected by the Australian Institute of Health and Welfare, the statistics show that between 2008 and 2020, cases of hospitalization due to self-harm in young women aged 15 to 24 doubled. To date, the most common therapies used with these young women have been Dialectical Behavioral Therapy (DBT) and Cognitive Behavioral Therapy (CBT), but neither of these therapies have been recognized as wholly effective.

In 2011, I was approached by the University of Queensland and the Royal Brisbane Hospital to conduct a pilot study using the techniques of Voice Movement Therapy (VMT) in a ten-week program for young women aged 16-25 who cut themselves. It was proposed to me that psychiatrists and psychologists working in this field were searching for something unique to fill an unidentified and unaddressed need and wanted to try a different approach, as they felt that the therapies they were using had mixed results. VMT offers an approach for an exploration of the self and the expression of emotion that cannot be found in its entirety in other therapies or practices. For me, this was an opportunity to work with a group supported by both the University and the Hospital. It was also an opportunity to be supported in research and to explore the efficacy of Voice Movement Therapy with a professional group that had asked for help.

In 2012, the results of this pilot study were published in the journal, *Music and Medicine* in a paper titled *Voice Movement Therapy: Evaluation of a Group-Based Expressive Arts Therapy for Nonsuicidal Self-Injury in Young Adults.*"[1] Both the study and the paper were an exciting development for the field of Voice Movement Therapy. The results, which I will detail later in this article, were positive and offered VMT as a new therapy to support these young women. Almost 10 years later, I am writing this article in order to expand on the pilot study. It is also my intention that it include not only my voice, but the voices of the participants taken from completed questionnaires and testimonies which were not included in the original published paper. Although permission was given to use the names of the participants at the time of the study, I will still be changing them to retain the privacy of individuals whose lives may have moved on.

The Process

With ethics approval from the University of Queensland Medical Research Ethics Committee, the workshops were designed to be held over a period of 10 weeks for 2.5 hours a week at the University of Queensland initially and then in other locations for later groups. The young women who volunteered to be involved were all currently struggling with self-injury and all expressed a hope to stop. While reflecting on why she had come to the workshop, one participant stated, "Quite simply, I felt like this group might be my last chance to overcome self-injury." As part of the requirements for the workshop, the participants all had to be currently supported by a therapist. This was required to provide additional separate support should the participants need it. None of them were required to know anything about voice or singing prior to attending the workshops. Voice Movement Therapy uses an approach to voicework that doesn't require previous experience or skill with the voice, only that participants are willing to explore it.

In their study of self-mutilation in female adolescents and young adults, MacAniff, Zila and Kiselica talk about two main issues arising within young women who self-harm: firstly, that they have difficulty verbalizing their emotions and secondly, that they are "functioning from the notion of a 'false self' and that this false self is brought about by denying their thoughts and emotions over a long period of time.[2] In these workshops, I hoped to encourage the participants to "talk" about their emotions through creative writing, drawing and, most importantly, vocal play. I also hoped to encourage them to start to explore themselves and their feelings using Jungian archetypes such as the Trickster and the Mother, and perhaps to create their own archetypes and subpersonalities based on their life experience, and then to explore these in various vocal and creative forms such as writing a letter or creating a song. I hoped to help them start to connect their body and their voice with their feelings, and looked in particular at *alexithymia* (the inability to express feelings using words) which is often associated with self-injury and hoped these young women could start to express and describe their emotions through body and voice.

I created a 10-week program based on key components of VMT which ensured that each session was supported by the structure of song. I also wanted to ensure that the focus of each week would be the same throughout the four groups in order to compare data. However, as VMT allows for and gives space to the individual and their psyche and voice, I knew that there would be differences between groups whilst keeping the structure the same.

In order to collect data for the study, five questionnaires were chosen to take pre-test and post-test, with a follow-up 10 weeks after the final session of the study. The questionnaires used were:

1. Difficulties in Emotion Regulation scale
2. Toronto Alexithymia scale
3. Rosenberg Self-Esteem scale
4. General Health questionnaire
5. Self-Injury questionnaire

The Sessions

Voice Movement Therapy offers an approach to exploring challenging subjects that provides both structure and flexibility in exploration. Using the 10 Vocal Components (see page 19) as a framework for the 10 sessions meant that the focus of this pilot study inside the workshops was not on self-harm, but on the story revealed by the participants' voices and creative selves. In working with these young women, I made a deliberate choice to focus not on the self-harm, but on their overall well-being and what they could do to give voice as an expression of self.

Each session was designed to involve a warm-up exercise, targeted creative exercises on different components of the voice or aspects of the self, group sharing, and a final group exercise. I was aware that the women I was working with might have had challenging experiences talking about self-harm, particularly in hospital settings, and also might have never had experience using their voice in other ways in group activities. The approach I took was one of gentle encouragement and playfulness, observing their body language and listening acutely to what the participants needed to feel safe in order to begin to identify and give voice to their feelings.

One of the aspects of VMT that I focused on early in the workshops was the creation of songs evolving from the experience of the participants within the group. This was important for two reasons: firstly, that overall, the participants were withdrawn at the beginning of the program, making limited movement and sound in exercises. I needed to encourage their feelings of expression to grow and expand through echoing a word, phrase or movement back to them, using the group to support and join in, allowed a natural growth in trust and strength of sound and movement which increased engagement. Secondly, creating songs in the moment not only brought the focus of everyone in the room into the same point in time, but also provided an opportunity for them all to feel truly heard and seen. This was often a powerful experience.

One participant described the sessions this way:

> To me, VMT is singing, walking, sitting, breathing, talking, writing, and sticking feathers and beads to colored cardboard; it is moving and thinking, challenging and expressing myself; drawing, stretching, lying down and imagining, laughing, smiling, yelling, creativity and silliness. Sometimes it is difficult and uncomfortable, but never unbearably so.

The Results

This was a small but promising study. Of the 27 referrals to the program, a total of 19 young women from the four groups completed the program. The results of the questionnaires were published in the original article on the pilot study, the key findings of which were:

In the four weeks leading up to the workshops, 89.5% of participants reported having self-injured. During the ten weeks of the program overall, there was a small trend of reduction in self-injury and six participants reported no self-injury in the last month of the program. Importantly, this reduction and elimination was sustained at the ten-week follow-up after the program had come to an end. Nearly ten years later, when I contacted one of the participants to ask if I could share her feedback in this article, she reported to me that the program had been a real turning point in her life. She said, "Learning to better understand my voice and body was like a missing piece of what I needed to begin to move through a lot of issues I'd been struggling with." She also reported that she had only self-injured once in those ten years and had managed to help herself through it with the tools she had learnt.

Another exciting finding to come out of the data collated was significant improvement in emotion regulation, impulsiveness, identifying feelings, self-esteem, anxiety, and social dysfunction, with gains maintained between post-treatment and follow-up.

Most importantly for me was to hear the voices of the participants in feedback forms reporting to me, for example, that;

> The movement aspect of this therapy has taught me different things about how my body reacts and carries different situations and feelings. I have a greater understanding of how my body and mind are connected... Cognitive Behavioral Therapy helped me understand my thoughts, but Voice Movement Therapy made me feel like a real person.

NOTES

1. Sophie Martin et al, *Music and Medicine*, "Voice Movement Therapy: Evaluation of a Group-Based Expressive Arts Therapy for Nonsuicidal Self-Injury in Young Adults," *Music and Medicine* p. 5, no.1 (2013).
2. Laurie MacAniff Zila, Mark S. Kiselica, "Understanding and Counseling Self-Mutilation in Female Adolescents and Young Adults," *Journal of Counselling and Development,* p. 79, no. 1 (2001): pp. 46-52.

FACILITATING CHANGE—BODY, MIND AND SOUL: THE ROLE OF VMT IN AN ADDICTIONS TREATMENT CLINIC

Ben van Rensburg

> Editor Note: This article is a section on group work from Ben's VMT qualifying thesis, slightly condensed by Anne and Deirdre Brownell. As the most in-depth documented work we have on holding VMT groups for people with addictions as a regular part of their basic treatment in an established clinic program, the editors felt the inclusion of his work in our book was essential. He is now deceased, but his work stands.

The following group sessions were conducted in a clinic which was a licensed psychiatric hospital dedicated to the treatment of chemical addiction to alcohol and drugs as well as behavioral addictions such as co-dependency, compulsive gambling, eating disorders, and sex-and-love addiction. It consisted of a highly experienced multi-disciplinary team, including several psychiatrists, a clinical psychologist, registered nurses, an occupational therapist, a social worker, and qualified addictions counsellors such as myself. As part of a more holistic approach, it also included an art therapist, a drummer and, in addition to my role as counsellor, I introduced Voice Movement Therapy into the ongoing group work on a regular basis.

This institution was committed to blending diverse skills into a 12 Step-based, holistic program that offered a rich, life-changing treatment experience within a structured, supportive environment. It specialized in the treatment of dual-diagnosis clients, for whom effective treatment of both the addiction and any co-existing psychiatric disorder is essential to recovery.

The Primary Care Program consisted of a four-week intensive that incorporated the most recent evidence-based practices, including a detoxification regime. A Secondary Care facility was also available to clients who needed to work on significant emerging issues that might accompany their addiction, (i.e., specific psychiatric diagnoses, childhood trauma, or behavioral difficulties). Client-specific combinations of effective therapeutic approaches included Focus-Oriented Psychotherapy, Cognitive-Behavioral Therapy (CBT), Dialectical Behavioral Therapy (DBT) and Voice Movement Therapy (VMT). The multi-disciplinary team developed goal-orientated treatment plans for each client, utilizing specific combinations of therapeutic approaches to effectively address individual needs.

Much of the therapy took place in groups and was supported by individual counselling and facilitated family sessions with the client. Through these groups, lectures and experiential exercises, clients learned about addiction and its physical, psychological and spiritual impact on their lives. They were given the tools to cope with the challenges of real life without resorting to their addictions. Relapse prevention formed a key element of the treatment program. Clients were helped to identify and prepare for risk situations that could threaten their recovery. Specific individual psychological issues that might interfere with recovery were identified and worked with.

Experience has taught us that, while it may be difficult to stop addictive behavior, staying stopped is the real challenge. To this end, clients were introduced to the appropriate 12 Step Fellowship meetings, helping them to begin a program which they could apply, learn from, and enjoy for the rest of their lives.

All healing includes a spiritual component. Spirituality means different things to different people. Clients were assisted in defining what spirituality meant to them and encouraged to work towards enhancing this area of their lives through walks in nature, meditation groups, and further exploration of themselves through Expressive Arts Therapies. During the time I consulted at the clinic, I introduced two different VMT groups as integral parts of the weekly schedule. The purpose of the first group was to introduce the use of key VMT concepts adapted to clients struggling with a variety of addictions.

The second group, "Body Mapping," was an image-based way of actively using the visual arts to personalize and then reflect on key issues generally encountered in treatment.

During my VMT training, Anne Brownell introduced the concept of Active Supervision. This was a new experience for me in which you have to put yourself in the place of your client by taking on their stance, trying to find the qualities of their voice within yours, and doing their movements and vocalizations with your own body. This enabled me to connect on a very physical level with what the client might be struggling with, as well as highlighting areas of any residual emotions or experiences that might be left in me from a previous session. I discovered new awarenesses of issues or blockages which I was then able to take to formal one-to-one as well as team supervision.

I had ongoing weekly supervision with a clinical psychologist who was also well-informed and qualified within the field of Expressive Arts Therapy. Group supervision took place weekly in the form of a review of each client and was attended by the whole counselling team. Every client was presented by their individual counsellor in a progress report, followed by an open discussion. This was a particularly insightful way of working with any transference and counter-transference issues that might arise. The input by others also created a wonderful platform for incorporating fresh approaches in regard to a client's treatment plan. The following description of the group work is presented in the present tense and client names have been changed to maintain confidentiality.

I. GROUP ONE: BASIC VMT PRINCIPLES APPLIED TO WORKING WITH ADDICTION

All clients participate in and complete a full four-week program (28 days) which incorporates all group lectures and experiential sessions on the general schedule, including the two VMT groups that I facilitate. These groups are big, consisting on average of about 30 people. The focus of the first VMT group is to introduce clients to the use of some of the Non-Vocal Components of VMT: Breath, Sphere, Shadow, and Feline/Canine (see page 21). Due to the large number of clients attending, as well as their varying physical and emotional conditions, these groups are kept very simple. Bringing these concepts into their treatment plan is very beneficial for later therapeutic intervention and also becomes part of their "toolbox" for dealing with the challenges of addiction.

Week One, "Breath: Where Life Begins," I start the group with some stretching exercises, partly as an icebreaker and in order to create group cohesion. This is kept "light" in both movement and explanation. It also incorporates the VMT principle of Convex/Concave: that all movement is on a spectrum between these two extremes which can be observed and grows out of the action of the breath in the torso.

We start in a circle with an imaginary "arms over the ball" exercise: Arms are in concave to the front of the body, as if holding a large beach ball. Everybody then turns to the left as far as they can, as if handing it over to the person next to them, then to the right with the same intention. It is repeated five times to each side. We do not do the fourth position, leaning backward over the imaginary ball, as it can make people feel too vulnerable. Instead, we do the "Titanic" in which both arms are stretched behind the body, putting the back in concave and the chest in convex. Next, we do the "ballerina": left arm above the head in an arc, right arm down the side in a smaller arc facing into the body. We then start alternating the arms as we move, often creating lots of laughter as we twirl about. Clients are then given permission to move freely around the room using these various positions, returning to the circle in a few minutes.

After everybody has re-gathered in a circle, we all sit on the floor and catch our breath. I then introduce the three areas of expansion prioritized in VMT breathwork–chest, ribcage, abdomen–which they have just experienced, un-named, through their work with the imaginary ball. At this stage, I ask permission to use "appropriate touch," if necessary. I explain that touch does not normally form part of therapy, but that I am qualified to do this in a particular therapeutic manner for the purpose of freeing up the breathing mechanism, allowing one to take fuller and deeper breaths. It is clearly stated that "not wanting" to be touched is also acceptable and that no one should feel forced.

I start by asking one of the clients to place their hands on me to see if they can feel or observe movement in each of these three areas of inspiration and expiration. They are then asked to pair up with someone of the same sex with whom they feel comfortable and duplicate this exercise to see if there are any areas each needs to become more aware of in their own breathing. If either partner does not feel comfortable with direct touch but would like to try it, they can ask that their own hands be placed under the hands of the person working on them or on top of the hands of the person they are working on.

Whenever I refer to VMT Breath, it has been explained to the clients as the process of learning to prioritize each of the three areas of expansion–chest, ribcage, abdomen, or clavicular, thoracic, abdominal–in order to strengthen and eventually combine them to facilitate a more deep, complete and powerful breath.

After identifying some of the areas they might struggle with, I introduce some examples of different breathing patterns and how they affect us on a physical and emotional level. A typical example is the "fight or flight" (angry/scared) breath. An example of how this quick, shallow breath increases the heart rate normally resonates well with the group. Clients are then encouraged to incorporate a breathing exercise regime into their day. During emotional distress which can easily result in cravings, they can use their breathing as a relapse prevention tool, both to calm and to fill themselves in a different way.

We then move freely around the room again and clients are encouraged to start a process of "audible breath" so that they become aware of the way they are breathing. After about five minutes, we close the group in the circle that acts as our container. I reflect on the process of breathing and the relationship between breath and spirituality. For example, breathing not only begins and ends physical life, but is its animating force and has for centuries and in many cultures been directly connected to the spirit, the divine breath from which all human life comes. Clients are asked to reflect on the fact that life starts with the in-breath and ends with the out-breath, and everything else happens in between. The group closes with three slow, full breaths.

Week Two, "The Sphere and Boundaries: Mine and Not Mine," I introduce the Sphere, an imagined container or womb for the self in the world, with the term "fluid bubble." Whereas the circle provides an excellent structure for group cohesion, the Sphere, being so specifically 3-dimensional, provides an all-encompassing imaginary container for each individual.

We start off in a sitting position and I encourage clients to follow my example by physically reaching out in as many directions and as far as possible. Clients are also asked to make sure that they keep sufficient distance from others and not allow their own "Sphere" or "bubble" to be penetrated. After clients get comfortable with this, they are encouraged to stand and slowly start moving around. This concept also relates well to the concept of "boundaries" which is an issue addressed frequently in their overall treatment. After moving freely, they are encouraged to find a place in the room where they feel safe and sit down.

I then ask them to stretch out their arms whilst concaving or gently bending their wrists in order to see the palms of their hands. They are asked to focus there for a while and notice how clearly they can see the lifelines on their palms. After they get comfortable with the inner space of their Sphere, I encourage them to focus on something outside of their palms while keeping them in the same position, in order to connect visually with what is outside their own sphere. By doing so, they get a better idea of what is theirs and what is not, the "mine" and the "not mine" of their lives. This then becomes a crucial element in taking responsibility for what is theirs and letting go of control of what is not theirs.

About fifteen minutes are used for exploring the inside of their Sphere while spending some time in exploring some parts of them that are "strong and want to be alive" compared to what they see as "weak and just surviving." During this time, I will freely move between the clients to ensure that they feel safe and contained.

We close this group with the saying of the "Serenity Prayer," originally known as the Prayer of St. Francis: "God, grant me the serenity to accept the things I cannot change; the courage to change the things I can, and the wisdom to know the difference." The majority of the peer group will know this prayer at any stage of the treatment, as they use it daily during focused Serenity Time. Closing with us all saying this prayer together creates a wonderful "voice container" for the group.

Week Three, "The Shadow: The Part that Fuels Addiction," the Shadow gets introduced simply as that part within us that turns to drugs and alcohol or "process addiction" (for example: gambling or compulsive sex-and-love behavior) when we are faced with difficult or overwhelming feelings. It is thus normalized, named as a simple and well-known fact–not shameful–that all addicts turn to their drugs when they experience overwhelming emotions. We "use" on feelings! By starting a process of getting to know our shadow, we are better equipped to deal with emotional situations when they arise. The participants are reminded that addiction is physical, emotional and spiritual.

Clients are then given paper plates on which they are instructed to draw two faces. The first face is what they habitually present to the world: their sometimes false, happy angelic face. On the other side, they draw the face that often lies underneath: maybe their sad, angry, or fear-face.

Without showing their peers their "other side," they hold up the side they project to the world. They are encouraged to move around freely and notice if they have any connection with the masks of other peers. After about five minutes, they are asked to turn their plate faces around and match a sound with the shadow-self depicted. They are again encouraged to move around freely, but this time to start forming subgroups of sounds that match theirs or that they feel comfortable with.

After about ten minutes, since it often takes longer for clients to get comfortable with sounding rather than just moving, the different groups are asked to form a circle. Each client is then given the opportunity to introduce this "other" side of themselves to their peers and give a short explanation of where the sound/feeling/face comes from.

I close the group by encouraging clients to join the big circle when they feel ready. I also encourage them to continue engaging with their shadow-selves and to share their experience with each other and their counsellors outside the group.

Week Four, "Feline/Canine: Working Towards a Roar," the main aim is to start a means of investigation toward fuller expression and voice projection by experiencing different timbres or qualities of sound.

We start by sitting on chairs and I introduce Homo Erectus: upright, highly cognitive human, frequently very "uptight." Just the name is enough to start a level of humor that is quite necessary to get them to allow themselves the freedom required for this group. I then ask them to remove the chairs and stack them in a corner. They are tasked to move around and ask fellow peers, "How do you feel?" replying "Fine." I also introduce the "treatment acronym" for "fine:" Fucked, Insecure, Neurotic and Emotional. This immediately creates a lightness that is required in order for them to begin to embrace the more instinctual positions of Primate and Feline/Canine. Clients spend about fifteen minutes on this exercise.

After Homo Erectus, Primate is introduced, as well as the movement that accompanies it. This is the position between the cognitive and the instinctual. Normally the movement of a drunken sailor will be interjected to encourage the progression towards less held, less constrained movement.

Last, we move over to Feline/Canine, the most instinctual of the three positions/postures. At this stage I have been able to observe which client is responding exceptionally well to this form of exploration and the two of us will take to the floor to demonstrate a more instinctual form of sound-making while the rest witness. I do not allow for too much time in setting an example, as I am aware of how evocative this exercise can be.

Clients then pair up in groups of four and start growling at each other. Again, I do not allow too much time on this before splitting the whole group in two. They form two straight lines across from each other at opposite ends of the room. One by one, each client is then afforded the opportunity to start projecting a growl to the person opposite them, allowing time and opportunity for a response. I might intervene with individuals with some physical manipulation at this stage to increase the volume of tidal airflow in order to help them release and amplify their sound. This progressive series of movements or postures enables the clients, without thinking about it, to start widening and lengthening their vocal tract at the same time they are loosening up their bodies. Vocally, this process of physically moving from Homo Erectus to Primate to Feline/Canine has the effect of widening and lengthening the vocal tube and changing the timbre or quality of the sound emitted. For someone who is overly controlled and with a constricted voice, it can provide a way to loosen up both physically and emotionally and produce a more powerful sound; for someone who is always "roaring" and barely in control, moving from Feline/Canine through Primate and back up to Homo Erectus can help that person regain control of how they move, what they say, and how they say it.

We end this session by engaging in a group-roar, to see if we can scare the other counsellors away!

II. GROUP TWO: BODY MAPS

These sessions are also attended by all clients. Prior to attending the first session, a new client will have outlined their body map with the assistance of a "buddy," another client of the same sex who has been in treatment for more than a week who will trace an indelible line around them as they lie on a strong piece of paper.

The material that we use for this is a thick poster paper that is pre-cut into sheets of 1.5 meters by 3 meters which enables an outline of the whole physical body. The art materials consist of water-based paints, oil pastels, charcoal, crayons, chalk and pencils.

After the introduction of the weekly theme, I play a CD containing mostly sounds of different singing bowls. My reason for doing this is that, due to the large number of clients attending the group, I find this helps to ground them by softening any noise from outside; it also helps them focus on their own process, instead of investigating what others might be doing. The sessions start with a short period of relaxation and breathing, and each week I introduce a different related theme. For the four groups I give the following directions:

Week One, "The Inner Self": Think about your source of inner power or energy. Where does this lie in your body? Where do you feel your energy and strength come from? Find this place and then imagine a personal symbol for your power source. For example, you might choose a winged heart in the chest area, or a growing plant in the stomach area, or a trumpet in the throat. There is no right or wrong. Let the symbol come freely to mind. You do not need to understand why you chose it. Then do the following:

1. Draw your symbol in the place where you feel the power source in your body. Use pastels or crayons. Then draw lines to show energy moving out from that power source. Choose the direction of the lines. Do they zigzag or spiral? What parts of the body do they go to? Do they move outside of the body outline?

2. Trace around your hands or feet near your body outline. Think about where you would like to place your hands: for example, they might be on either side of your head or holding your stomach. Use white crayon and pastel to do this.

3. Now write some words on this Map of Your Self and use wax crayons or oil pastels. Write in any language, style or size. Think carefully where to place each word. Use the following guidelines to write your words:

4. Write 5 words that best describe who you are: for example: student, Italian, artist, long-distance runner.

5. Write 3 positive or good things that family or friends or other people have said about you in your life. They might be positive comments on your

personality, your work, your skills or talents. For example: kind, good listener, creative.

6. Write down a phrase or saying that guides you in your life. It might be a motto, a prayer, a proverb, or the words of a song. It might be something you say to yourself when times are difficult. For example, "Be true to yourself," or "I am beautiful."

Week Two, "Your addiction":

1. Sit or lie down on your Self Map. Close your eyes, take a couple of deep breaths. Bring your time of active addiction into your mind.

2. Think about your drugs or behaviors of choice and how these have progressed. Think about the unmanageability, the lack of control, the damage to yourself and others. When you have this in mind, think about your addiction in terms of the inside and the outside of you.

3. Inside and Outside: Perhaps on the outside you may have marks, scars or tattoos that are linked with your addiction? On the inside, are there any thoughts, feelings, images, colors, textures that come to mind as you think about your illness? Where does your addiction lie in your body? Does it take a particular form or shape? Is it a particular color or various colors? Is there maybe an image that comes to mind or a symbol? Work quietly in your own space to express your addiction somewhere on your Self Map. Remember there are no rights and no wrongs.

Week Three, "Your Masks": Think about the concept of the mask. To mask something means to hide or disguise it as something else. A mask is made to wear over the face, hiding the true identity of the wearer and creating a new identity. Masks can have the facial features of a person, an animal, an imaginary creature or spirit. Masks can transform people so that they seem to enter another world, or feel differently about themselves, or make other people see them differently.

As human beings, we often mask or hide our true feelings or inner selves through using a variety of defenses and through changing our outer appearance and facial expression. It is normal for all of us to have appropriate masks, personas and defenses. However, what often happens with addiction is that the inside and outside become uncomfortably different and this is what we call being incongruent: there is a clash, a conflict, between the inner and the outer self. For example, often we feel sad or angry on the inside but put on a smiling, happy face. Or we feel afraid of life and others, so we put on an angry, intimidating mask. Our clothes, hair, shoes, make-up, accessories, body tattoos and piercings often form part of this mask or image that together give out a particular message to others.

1. Think about yourself and the masks that you wear. What are your most common masks? Smiling, angry, sad, scared? Try to identify at least 4 masks that you use in different situations for different reasons.

2. Think about the rest of your appearance. Do you cultivate a particular image for a particular reason? Think about the kind of clothes you like to wear and the kind of shoes. Do you wear make-up and how much?

3. Work quietly in your own space and draw at least four different masks that reflect different sides that you show to the world.

Week Four, "Your hopes, dreams and goals for recovery:" Take a few minutes to reflect on your hopes, wishes and dreams for your life in recovery. You may have had dreams, goals, activities, passions prior to your addiction and these have been lost, dropped, eroded. Depict these hopes, dreams, wishes and goals around your body on your map using colors, images, textures, and even symbols. (Clients take great pride in their body maps, the actual size of which is 1 meter x 2 meters.)

Conclusion

My progression with VMT took me on many amazing journeys. In some of those journeys, I witnessed the transformation of a client and in some of them it was my own. During my training, I was introduced to a working experience of the Sphere. This had an immediate and significant effect on me. I started experiencing what it feels like to be vulnerable and yet safe at the same time. Using this flexible yet strong container with my clients became an important VMT principle that I employed during individual and group sessions to create a place of safety.

I also encouraged clients to be aware of the Convex/Concave movement in the abdomen where tidal airflow and vocal power are primarily generated. By stretching out an arm and concaving the wrist so that the inside of the palm is clearly visible to the client himself, I created a new dimension of "what is mine." The opposite effect was created with a convex movement of the wrist, with the palm of the hand facing away from the client, thus creating a natural barrier to "what is not mine." The therapeutic significance of this simple exercise cannot be overemphasized and I have used it with great effect.

SOUNDING OUR WAY TO WHOLENESS: LINKING THE METAPHORICAL AND PHYSICAL VOICE WITH WOMEN EXPERIENCING EATING DISORDERS

Irene Kessler

(Excerpted and summarized by Deirdre Brownell)

Since this was the first time VMT was used as a primary modality in a preliminary quest for information on the effectiveness of VMT with women with eating disorders who are metaphorically "voiceless," we felt it was important to include it. Although now deceased, we feel that Irene's dissertation, conceived of in her Ph.D. dissertation as a pilot project, belongs here.

Dr. Irene Kessler, a psychologist and a registered Voice Movement Therapy practitioner, relates in "Sounding Our Way to Wholeness: Linking the Metaphorical and Physical Voice in a Pilot Study with Women Using Breath, Voice and Movement"[1] how she worked for a year with a group of seven women with eating disorders to discover if breath, voice and movement would result in any noticeable attitudinal and behavioral changes. She also employed journaling and art, but the main focus was on voicing, listening and being heard. This combination of methods provided a holistic body-centered approach to eating disorders which sought to address the role of disassociation from the body and the use of food to numb the physical self and ignore feelings.

Using such Voice Movement Therapy concepts as Convex and Concave (see page 21), positions evolving from the actual body movement of the breath in the torso, and spherical space, or the Sphere, conceived of as both kinesthetic or reach space—How far can I reach using all the parts of my actual body? and energetic or emotional space—How much space do I feel I take up today?—Kessler shows her research participants how to construct an imagistic safe space that they can claim for themselves. In this way, she provides them with a safe container which is both physically and imaginatively based from which they can relate to the world around them. The movement exercises make the women aware of how uncomfortable they feel in their bodies, and they struggle with this. The vocal exercises prove to be easier for them, involving less outward or obvious movement, and they can limit the amount of visible physical exposure required. The voice can grow in volume while one remains in a single place, whereas large movements, for them, feel more revealing.

In general, the women's experience of using body and voice as tools for self-exploration brings on feelings of not being in control because they cannot foretell the outcome. They are not used to allowing expression of feelings at a physical level and tend to over-intellectualize to maintain distance. It is difficult for them to express the feelings they are used to holding back. One woman says, "I knew I had a tear, but it stopped."[2] Most talk about these experiences as if they are not happening in the present.

However, as their work progresses, they become better able to acknowledge their feelings and begin to accept and work with them. For these women, taking care of themselves means not taking care of someone else, meaning they feel that by taking time for themselves, they are literally taking it away from a husband, a parent, or other family member or friend. A movement exercise in opening and closing, giving and receiving, enables them to practice the receiving part of relationship which, for them, is difficult.

These women have been shamed and isolated by their condition, and unheard. The point of this group is for them to experience being heard and hearing others with some regularity. By participating in this group through moving and vocalizing with and without words, the women begin to develop "a sense" of the body as having a spatial existence as it is vibrated from the inside out and from the outside in. They can feel the vibrations in their own living bodies and from the group voicing around them, giving them a kinesthetic sense, a sensory awareness that their body is an actual physical entity and perhaps an acceptable thing. By making sounds and discovering different voices for themselves, they begin to connect their child voice with their adult voice.

When we look at someone, we cannot know how they experience themselves, whereas, as Kessler says, "When we hear them vocalize, the sounds as vibrations enter our bodies and the ear functions like an antenna, letting us know where we are in relation to the sounds around us, as well as letting us get a sense of the affect another person is expressing and the mood he or she is speaking or sounding from."[3]

Kessler had done previous groups based on talk therapy which had included visual imagery and art, but not movement and vocalization. She explains that "Eating disordered women who cannot deal directly or openly with their feelings eat until they are numb."[4] She knew they needed to deal with that numbness: to become more aware of it, acknowledge it, and work with it. She had seen for herself in the past what talk therapy could accomplish and where it sometimes seemed to fall short. What she found in this group is that when working directly with body, breath and voice, she seemed to get results faster through making that connection. One of the women in the group said she thought she had accomplished more in one year with VMT than in four years of talk therapy. It seems that this issue, so directly related to the physical body and body image, responds well to an approach involving amplified moving and voicing.

According to this study, the sounding drew out the shame and anger of feeling worthless, being misunderstood, and being silenced. Of the seven women who began, four stayed for the whole year. The pre- and post-tests which measure psychological symptom patterns for the previous seven days and reflect the current clinical status of the respondent, and especially the Zung which measures depression, showed there was a decrease in sensitivity, depression, anxiety, and hostility. The participants who completed the year tested at a normal level in these categories.

Key to Kessler's work with the eating disordered women of her study is the affect of shame and its relationship to the voice. In discussing the general development of women's voices and using "voice" as a metaphor for one's sense of self, she notes,

> The general agreement that girls' voices, their connection to their inner self, begin to get shut down somewhere between nine and twelve years of age, is due in large part to the objectification of girls and women, especially the sexual objectification, which causes feelings of shame.[5]

Discussing the work of Carol Gilligan, she notes that the choice to speak or to be voiceless is played out in the body and the use of the voice. According to Gilligan, "The loss of voice is companion to the loss of self."[6]

According to Kessler, the cycle of hiding unacceptable parts of the self begins with a feeling of oppression. The false self, the self of many masks, gives birth to the chameleon. She references Winnicott's concept of the "false self" and describes it as a defense mechanism to hide vulnerability and worthlessness. It affects the way we present ourselves because, as she says,

> When the way we live in the outside world is not in agreement with the way our inside wants to live, we shut down our voices. There is a fear of doing, saying, and even wanting things that may displease those who hold our survival in their hands. The threat of disruption of connections—with our husbands, our friends, all those whom we serve to atone for inhabiting our unpresentable overweight or underweight selves—is perceived not just as a loss of relationship but as something closer to a total loss of self.[7]

In Kessler's words, "Shame is the feeling that the self is defective. It reaches to the core of our being, affecting our self-image." She concludes her study as follows:

> The human connection generated in the therapist-client relationship is created through resonance, the vibration carried on the breath. Resonance carries both words and sounds. Learning to allow sounds to spring spontaneously from the body is the path to freedom not only for the body but for the spirit and soul, as well. Here we have the true connection to the authentic voice.[8]

NOTES

1. Irene Kessler, from "Sounding Our Way to Wholeness," in Brownell, Deirdre "Re-Embodying the Voice: Uniting Body and Mind through the Voice to Strengthen the Self." Unpublished PhD. dissertation, Petaluma, CA: Meridian University: 2020, p. 79.

2. D. Brownell, "Re-Embodying the Voice," p. 79. These also have correct information.
3. D. Brownell, p. 80.
4. D. Brownell, p. 80.
5. D. Brownell, p. 81.
6. D. Brownell, p. 81.
7. D. Brownell, p. 81.
8. D. Brownell, pp. 81-82.
9. D. Brownell, p. 82.

BIBLIOGRAPHY

Kessler, Irene. (1997). "Sounding Our Way to Wholeness: Linking the Metaphorical and Physical Voice in a Pilot Study with Women Using Breath, Voice and Movement." Unpublished PhD dissertation, Los Angeles, CA: Union Institute.

Kessler, quoted in Brownell, Deirdre (2020). "Re-Embodying the Voice: Uniting Body and mind through the Voice to Strengthen the Self." Unpublished PhD. dissertation, Petaluma, CA: Meridian University: 2020.

Chapter Three

CHANNELS OF THE VOICE: AFFECT AND THE BRAIN

INTRODUCTION, MY BODY, MY ENEMY: A LIFE IN RECOVERY

Deirdre Brownell

This chapter is very close to my heart. Having been born with dyslexia (a reading disorder), dyspraxia (a disorder of the central nervous system), and an auditory processing disorder which caused my hearing to drop out often for a few seconds to a minute at a time, I was at a disadvantage to begin with. Because of these conditions, I did not move or think very fast and had little coordination. To make matters worse, my family life was often very chaotic and I found myself being dragged around a lot because I would go on "sit-down strikes" and shut off the world when I got overstimulated.

As an infant, things were not so bad, since everything was close to my face. I had another condition known as alternating strabismus which meant that my eyes did not approximate or focus together, so all I saw were dark and light blurs till I got bifocals and began eye exercises when I was six. Mostly, I relied on echo-location, like a bat using sound to bounce off of objects to know where it is in space. I also developed a very strong sensory awareness of my own body, which was not always good because my dyspraxia affected my nerves as well as my balance and the wind could sometimes feel like a slap and I had trouble dealing with myself in space.

Learning to walk was very difficult and I don't know how I did it, as I had little ability to know whether I was standing up or lying down. Also, the posture of standing caused my diaphragm to become compressed as my core muscles overworked to hold me up, with the result that my breathing became quite shallow. At 14 months of age, I developed croup, a type of respiratory infection caused by a virus leading to swelling inside the trachea which interferes with normal breathing, and I had to be hospitalized and put in a steam tent. I truly learned what it felt like not to be able to breathe and from then on knew the fear of dying without really understanding it. But the affect, the felt sense of fear, was ingrained in my body and remained there for decades. It adversely influenced how I lived my life for many years.

From early on, my outer life was complicated. My family circumstances continued to be chaotic and many times the one who spoke the loudest was the one who got heard. When I entered the first grade, it was obvious to me that I could not keep up, although it took a while for my teachers to recognize the difficulties I was having because I was very verbal, sociable, and happy. I had to return to kindergarten and be tested. I changed schools and started tutoring, which saved my life, but school was no longer fun; I was mercilessly teased by classmates and by my brother for my lack of coordination and the fact that I had no ability to stop thoughts from escaping my mouth, so often the things I said did not follow the progress of the conversation. This is when I started to feel ashamed. As a result, my own embodied voice became silenced for fear of ridicule and persecution. At the same time, spending so much time trying to learn to read and find the right words to express my thoughts and feelings, because of my dyslexia and other conditions, only furthered the disharmony between how I felt (my affective voice) and what I said (my cognitive voice).

As I moved through adolescence, I continued to improve, but I was always striving to put my learning disabled and uncoordinated self behind me. I pushed myself to do all the things the doctors said I never would do and to deal with what I originally identified as my brother's voice in my head. I now call it my "demon" voice, but because my older brother was so critical of me when we were young, and until I had the opportunity and tools to look at things more objectively, I heard it as his voice. But I never really dealt with it; I ran from it until a situation occurred in my early 20s that I couldn't deal with: I became suicidal and eventually had a nervous breakdown (Piece of advice: Don't ever try to be a full-time student and start and run a horse breeding business at the same time).

I knew I was in over my head, but I kept hearing my brother say that I would fail, that I couldn't make it on my own, and so I simply could not give up or admit that I was in trouble. Contained in this voice, as well, was my mother's, whom I believed didn't think I could do it, either. Because of her own fears about the world and my special needs as a child, she was over-protective and overly worried about me. So, I felt that fear and thought it meant that I should feel that way, too. After I left home, I was in therapy for two years, during which time I learned to distinguish between what were actually my emotions and what belonged to others. I should state that I am an empath, so I pick up on all emotions and had to learn to let go of the things that were not mine. After this period of finding myself, I decided to participate in the first American Summer School in Voice Movement Therapy (VMT), held in Somerville, MA in 2002.

I have always been a strong singer and music has always been a major part of my life. At around this time, I started to feel a tightness in my voice and my range was shrinking. My singing voice was the one part of me I could always count on, so this really freaked me out. I thought it was just mechanical, but as I continued through the weeks, I realized it was not. As my mother was co-teaching this course, I worked a lot with the other instructor, Christine Isherwood. Anne and Christine were the only people actively teaching VMT at this time, so I had no choice. For me personally, this was a good thing because it brought out issues that otherwise would not have been addressed: for example, my mother's over-protectiveness of me in physical and social situations and how this was no longer needed.

The biggest issue I addressed in these three weeks was my inability to scream. This was when I discovered what I call my three baby subpersonalities which I would not have discovered without re-experiencing these baby stages and sensations within a supportive group. Taking off my glasses and cooing and crawling around and vocalizing as a baby during some of the course's developmental work began, for me, the emergence of the transition from affect to cognition.

As I vocalized without words, I began to find sounds and sensations I had not felt in years, possibly decades. They had been buried. On the last day of the summer school, I was vocalizing and rolling around on the floor in this fashion and I could feel something emerging from my body. I was reaching for it within myself and I could feel everyone in the room urging me on, as they could feel it, too. Suddenly my vocalizing became screaming. I was screaming for the first time ever and I just could not stop because it felt so good! Finally, when I was hoarse, I stopped and opened my eyes and saw my mother. This was exactly what I needed, for looking up at her I had a vision of being in that steam tent as a baby and not being able to breathe. In that moment, I found Fear Baby, the subpersonality that had been holding me back from trying things for years. The physical feeling of fear, the actual body sensation, was translated through re-enactment into the cognitive emotion of fear which could be named and discussed. This illustrates the importance of moving and voicing these sensations and, literally in this case, taking it to the floor.

There were two other baby subpersonalities: Power Baby who has always been my 2-year-old self, keen to explore, incredibly sociable and never self-conscious. There was also Angry/Frustrated Baby whom I found when I was training in VMT in South Africa in 2012 in very much the same way I found Fear Baby. In exploring them both at this time, I discovered maladaptive breathing patterns that became emphasized in their enactment. In becoming aware of these patterns, I discovered the buried affects of frustration and fear caused by both my physical issues and my situational traumas, and how they continued to affect my life. The next phase in my quest for self-actualization was working with the cognitive emotions and maladaptive behaviors that stemmed from them.

In 2008 I started to study Imaginal Psychology at Meridian University in Petaluma, California (at that time, the Institute for Imaginal Studies) where I later received my Ph.D. Imaginal Psychology is all about finding "the soul's passion," what we are meant to do and what gets in the way of doing it. After working with VMT, I found that Imaginal Psychology added an important piece: the idea of an "adaptive" or false identity created by traumatic situations and how that is what keeps us from our fully realized self.

As I was working in VMT with the Fear and Anger babies, I began to notice a child in the back of my mind screaming at me to acknowledge her. In class at Meridian I was encouraged to engage with this child, so I would get up in front of the class using a system, adapted from the work of Fritz Perls, where there are three chairs which are occupied somewhat differently in Imaginal Psychology: in one sits the Self, in the second is the Child Within (who is still there), and in the third is the Gatekeeper who does not want the upwelling emotions to be worked with. The Gatekeeper's job is to protect the adaptive (maladaptive) identity. It originally appears to protect the child from a situation they can't deal with. The therapist (in this case, my teacher) guides the conversation only as much as is necessary.

Through these sessions I began to know my eight-year-old child subpersonality. She is the one I pushed away throughout my life. She is the awkward disabled part of myself, the one I never truly accepted. I was ashamed of her. But in dialogue with her, I learned she had much to teach me. She reminded me of where I came from and how far I had come. She is my compassion for others and my desire to work with people like me because my understanding comes from her.

We all need our past. We all need to be understood, and as a learning disabled child, I often felt unheard and misunderstood, so I stopped talking very much. As an eight-year-old, I became much more withdrawn, and shame caused the adaptive identity to form which I refer to as the Disabled Outcast. I wanted to believe that I had left my disabilities behind me, but they kept coming back. However, I cannot be a whole person without all of my experiences. I learned that they had value for me and could be used to help others. I cannot truly be my authentic, fully actualized self without accepting my past and all the parts of me. This makes me a better person, a better listener, and a better therapist.

In essence, what VMT did for me, in working to bring the affective and cognitive channels of my voice into sync, was to help me contact and bring forth material locked in my unconscious and create a bridge between what was trapped in my body—a body memory existing only as sensation—and what needed to be brought into consciousness in order for me to examine, confront and change it. At Meridian, it began to be conceptualized, named and worked with through my own continuing process of songmaking and through the enactment of the various subpersonalities that emerged. What Imaginal Psychology did for me was to define the process of taking these buried affects which VMT had uncovered and identified as recognizable named emotions and bring them into further cognitive understanding through the concept of the "adaptive identity," this "as if" or false self which temporarily helped me to adapt and survive in response to adverse life conditions. Of course, just as my voice continues to grow and change, so do new "adaptive" identities emerge which can be worked with and let go. This is a clarifying and life-affirming process.

In this introduction based on my own personal experience, I have presented examples of three main learnings I wish to illustrate in more detail by the articles in this chapter:

1. The relationship between the two channels of communication worked with in VMT: the cognitive (the words we use to convey meaning) and the affective (the tones of voice we use which reflect the bodily sensations which underlie them and convey how we are really feeling about what we are saying);
2. How and why maladaptive behaviors develop because of the splitting of the relationship between these two channels, focusing on how they influence the development or alteration of identity in those of us born with pre-existing conditions, either in the form of obvious special needs, or as what have been called the "hidden" learning disabilities because they are not obvious; or because of neurological or sometimes highly traumatizing accidents or events in the progression of one's life;
3. How to bring these two channels together to eliminate or ameliorate the resulting maladaptive behavior caused by the development of an "adaptive" identity.

The articles which follow are divided into two parts. The first three deal with individuals experiencing congenital conditions or accidents of birth, and the next three with individuals with emotional or physical conditions they were not born with, but developed during childhood or later in life. In "Dillan: Opening up Channels of Communication with the Person Trapped Inside," I recount my experience of working with a ten-year-old child with a pervasive dysfunctional chromosomal condition.

"Samuel: A Story of Healing Trauma with Voice Movement Therapy," by Sebastiana Black, concerns her work with a teenage boy with mild to moderate cognitive delays and behavioral issues and how the formation and growth of their relationship through sound and movement and his move into songwiting enables him to give voice to his feelings and become more calm and confident.

The third article, "Interviews with an Expressive Movement Educator, Three Young Men with Physical and Cognitive Delays, and Their Home Providers is about the efficacy of one-on-one sessions with Dr. William C. Freeman, Expressive Movement Therapist and teacher, with three young men in their early 20s with both physical involvement and cognitive delays, and their accompanying parent or home provider. The last session includes some adjunctive work I did with Dr. Freeman who also has taught on the VMT Training to increase the students' observational and interactive skills in movement.

The next three articles involve practitioners working with individuals with emotional or physical conditions they were not born with but developed early and/or later in life. The first, "A Case of Selective Mutism in the Work of Tracy Starreveld," is about an elementary school-aged child recovering from trauma-induced mutism and how this process is enhanced by a slow and careful process using breath, voice, and simple movement to reveal and work with emerging subpersonalities to affect her ability to socialize by helping her recover her voice. The next, "My Favorite Patient and How I Became the Singing Pastor," by Anne Maarman, tells of her work with a woman recovering from a major stroke, and includes her reflections when, two years later, she suffered a similar kind of stroke herself.

In the last article, "Singing for Joy: Creating Community and Sustaining Function in a Choir with Parkinson's Disease," Carol Grimes tells of her work with a choir in London, UK, composed of people in various stages of Parkinson's and other neurological disorders. What VMT provides in all of these instances is a way of working with a person's affect, or feeling state, to promote healing.

I. INDIVIDUALS EXPERIENCING CONDITIONS PRESENT FROM BIRTH

DILLAN: OPENING UP CHANNELS OF COMMUNICATION WITH THE PERSON TRAPPED INSIDE

Deirdre Brownell

This is the story of a young boy experiencing maladaptive behavior whom I was able to work with mainly by listening to and interacting with him in such a way that he knew he was not just being listened to but truly heard, even though he had very limited verbal speech and expressed himself mostly in high-pitched cries and tight movements. My training in VMT is what enabled me to decipher and find ways to match his movements and the affective tones of his vocalizations, which at that time composed the bulk of his "language." My passionate desire to communicate with him through what I had learned from VMT about the affective voice as opposed to cognitive speech made him want to learn to communicate better with words. His progress in this endeavor majorly changed his behavior and his relationship to other members of his residential school community.

Dillan (name used by permission) is a ten-year-old Afrikaans boy who is a residential student at the Alta Du Toit School for children with cognitive delays. He is the son of devoted but working parents without reliable transport to get him to school every day. He was born with a chromosomal disorder called Cri du Chat (cry of the cat), also known as 5P- (minus) syndrome. The main characteristics of this condition are:

1. A very high-pitched voice
2. Elongated limbs
3. Low-slung ears
4. Very wide apart eyes
5. Extremely tight muscles, including facial muscles
6. Sometimes genital abnormalities and
7. Sometimes severe retardation. With regard to this last characteristic, the prevailing opinion of those who worked with Dillan most closely was that he was not retarded but delayed, primarily because of his inability to speak.

Shortly after my arrival for my VMT internship, Dillan was moved from the junior or first class to the special or lowest functioning class because he was experiencing overstimulation and frustration resulting in violent behavior such as biting and hitting teachers and other students. Although both his teacher and the school psychologist were unhappy with this placement, they had no alternative at that time.

Even though Dillan barely spoke, they knew he understood simple directions for identifying and retrieving objects and following basic commands: for example, the teacher would ask him to listen and he would look at her and listen, and then indicate Yes or No by nodding or shaking his head. He showed more basic understanding than any other child in this group. However, when frustrated or angry he bit, hit or threw a temper tantrum. When he was feeling stubborn, he would not cooperate: for example, if someone tried to take him to the door and he didn't want to go, he would fight them or start grinding his teeth and picking at his face. His mother said he talked to her, but to most of the staff he only responded with actions and gestures. He communicated well with the other children through body language and they loved and looked after him as if he was a baby.

Initial Observations

I was interested in picking three students to work with individually. This was very helpful to the school in South Africa where I was interning as part of my Ph.D. program because they couldn't afford to work with students one-on-one, but only in groups. Since many of the students had language delays, the school psychologist was very interested in my working with some of these students more intensively. I was looking for the most delayed individuals I could find to test the usefulness of Voice Movement Therapy with this population.

The first student I picked was Dillan because I felt I understood and could connect with him. Not only did I think he was intelligent, but there was just something about him. He stuck out from the rest in the classroom because he seemed to have a curiosity and a desire to learn, in spite of his many handicaps.

What I observed when I first met him was that his muscles, especially his facial muscles, were extremely tight which inhibited speech. He did not cross the midline and functioned on the horizontal plane except for a lurching, unbalanced gate forward. His walk was still in bilateral toddler phase with no real diagonal movement of his limbs. He had very poor balance and didn't pick up his feet, but shuffled and would trip over anything on the floor all the time and I would catch him. Although he could sit, stand, lie and roll over, he had little awareness of space and his body in space. His voice was very high-pitched, accompanied by hand flapping. I was given free rein and the school psychologist was hopeful, stating, "We don't know if this is going to work, but what if it does? What can you do for him?" His possibility for further education was at this time tentative.

My main observations were that, in addition to extremely tight muscles, he was easily seriously overstimulated and, although affectionate, tactilely defensive because of acute sensitivity to touch. With regard to his other senses, loud sounds did not bother him and he noticed what was right in front of him but could not see well far away, either because his vision was bad or because there was so much information coming in, he couldn't process it. What follows are excerpts from "It's a Nice Day If It Doesn't Rain," an instructional Handbook on VMT written by Deirdre Brownell with Anne Brownell (2013) at the request of the teachers at Alta Du Toit School, Kuilsriver, Western Cape, S. Africa, at the end of my internship there.[1]

Dillan was at first very stand-offish. The first time, I only had him in the room for about 15 minutes. Very gradually, as we continued to meet and as he started to play with things, particularly the electronic piano keyboard, he would want me to watch and would check to see if I was doing so. Initially, that was our only interaction. Soon after, it became important for him that I become involved in what he was doing. I would sit and watch him play with the piano and from time to time I would sing "La, la, la" when he hit the keys. Eventually, he started requesting this by placing his hand to his mouth and then pointing to the keys on the piano, and then he would start to play a note and would indicate with his hand for me to match it with my voice, after which he would play a series of notes and have me match those with my voice. Then he started going around the room picking up other objects and asking me to name them by pointing to them and eventually trying to repeat the words back to me. As he began to feel safer, his interest and his desire to communicate with me grew.

Figure 7. Deirdre Brownell with student at keyboard. Alta du Toit School, Kuilsriver, Western Cape, S. Africa—2013. Photo: Anne Brownell.

I began to add more instruments, like the harmonica. Soon he wanted to combine sounds, like his piano playing with my harmonica playing or singing. He would pick up the harmonica and give it to me and point to my mouth to indicate his desire. He had also been trying to match notes on the piano with his harmonica and he was getting closer. He would play a note on the piano and then try to find that note on his harmonica.

Once Dillan felt comfortable in the room with me, I realized it was time to start him socializing in a larger group and so we began attending the VMT Music and Movement Group in his classroom with his classmates that I had begun with Anne Brownell. At first, he wanted only to cling to me while someone else led the group, but soon he and I were sitting on the bench side by side and then, soon after that, he would sit with children several seats away from me. Gradually he became more independent of me when with his group. He would also interact with the other children as well as me. After a few times in group, I would not take him right after class and would do his individual session on another day. In this way, he learned not to depend on his session being right after group and would therefore not try to rush through the group session in order to get to his individual one. As a result, he started to get more involved and enjoy the group sessions. The other important thing about group sessions is that he started to see me in different situations and it became less strange to encounter me in the hallway or in the hostel and he would smile and give me a hug.

In the last few weeks of our time together, our schedule got interrupted quite often. I had been coming to his class twice a week, on Tuesdays and Fridays, but one week he was taken out for testing by a visiting psychologist, another week it was for something else, and the third time it was Market Day right after our Music and Movement group. Since our schedule had been interrupted and he had been disappointed in his expectation of our time together so often recently—and since he had handled all the changes so well and it was getting a bit much for him—that day I went to market with him. In some ways it was good that we had a lot of interruptions in our work together because I wanted him to understand that things change and that yelling and screaming wouldn't help him to deal with the changes. Dillan is a first-class example of a person who doesn't transition well. He needs more time to go from one activity to another because of his own built-in problems that he must learn to deal with. The extremely sensitive nervous system which he was born with is already over-responsive and hyperactive. There is already too much going on inside him that is confusing and distracting. So, when there is a lot of unpredictable activity going on outside, as well, i.e., not what he is used to and has come to expect, it can be quite overwhelming.

One thing that is helping Dillan both to adjust to changes and to socialize more is his increased use of language to express his wants and needs. When I use words with him, the point is not only to name objects and actions, but to watch for his efforts to say the words and to help him develop and add to the language he already has, including his non-verbal movement language. When Dillan indicates that he wants something or asks what it is called, I say the word and two, three or four sessions later he'll say it to name that object.

For example: he walks into the room and starts playing the piano and I say, "piano." Pretty soon he recognizes the connection of that word to the object he is playing with and tries to make the sounds that identify it, like "eano." Later on, he starts creating his own way to represent an object or an action.

Another example: We had been taking pictures in the Music and Movement Group in his classroom and he wanted to take some pictures in our room. So, he put up his hands on either side of his face, palms open and framing his eyes, and said "camma," creating his own gesture to accompany his attempt to say the word. In this way he communicated what he wanted to do. Then he started making a patting motion on the floor to indicate that he wanted me to sit down. I asked him, "Do you want me to sit in a chair while you take my picture or do you want me down on the floor? He pointed to the floor and said "Down," or as close as he could get to that word. For example, the "d" is easy for him, but the "ow" sound of "down" is hard because of his difficulty making that shape with his mouth.

When looking at Dillan, sometimes it will appear by his facial expression that he's very distressed when he may only be trying to concentrate, so you have to look at his body language. Is he running around or is he simply staring? If he's running around, it may be because he's looking for something, so I ask him "What do you want?" and listen for what sounds come out and try to figure out what he is saying. Sometimes you have to guess. At other times it is very clear.

For example: One morning in our room he was trying to find something in the cabinets. He was running back and forth, but not just pulling everything out and dumping it on the floor, so I asked him "What do you want?" and he kept saying something that sounded like "puh," "puh." So I began naming different things that sounded like "puh" until he found the four cassette tapes he was looking for. Perhaps "puh" indicated the way one pushes the buttons to make it work. So I learned that, for right now in his ability to say it, "tape" was "puh." I then said, looking at him and pronouncing very distinctly with an exaggerated facial expression, "tape." He began to be able to make the sound "t," and now he is beginning to be able to say "CD" instead of "Ti-Ti."

The first sounds I noticed that Dillan could make were "eee" and "uh." The main consonant sound that he used was "buh," buh." Now, in playing with a toy car, he can say "car" and it sounds like "caar." In other words, it is elongated, or held out a little bit, in order for him to get all the sounds out. When he first tried to say the word "guitar," it came out "gi-gi," and eventually "gui-gui-guitar." Now he can say this two-syllable word outright, but it must be remembered that this takes a great deal of muscular effort and concentration because his facial muscles are so tight.

The main thing to remember with Dillan is that he has to know you are listening and you really have to look at him while you speak because he needs to see your gaze to understand that you are speaking to him. Otherwise, he may be experiencing both too much internal and too much external distraction, which causes him to remain somewhat lost and out of contact with you.

If Dillan actually is distressed, the best thing I have found to do is to look him directly in the eye, put a hand on his arm or shoulder and ask him,

"What do you need?" Even if he can't answer or doesn't know, this simple act of speaking to him while you make physical contact can be enough to calm him down, to calm his system. It is important to maintain a calm but attentive presence because that helps him to learn to develop and maintain his own sense of calm.

How I worked with Dillan was in terms of what I could see, hear, and sense. In the beginning, he couldn't sit still and he was scared because he didn't know who I was or what I wanted. I knew that he had been born with this neurological condition "cri du chat" and that meant there were certain limitations that he would be struggling to overcome. I had never worked with or met anyone with this condition before.

One needs to remember that Dillan's body and face are long and narrow and his muscles tight, or hypertonic. When trying to walk forward, he mostly goes from side to side and his balance is not very good. If there are objects on the floor, he will fall over them, or he may bang his head on a cabinet when trying to take something out of it if he is not paying attention. His coordination and concentration are not good and he has trouble picking up his feet. Dillan's face, both when at rest and when trying to talk, shows great physical and muscular tension. When concentrating, his mouth is in a straight line and his jaw is habitually pulled down and very tight. It is an effort for him to open his jaw further to say "buh" and even harder to stretch his mouth across on either side toward his ears to say "eee." The hardest is probably the sound "oh" which requires rounding his mouth. But he wants to learn, he is curious, and he has intelligence. It is just that he has a lot to struggle against, a lot to overcome and find ways of compensating for.

It is important to know that Dillan is intelligent but needs guidance. There is a difference between letting him do whatever he wants to (a false, unproductive kind of "kindness") and giving him some freedom to explore within the structure of guided play because for him every such opportunity is a learning experience. If you watch, you will see that he is quite frequently asking for guidance or information through either movement gestures or voice. For example, if he wants to play piano (the electronic keyboard) when he comes into the room, I ask, "Is everything on?" and he will go to see if everything is on before he tries to play. If he plays something and there is no sound, he will go back again to see if all the switches are on. This is learned behavior of a very positive and functional kind.

Or, another example: He no longer randomly pulls toys out of the cabinets, but searches through the boxes trying to find particular things. In the beginning, when he used to pull everything out and strew it around the floor, he would then trip over things. Rather than just saying, "No, don't do this" (because it is bad behavior and also will take me a long time to pick it all up), I pointed out that having all those objects on the floor would just make him trip and not get him what he wanted. This made sense to him and so he found another, more satisfying way. It was satisfying for me, too, not only because of what he had been able to learn, but also because it saved me the time and effort of trying to get him to pick everything up and put it back or having to do it all myself.

Dillan is a very sweet, intelligent and affectionate little boy. He has a smile that lights up a room. When Dillan smiles, his whole face changes and one can see not just the disabled child but the actual person who is inside and working hard to come out and be known. He is very quick to pick up on things as long as you keep a few things in mind:

First: Always look at him when you are speaking so he knows you are speaking to him and he can concentrate on you, which is hard for him because of all the internal and external distractions.

Second: Watch to see if he is trying to communicate. If he comes up to you and points to something, he may want you to name it so he can learn it. I think part of the reason he gets angry and fights is because he is trying to communicate what he needs and feels that no one is listening. Sometimes just naming something for him is all he wants. He needs attention of a very positive kind because that is what will stimulate him to talk more.

Third: Dillan's oversensitive nervous system will pick up on the energy of the people around him. If he becomes agitated and starts to fight or become distressed, try to keep yourself calm, touch his shoulder or arm, and look him in the eye and say, "What do you need?" He will react to your energy or mood and, if you are calm, it will help him to calm himself. This will help teach him to control his own behavior and not get so distressed. If the energy of the person around him is agitated, this will worsen his behavior. Some behavior can seem to be purposefully bad, but for Dillan this behavior is just out of frustration. The world is a scary place when you can't control your own body. Following these simple steps will, I believe, help to improve Dillan's behavior and ability to communicate and make him a happier, more productive child. I believe he has the ability and the intelligence to become a productive member of the community.

A Closer Look

When I began to work with Dillan he was fearful and his standoffishness was caused by that fear. He didn't know me, it was a new space, and he had no idea what to expect. He was very used to being evaluated and judged. I dealt with this by letting him leave when he wanted to and let him set the pace. I introduced him to different instruments and toys and he chose what he wanted. I made it clear I was there for him.

What made him want to stay was being allowed to play with the piano switches and making it sound, and realizing I was there to play with him and not just another person come to evaluate him. When he realized it was his choice, he wanted to stay. The first big change was when he experienced this difference in relationship. Children know when they are being judged and this was different.

The second big change was when he moved from parallel play–he would be playing the piano and I would be singing at the same time but not really together–to actually wanting me to accompany him by singing along to his playing, creating a kind of duet. This built upon his favorite classroom activity which was group singing while the teacher played piano. But now it was a direct form of communication solely between me and him.

At about the same time he began to push the on/off switch to control the power and I would say "on" and "off." He then began waiting for me to say it by looking at me after he pushed it. After a while he began to say the words. This was our first intentional communication in words and led to his pointing to toys for naming by me and then he would attempt the words after hearing them enough.

Next, I bought him a remote-controlled toy car. He learned to control the car with his thumbs and his next word was "c-c-caaarrr."

The next major hurdle was to increase his understanding of his effect on space. After all the falling down because he pulled all the toys from the cabinets so I could name them, I demonstrated to him taking out one toy, naming it and putting it back in the box. I then showed and told him he would not fall on the toys if he put them away. By doing this I was showing him that putting the toys away was for his comfort and safety and not just because I said so, not a necessary response to the authority or convenience of an adult. I was told later by the housemothers that he was not only picking up after himself with me. but also in his living area.

Around session ten, he wanted his classmates to see him play the piano, so they all came and watched him play and then he wanted them all to go away so he could have me to himself again. That was when I decided we needed to start working in his classroom. I accompanied him like a classroom aide and Anne Brownell led the music and movement class we had created for when she was in town. As described in the previous section, I found more and more ways to help him separate from me.

There were two further steps in my work with Dillan. One was the in-service training sessions I gave to the staff. The content of these sessions is documented in the VMT Handbook, *It's a Nice Day If It Doesn't Rain* which I was requested by the staff to write as a guide for them and which was the final step of my work at the school. The main points of those sessions were:

1. To allow the teachers to experience for themselves the facial configurations described in VMT and how they related to speech in children like Dillan,

2. To explain the importance of allowing a child to experience something for him/herself rather than doing it for them and

Figure 8. Deirdre Brownell with child with helmet and drum, Alta du Toit School--2013. Photo: Anne Brownell.

3. My explanation to the teachers of my somatic empathy with Dillan.

The two teachers of Dillan's class actively participated in the final in-service session when we did a sample beginning of a group where I and the two teachers each played a student from that group and all the rest of the staff knew exactly who each one was because of the way we were able to inhabit their movements, gestures, and sounds.

It was a wonderful moment when these two teachers, in their excitement, asked me if they might speak in Afrikaans in order to explain more easily to their peers why they found this work so useful. The in-service helped Dillan, too, as demonstrated by the fact that the vice-principal told me that Dillan had come up to him after dinner and said "e e" and the vice principal realized he was asking for a cd that he really liked. This showed the man's new awareness and willingness to spend a few moments learning to understand Dillan's words and gestures in his attempts to communicate. The house mothers, who were not present at the in-services, also asked me to do a session specifically with them, and I did.

Conclusion: What Worked and Why

My major goal in working with Dillan was to see if the practice of Voice Movement Therapy could improve his ability to communicate. What I discovered was:

1. My knowledge of the three areas of respiration led me to conclude that his shallow breathing was mostly restricted to his upper torso, the clavicular area, and that it, combined with the tension held in his narrow body, contributed to the production of his high-pitched sounds;

2. My ability to understand and use the facial configurations, which in VMT accompany learning to produce the timbres called Flute, Clarinet and Saxophone, helped me to discover what sounds were easier and what were more difficult for him to make and how he could mobilize his muscles further;

3. Through the principle of amplification of voice and face and gesture, I was able to help him to increase and vary his sounds. In the course of our work, as he relaxed more, his voice deepened, his face and body muscles became less tense, and he began to achieve greater success in his ability to communicate.

I was also able to teach these concepts to staff members so that they could use them in a more general way. My approach of meeting a person where he is and giving him some control over what he does allowed Dillan to own his own actions and to know that he could to some degree take charge of himself and assert himself in a non-threatening way.

On a personal note, I developed a real somatic empathy with Dillan. Having experienced hypersensitivity, hyperactivity, tactile defensiveness, balance issues, and extreme frustration from not being understood, I recognized his hunger for connection and the longing for someone who could help him bring out his knowledge and express it to others. The final step in my work with Dillan was to have a bag made with his name on it that contained all his toys and to leave him the keyboard. I also had a picture book of us made up so he could remember our time together, as well as a copy of my own cd of songs which I had made several years before in which he always recognized my voice. These were my transitional objects for him.

I learned a lot working with Dillan and it was hard to leave. We had grown so close and all the staff saw it and knew it would be hard for him when I left, and so I prepared them for this, as I knew he would act out, leaving them suggestions and instructions about how to continue the kind of work and approach I had been using. No one wanted me to leave and I was told that I would be welcome back at any time. I will always treasure my time at the school as a growth experience and an amazing time with wonderful people who really cared about these children and were not afraid to try something new on the chance that it might work–and in this case, it did.

Together, Dillan and I created an affective language through his high-pitched vocalizations and body movements so he could express himself and communicate with others while he was learning to speak actual words. This began to bring the affective and cognitive voices together and stopped his biting and lashing out behaviors because now he was being heard. Teaching the staff to recognize his attempts to communicate and learn to respond to them has enabled him to continue to improve, in line with his innate desire to learn.

"SAMUEL": A STORY OF HEALING TRAUMA WITH VOICE MOVEMENT THERAPY

Sebastiana Black

Voice Movement Therapy can offer young people with adverse childhood experiences a safe space and diverse tools to give voice to a wide range of experiences and connect to others in a more embodied way. It comes as a relief to a young person who has endured many changes and losses to discover the means to process and express verbally, or nonverbally, some of their feelings with the support of a compassionate adult. In Voice Movement Therapy, practitioners meet clients "just as they are" by offering opportunities for creative expression in the context of a therapeutic relationship. Movement, rhythm, improvised melody, words, and singing or rapping in a therapeutic context allows the young person to marry the spontaneous creativity of their mind and imagination with the bodily sensations of hearing, vocalizing and moving, and brings to light what was previously hidden and silent. Both implicit and explicit memories take new shape and are heard and seen in the context of the therapeutic relationship. The young person has an opportunity to enjoy, integrate and often transform their story and the way they perceive themselves.

In 2012, I was fortunate to receive some funding and was able to offer Voice Movement Therapy individual and group sessions at a children's residential home in Norfolk, England. At the time I was also training to become an integrative arts and adolescent counsellor which supported my engagement with the young people. One of my clients was a 13-year-old boy who I will call "Samuel," a lively, friendly and angry teenager. In many ways he was a typical teenager with mood swings and friendship struggles, but Samuel also suffered developmental and relational trauma. This left his body and mind vulnerable to emotional dysregulation (he was diagnosed with ADHD) and frequent conflicts and urges to run away.

Samuel has mild to moderate cognitive delays and behavioral issues. Our Voice Movement Therapy sessions turned out to give him an opening to connect with his turmoil and tell his stories and predicaments in song, movement and enactment. Our sessions often began with games of mirroring each other's spontaneous vocal and body expressions, catching and throwing soft balls with varied speeds, playing hide and seek, and improvising with musical instruments. The relational and rhythmic quality of these interactions helped Samuel to build a sense of trust and safety as he felt met in the multitude of his states. He experienced a reciprocal engagement where he was both able to take and let go of control. The vocalizations that I initiated gave him permission to experiment with his voice and therefore communicate different aspects of himself. Sounds that he uttered in our call-and-response exchanges reflected joy and mischief, urgency, impulsiveness, and strength. Others sounded resigned, soft, unsure or sorrowful. His vocal expressions and dynamic movements were recognized and confirmed in my echoes, giving him a sense of agency, being effective and reinforcing his feeling of physical identity.

The rhythm of these interactions seemed to regulate Samuel, too. When he arrived at his session in a solemn withdrawn mood, we began to interact quietly through the sonic flow of musical instruments, each choosing an instrument that we were drawn to. This non-threatening but attuning form of interaction helped Samuel slowly to emerge from his shell and bring himself into the room. When he was hyper-aroused and agitated, our mutual meetings, engagement, and the structure that I gently brought in regulated him into a more receptive state. The predictability of the space and the resources we used, the regularity of some of the exercises and games that I took charge of, as well as taking turns, allowed Samuel to feel safer and more in control of his nervous system.

This didn't always work, of course. At the time, he was going through periods of intense anger and rage as he was working through feelings of rejection and loss to do with moving to a new home for adolescents. Some sessions Samuel spent sitting quietly in his own space whilst I intended to reach him softly with the sound of music I played or sang. I imagined that way he was not alone, that the improvised melodies were building bridges between us.

In Voice Movement Therapy, we incorporate into the notion of a "song" any vocal utterance, either verbal (one word or more) or non-verbal creations. This makes songwriting more accessible and allows for songs to evolve into creative containers for personal stories, explorations and expressions. Not many of my young clients at the Home, or in general, chose to or had the confidence to write songs in the traditional sense of the word. However, Samuel often took a piece of paper and eagerly started to put down both lyrics and a vocal arrangement, specifying where verses, choruses and repetitions would occur. Perhaps he sensed the purpose of this work: my intention to support him to venture safely into his unique universe. Or was he primed by the permissive guidance he received from me and the consistency of our weekly playfully attuned encounters?

Often clients come up with words but lack the confidence to weave them into a tune. However, Samuel wasn't deterred by the challenge of singing his songs and opted for rapping them. In these songs, he explored experiences connected to his relationships such as heartbreaks, fear of loss and disconnection, asking for help, and seeking a sense of safety. The form that he used in his songs included a lot of repetition which I sensed as empowering and emphasizing the point he was making. The process of organizing his expression into a song seemed to focus his attention and bring some level of regulation into his internal world.

He arranged his songs fairly quickly and was soon ready to "perform" them for me. He found a spot in the room where he created himself "a stage" whilst I was keen to hear his voice in "the audience." Occasionally he wanted me alongside him. I joined him either by accompanying him with a gentle hum or a percussive musical instrument. Other times I felt drawn to respond to his songs by echoing some of his words back to him to let him hear them, too, and allow them to land in his consciousness. He seemed up for that and it may have helped him to stay with his creative expressions longer.

For example, I repeated the chorus with him in order to validate and punctuate the content. My voice mixed with his on the chorus of a song that was exploring his safe place, as we both rapped his words, "Hermit crab, hermit crab, hermit crab, hermit crab...." Or when he creatively dived into his feelings, I reflected back the poignant juxtapositions that he was uttering with passion: "Love, love, love, love, love, Hate, hate, hate, hate, hate" or "Mad, angry, furious" every word restated five to ten times, each time with more vigor which I encouraged by modelling an increase in volume and using a harder glottal onset (see page 19).

If the words communicated more vulnerable feelings like fear, "feeling scared, can you help me, please?" or "I feel trapped...I feel stuck... " I vocalized with softer vocal qualities like Free Air (similar to breathiness) more quietly or with some pitch fluctuation (see page 19). I also often responded to his songs with movement so he could see its effect on me and subsequently feel it more within himself. My choice of vocal and movement responses as well as where I would position myself in the room (further or closer) were based on somatic countertransference, what I sensed through my body as I witnessed his expression. I then chose in the moment whether I would match, amplify or alleviate its affect with specific vocal qualities, movements or gestures.

Samuel appeared to get a lot of satisfaction from the whole process of his songmaking: the writing, the performing, the sharing of his world with me and receiving my creative and therapeutic input. The songs gave him a sense of mastery and strength. The creative container of the song normalized his challenges and therefore increased his resilience. His songs were both cathartic and soothing in their nature. I believe that the unconditional nature of my support and guidance and my overt appreciation of his authentic expression felt healing to him and gave him a taste of what a secure relationship might feel like. We both enjoyed his creativity which bolstered his confidence. He learned that one can communicate beyond words. At that point, for Samuel in his life, Voice Movement Therapy was far more accessible than talking therapy would have been. It offered him permission to let go safely into the containing and transforming power of this modality.

Voice Movement Therapy has also informed my own voice and how I use vocal prosody in my clinical practice. Working with young people requires an engaging tone of voice. A monotonous one can be threatening for young clients. Furthermore, the therapist's ability to tap into different vocal qualities can aid the therapeutic process in terms of matching the client's affect vocally, or joining them in their enactments, role plays and other creative expressions that require a variety of vocal sounds. Change of vocal tone can facilitate change of pace and subsequent calming or energizing of the nervous system.

I have been integrating Voice Movement Therapy principles and practices into my work with young people for over a decade now. I have witnessed many times how engaging a withdrawn child, whose voice has been silenced by trauma, in non-verbal vocalizing can begin to draw out their psyche from a frozen, dissociated state. They can express something that is unspeakable and share it in a safe and playful way within the context of a therapeutic relationship. They don't have to explain and describe something they don't have words for, yet they are heard. They can experience reciprocity, being seen, validated and accepted as they are, words or not. Voice Movement Therapy is an experiential bottom-up approach that allows for meeting the young person where they are developmentally, often starting from early missed experiences of needing a secure attachment where they can learn to focus and experience shared joy, co-regulation and other important intersubjective experiences.

BIBLIOGRAPHY

Brownell, Anne. "The Theoretical Pertinence of Voice Movement Therapy" (VMT class notes) 2008.

Kraybill Gertel, Odelya, "What Is Developmental Trauma? A framework for building secure attunement." *Psychology Today,* eds. Malchiodi, Cathy A., Crenshaw, David A. (2014)

Malchiodi, Cathy and David A. Crenshaw, eds. *Creative Arts and Play Therapy for Attachment Problems.* New York: The Guildford Press, 2015.

Mc Niff, Shaun. *Integrating The Arts In Therapy.* Springfield, Il: Charles C Thomas. Publisher, Ltd, 2009.

Stern, Daniel. *The Interpersonal World of the Infant: A View from Psychoanalysis and Developmental Psychology.* London, UK: Routledge, 1985.

Perry, Bruce and Erin Hambrick. "The Neurosequential Model of Therapeutics." Chicago, Il. Child Trauma Academy, 2008

INTERVIEWS WITH AN EXPRESSIVE MOVEMENT EDUCATOR, THREE YOUNG MEN WITH SIGNIFICANT PHYSICAL AND COGNITIVE DELAYS, AND THEIR HOME PROVIDERS

Deirdre Brownell

In the winter of 2017, as part of my research for my Ph.D., I journeyed to Vermont to observe and experience Dr. William C. Freeman at work with clients. William has regularly been a teacher on the VMT Foundation Training, adding to students' awareness and sensitivity in observing and working with an individual's natural movement. He describes himself as a Movement Therapist who works in educational settings facilitating movement experiences with students and those who work with them by focusing on the development of expression and communication. As he describes it,

> Therapy, in my view, is an extension of education which enables the individual to pursue his or her goals with greater focus and depth. In the process of therapy, it is valuable to allow the individual to explore feelings, issues and themes not just by relating to them in words, but through actualizing the self physically, emotionally and creatively in the process... By being in the moment with children and actively involved in the movement experience for oneself, both child and facilitator feel affirmed. It is in these moments that relationships are developed and through this process accommodations and applications are made in a way that is responsive to the individual needs of students in the movement experience as it unfolds.[1]

In order to be able to witness and report on this kind of experience directly and also to collect feedback—a kind of personal assessment about the value of Movement Therapy from the individuals most directly involved—I, the reviewer, who had had opportunities using my skills in VMT to assist Dr. Freeman in client sessions in the past, conducted three interviews within the context of one individual session each with three of his clients and their accompanying home provider or parent in Weston, VT.[2]

"Mike"

Client 1, Mike, is a young man with cognitive delays and limited skills living with his home provider, Rose. He works as a janitor. His mother put him into the care of the state when he was quite young and he has had several placements and home providers since he was a child, and therefore has attachment issues. He is rather large and athletic and carries a lot of anger, so many people are afraid of him. His main therapeutic issues seem to be dealing with regulating and verbalizing affect, connecting with others, and recognizing and respecting the feelings of others. When specifically questioned about events or feelings in his life, he responds very factually in short, abrupt sentences. In terms of his general appearance, he has two main ways he presents himself: first, through a depressive posture with head hanging, shoulders slouched, chest concaved, and gaze not meeting another's; and the other a very animated self when doing physical activity such as playing basketball. He does not modulate well between these two states and has very little middle range in terms of energy and affect.

At the beginning of the session, Mike arrives angry, grumpy and unfocused. Freeman begins and ends all sessions with the affect the person is presenting with. Noticing the state that Mike is in, he does not just ask him how he is; he works with his affect in movement and dialogue, verbal and non-verbal. He invites the home provider to go inside into the treatment room and begins with Mike one-to-one outside. Using a basketball, he plays catch with him while they exchange words and sounds about how he is feeling. Freeman modulates between hard throws and soft throws, long throws and short throws. Then, after some of the energy and bad feeling has been discharged and dissipated, Mike is able to come into the room and be focused in the session. When asked about the usefulness of Movement Therapy, he says, "It really helps get the anger out and clears my mind." Freeman says, "It helps you start to focus more; you are able to name what is going on inside and what you are feeling, and to use words more effectively."

The interviewer asks questions and Mike is very clear in his answers; but then, for him, the talking goes on too long. He starts to lose concentration: his eyes lose focus and he begins to become distracted. At this point, Freeman gets him up on his feet and engages him in physical activity. They jump up and down, exclaiming Hah! loudly on each jump. Then they engage in mock wrestling, lightly pushing and pulling each other, which starts a banter between them, with Freeman saying how perfect he is and Mike giving him grief and saying he could beat him any day. At this point, Freeman has Mike look in a mirror so he can see how others perceive him and he notices the change in his facial expression and body posture. He is now alert, energized, smiling and focused.

As Freeman speaks to his home provider Rose about the issues at home, she praises Mike and Movement Therapy for the transformation she has seen in his behavior over time, noting a change in attitude, being more happy which reveals the sunny part of his disposition, and being better able to handle his negative affects with less swearing, slamming of doors and breaking things. Freeman notices Mike looking in the mirror and asks him about what Rose has just said and if it is hard sometimes to see himself. His answer is, "I'll get back to you on that," at which we all laugh.

When Mike is asked by William what is the best part about Movement Therapy besides having fun, he says, "Seeing you." This illustrates the importance of the connection between Freeman and Mike. The relationship between therapist and client is critical and Freeman is able to meet and accept his client "right where he is" in movement, body language, gesture, kinesthetic presence, and mood. This approach, which is grounded in the body, stimulates the client's desire to communicate verbally and allows him to speak about difficult things. Through this multifaceted method, Mike can physically feel the extent to which Freeman understands. Freeman doesn't just rely on cognitive words; the experience has to be visceral. Mike has to feel it in his body and hear it in Freeman's voice, not just see it in his eyes or try to comprehend it through his words.

In this session, when asked about problems in his home living situation, Mike is able to admit that he often gets angry at Rose and doesn't always see her in the present, but in relation to another situation. When asked, he can only refer to whatever he is thinking by naming the town of a previous home placement that was not a good one. The impression one gets is that the home provider was not a good one, either. Freeman then asks if that is why, knowing that smoking adversely affects Rose's health, he smokes? He says no, that he smokes to relieve stress, but later admits that it is only partially stress, saying, "But I don't want to kill her." Freeman says, "Maybe just mess her up a little," and he admits, "Maybe." Freeman then asks why he doesn't talk to her when he is angry and he says he is afraid to talk for fear of getting yelled at. "Like in a past situation?" Freeman asks. No answer. When asked if he thinks he loses awareness at such moments and goes back to somewhere else, he again repeats the name of the town where he had the bad placement. He admits that he can "go away" in his mind and does not know when he does that. This realization is a huge step for him. Rose states that when he dissociates, she is afraid because she does not know who he is or what will happen. However, she is relieved that he has made this connection right now.

We also discover that Rose is often not meeting Mike's affect. She offers that she is more upbeat and likes things happy, whereas Mike's comfort zone is to wrap himself up in depression and isolation like a warm, wet blanket. Freeman talks about honoring each other's feelings and asks could they work at respecting that? They each say honestly, "I don't know." This is a major step forward in their relationship because they both are acknowledging the issue, but also being realistic toward reaching the goal, and both are willing to try.

It is the opinion of all those who work with Mike, professional staff and provider family members alike, that Movement Therapy has been essential to his progress. Everyone is deeply concerned that when he moves shortly to a new placement in a different town where he will only have conventional talking therapy, that it will not be sufficient. They have noted that the moving and accompanying vocalizing is essential to his being able to express himself verbally. The effect of movement in helping him with both fine and gross motor control is also noted, as is the discharging of affect and energy through movement which leads him to being able to modulate his behavior.[3]

"Ryan"

Client 2, "Ryan," is a young man in his early twenties who has cerebellar ataxia, a slow death of the motor nerves in his cerebellum which control, among other things, movement and speech. His main issue is control, both physical and emotional. His movement attributes are strength and quickness because to move slower requires more sustained coordination and muscle control for balance. He likes to do Movement Therapy because he has fun and feels powerful doing it, which makes him feel better. He doesn't have much control and power in his life, can't get a job or a girlfriend, and it is hard just to make friends. It is very easy for him to say he feels angry, but he has to be prompted to identify the feelings behind it of sad, worried and helpless. He can sometimes feel happy and his desires are clear: to get rid of the ataxia; to get people to do what he wants them to do; and to have friends, a car, and an apartment.

Ryan has made tremendous changes, in spite of the fact that his ataxia is, as he says, "a nightmare." Movement Therapy helps him get through the feelings he lives with every day. When he lets the anger and energy out through the exercises and games he and Dr. Freeman play, he feels better. He has learned not to "blow up" when things don't go his way as long as there is someone around to help him regulate his feelings. Gradually, he is learning to do this more himself. He describes what it feels like when he "blows up," that he feels fast and powerful and doesn't want to listen to anyone. As he says, "I get hot and my feelings rise up." If they are not expressed, they "come out sideways" at someone else.

His home provider, Lisa says, "He's scary when he's gone, checked out, throwing things. Dr. Freeman is priceless. More and more, Ryan can get through such feelings because he can come to William, discharge them in a safe space, and then process them. Verbalizing his feelings helps him to retain what he's learned and this learning comes through being able to discharge those feelings and work through them in movement with a trusted person on a body as well as a verbal level." When asked what he thinks about movement Therapy, Ryan replies, "I wouldn't be doing so good without it." His home provider adds, "This kind of learning and increased ability to manage his feelings doesn't happen for him without it."

"Jack"

Client 3, Jack, is a young man with tardive dyskinesia (involuntary muscle movements) and a fused spine. He has some semi-paralysis on one side and leans forward when he walks to maintain balance. He and Dr. Freeman have developed a wonderful visual image of an ice cream cone which drips jimmies when his head goes down and he starts to lose balance. When this happens, it is accompanied by the sounds they make of slipping and slurping, with much laughter.

Jack is so excited when he comes in; he loves doing this work. Freeman immediately starts working on his shoulders in a sensory preparation sequence to recorded music which, after a few minutes, helps him to bring his eyes into focus and causes the tardive mouth movements to almost completely disappear. They stand and move into balance work, shifting their feet from side to side while holding hands facing each other. His legs start to bend and move more naturally and there is much laughter as they exchange jokes and humorous sounds.

Freeman asks the interviewer to join them to do some voicework and we start with growling in order to help him move his voice to a lower register. I employ shoulder and back massage while he attempts Santa-like belly laughs and then together we practice ascending and descending a scale with our voices. His short vocal sounds are like his quick movements, but gradually I am able to help him sustain them longer and longer and make new sounds which please him. For a young man like him, full of tension and having to make a great effort to put himself "out there" in social situations, it does not help to be speaking in such a high, light voice. He likes the persona he can create when, through this work, he is able to relax more and lower his voice to a more "masculine" range. Working this way, sounding and moving while being massaged on chest and shoulders, and being encouraged to expand his ribs and feel movement in his abdomen, increases his volume of breath and helps him sustain both moving and voicing more easily.

The experience of moving in balance and making sustained sounds while being helped to breathe deeper is calming. It also helps unite Mother and son when she is invited to join in the dance, moving together in quick, small steps and even turning in half circles. This movement pattern enhances his greatest ability which is small and quick movements and sounds which then can be elongated, paused and sustained.

When asked, Jack says he finds the moving and sounding both energizing and calming and it helps him. As he relaxes and focuses more, he is able to speak more easily and clearly. When he is asked what he is feeling inside, he says that moving to the rhythm feels good. It helps him connect his upper and lower body, helps him slow down, even helps him with his fear of the dark which he says represents "Everything that is unknown." As one who has had many surgeries and long hospital stays and never knows when his body, simply in navigating daily life, may let him down, he has more than his share of both conscious and unconscious dark images. In spite of this fact, he finds that more and more he is able to step out into the world and try new things. "Movement Therapy," he says, "is like riding a bike. You're not going to get anywhere in the beginning, but if you keep at it, it will come. I'm getting a lot further than I ever thought I would in my life."

His mother comments, saying "Jack is so much more confident, so much more willing to go out and be social; when he gets stuck, he has some real movement strategies for getting unstuck and he is more able to move around in his space and connect with others in theirs. He is much more aware of what he is feeling and is able to express it. His biggest gain is self-confidence."

Freeman uses sound in combination with movement, with an awareness of the affect his voice carries as well as its cognitive message. He does not explore the affective voice in any systematic or methodological way because that is not his orientation. The vocal strategies he employs were learned working in tandem with Voice Movement Therapist Anne Brownell. He is interested in working with more Voice Movement Therapy practitioners because he wishes to be able to translate the gains made in movement more effectively into speech, not just in terms of articulation or modulation of tone per se, but as a way of expressing emotional meaning while working on such things as modulating the vocal extremes that often exist in individuals with major physical issues, in order to help them be more socially appropriate and communicate more effectively in social environments.

In a recent communication with Dr. Freeman, he stated:

> I encode through movement and decode through vocalization. The first thing I look at is the nonverbal behavior in order to match and connect and understand the movement. The voice comes afterward. When I have observed Voice Movement Therapists work, they first decode the voice. The decoding and encoding happens with the voice much quicker because of the capacity they have developed, just as my expertise with the movement usually happens faster than that of a Voice Movement Therapist. This decoding of nonverbal behavior and encoding one's response to it is about connecting with the affects through one's primary mode of expertise.[4]

The point of view of Voice Movement Therapy is that what everyone needs is a voice so that they can express their feelings and communicate their needs, wants, and ideas. Whether this voice is affective only or is able to combine affect with the cognition demonstrated through words, the act of giving voice is essential. The reason for most acting out behavior, as well as for withdrawal, is the frustration of an inability to communicate with others in order to connect and belong. If one is unheard–or misunderstood, isolated, unseen–one will not be able to develop as a fully realized self. One's sense of self-worth and self-image will be too severely compromised.

NOTES

1. William C. Freeman (1999), "You're O.K. Right Where You Are: Expressive Movement in Education." Unpublished Ph.D. dissertation, UMI: Ann Arbor, MI, 1999), p. 7.
2. Freeman (1999), in D. Brownell, "Re-embodying the Voice to Strengthen the Self," 2020, p. 105.
3. D. Brownell, Appendix 14, "Assessment by Diane Dulicai of "Mike" for Developmental Neuroscience Research and Dance Movement Therapy Services," in Re-Embodying the Voice to Strengthen the Self in D. Brownell, Appendix 14, 2017 p. 139.
4. Freeman (1999) in D. Brownell, Re-embodying the Voice to Strengthen the Self, p. 116.

BIBLIOGRAPHY

Brownell. Deirdre. "Three Interviews with an Expressive Movement Educator, Three Young Men with Significant Cognitive and Physical Delays, and Their Home Providers. Weston, VT: New Thought Vermont, 2017.

Brownell, Deirdre, "Re-embodying the Voice to Strengthen the Self." Unpublished Ph.D. dissertation, Meridian University, Petaluma, CA: 2020.

Dulicai, Diane. Appendix 14, "Assessment of Mike by Developmental Neuroscience Research and Dance Movement Therapy Services," Washington DC, 2017.

Freeman, William. "You're O.K. Right Where You Are: Expressive Movement in Education." Unpublished Ph.D. dissertation, UMI: Ann Arbor, MI: 1999.

II. INDIVIDUALS EXPERIENCING CONDITIONS BROUGHT ON BY EMOTIONAL OR PHYSICAL TRAUMA

A CASE OF SELECTIVE MUTISM AND THE WORK OF TRACY STARREVELD

(Condensed by Deirdre Brownell from a longer case study)

An example of re-embodying a lost voice alienated from its surroundings by the lack of a sense of power and belonging is found in the work of Voice

> Movement Therapy practitioner Tracy Starreveld in her case study of a young elementary school child with whom she worked during her Voice Movement Therapy internship, supervised by Expressive Movement Therapist and Voice Movement Therapy adjunct teacher William C. Freeman and Training Director Anne Brownell.

At the age of five, this little girl had witnessed an act of extreme violence in her home and lost her voice for a long period of time. Starreveld describes her as follows:

> This eight-year-old girl, who was selectively mute when she came to the school three years ago, is making progress but still behind academically. She is also struggling to speak up in class, participate in group activities, and seems ill at ease with new people and new situations. Her reluctance to use her affective voice and to speak above a whisper limits her both academically and socially. She is a slow processor, hard worker, eager to please, and likes creative activities, especially artwork.[1]

Starreveld's initial observations of how the girl's movements reflected her affect included the following:

> She is very observant and watches everything closely. In terms of body attitude and gesture, her face and body are very still, but when nervous she fidgets a lot with her mouth and tongue, blinking and squinting her eyes and fiddling with her clothes. Her upper body is held, with shoulders up, chest rather tight and concave, arms held stiff by her sides, head often tilted, with knees and pelvis locked. Her movements are very light and rather bound.[2]

Starreveld then describes how her voice also reflects affects:

> In terms of voice and breath, she has shallow breathing, especially in the chest area. Her voice is not synchronized with her movement and exhibits long delays or no sound at all. Her voice is very small and quiet, with some resonance and depth of pitch, but overall very hesitant. Her general disposition is shy, nervous, anxious, but occasionally lighter and happier. She is happy to follow, but lost when asked to lead and exhibits a very limited emotional range.[3]

Starreveld's stated goals were to help her increase her confidence and ability to communicate with others by: 1) Improving her posture and breathing, 2) Increasing the volume and range of her voice, 3) Working on having her lead as well as follow, through trying different pacing (fast, slow, medium), and 4) Increasing emotional expression.

Starreveld's main method of working with the girl was by extending her breath with movement games designed increasingly to prioritize vocal expression. An early exercise was blowing a napkin back and forth across the floor while moving with each other on hands and knees. This required deep breaths as she progressed from tiny puffs to big gusts which began to strengthen her under-used intercostal muscles.

Faced with the problem of using Voice Movement Therapy with a client who does not want to vocalize, Starreveld's early sessions focused on movement with very simple soundmaking to build vocal expression. A game of copycat, leading each other in movement to the sounds of recorded music, challenged the girl to take the lead and deepened her connection to Starreveld. In this game, the girl was also encouraged to explore her center of balance as well as more Convex and Concave movement (see page 21) and revealed what Starreveld refers to as a "lovely, light and lyrical disposition."

In the seventh session Starreveld introduced the notion of small, medium, and big voice, working on a spectrum from quiet to loud in order to open the vocal tract or "tube." Using three balls of different sizes, they explored different degrees of openness in body, breath and voice. In the process, Starreveld discovered that the girl actually had an enormous mouth when wide open which she had been keeping small, tense and closed most of the time. Starreveld asked her to memorize and practice speaking a poem about opening and closing flowers, as a way for her to explore Concave and Convex in her body posture. Starreveld also encouraged her to practice speaking the poem while standing further and further away from her. In this way her voice began to develop in power, volume and confidence. However, when they started exploring the idea of small, medium, and large animals and began voicing these, the girl froze on seeing and hearing Starreveld portray a mouse. She would not join her in the sound and movement and only re-engaged with the exercise when they both became big and explored big sounds and movements which led her from a scared to a happy state.

Roughly halfway through these twenty sessions, others at the school began to comment on the girl's increased confidence, cheerful disposition, groundedness, greater willingness to speak, and louder voice. All of this was very much embodied in the sessions with Starreveld when exploring the character of a warrior through voice and movement, where she would leap into a dynamic stance with a loud and enthusiastic "Hah!" as if to say "Here I am!" Over the rest of the twenty sessions, the change was dramatic.[4]

Using Voice Movement Therapy methods, Starreveld was able to reach her goal of helping the girl become visibly more relaxed and confident in herself and with others. Using Convex and Concave movement to increase flexibility in the torso and increase tidal air flow, the girl's posture and breathing also improved. By focusing on making dyadic movements of voice and body together, Starreveld both modelled and encouraged vocal discourse as a natural part of the girl's day-to-day life which facilitated her communicating much more effectively with others.

By working with sub-personalities like the mouse and the lion and uncovering the unconscious meaning of each for this child, Starreveld facilitated the girl's readiness and desire to embody a warrior stance. Now she could truly embody her voice through a wider range and more effective delivery, with increased volume and expressiveness. All of these things worked to improve her overall understanding of affects and she was better able to regulate them according to the needs of the situation, which improved her ability to communicate with others. She had even been able to identify and understand, in these sessions, that her "small," "medium" and "big" voices might all be useful to her at different times in her daily life, such as in class or on the playground. From an academic and cognitive point of view, her reading fluency scores had nearly doubled by the time the sessions came to an end. From a social-emotional point of view, her ability to take her place among her peers greatly improved. From a Voice Movement Therapy point of view, she was able to make great strides in embodying her voice to effect personal change and inhabit a new and more powerful subpersonality, a warrior, while rejecting the dreaded mouse.

In this case, the selective mutism was a maladaptive behavior created by the trauma, and the subpersonality the child took on was the mouse. This very clearly illustrates how the behavior was changed and her view of herself changed as she was able to explore her range and play within the different pitches and modulations. This created confidence and self-esteem.

NOTES

1. Starreveld, Tracy. Voice Movement Therapy Internship Case Study at Ripton Elementary School, Ripton, VT, in Re-embodying the Voice to Strengthen the Self, unpublished Ph.D. dissertation by Deirdre Brownell, Petaluma, CA; Meridian University, 2020, p. 2.
2. Brownell, D., Re-Embodying the Voice, p. 2.
3. Brownell, D., p. 13-17.
4. Brownell, D., pp.16-17.

MY FAVORITE PATIENT AND HOW I BECAME THE SINGING PASTOR: A CASE STUDY OF A PATIENT RECOVERING FROM A STROKE

Anne Ross Maarman

I work as a chaplain and pastoral counsellor in a residential medical facility in George, South Africa. "Lucy" was one of my favorite patients. Not only did she fight for life from an early stage after her accident; she somehow stole our hearts. We, the hospice interdisciplinary team, all saw her as a model patient from the beginning. The following is an account of how I used VMT in my work with Lucy. This case study formed part of my VMT qualifying requirements.

INTRODUCTION

Lucy was admitted to us with cerebral vascular accident (CVA) and was unconscious on admission, which makes recovery more uncertain. This 42-year-old lady had three sons and was the star of her family. They were proud of her because she had fought her way through life. She was a well-educated woman, qualified as an engineer, and basically functioned as a single mother because her husband was a drug addict.

After the admission of any patient to the hospice, the interdisciplinary team has a family conference to discuss with them the progress and the total care of the patient. During their conference, her three sons asked me to help their mother. It was a spiritual wish. They were scared that if anything else happened to her, they would be devastated. Initially, she was more of a rehab patient, coming to us to be treated primarily physically by the physiotherapist and the occupational therapist, with me supporting the family emotionally and spiritually.

Lucy's History

In my first assessment with the family, it became evident that Lucy was the only daughter of a broken family. Her parents divorced after she was born and she was brought up by her grandparents in a very religious and well-educated household. According to her grandparents, she had been a healthy child. She went to university after high school, was an outstanding student, qualified as an engineer, and went on to work for local government, earning well and supporting her three children through their education; the youngest was still studying. She had, however, had hypertension for some years due to the high level of stress in her life. She and her children lived with her grandparents. She was generally calm and collected, always pleasing others. She had a strong personality and knew what she wanted in life. Her grandparents were both teachers and they loved her assertiveness. Her husband was absent during the admission and it was obvious that the family didn't have much respect for him or trust in him.

Lucy had enjoyed creative expression when she was younger. She started dancing in primary school and later took drama when in high school. When I found out that she loved singing when she was alone, I immediately asked the family if there was any song she particularly liked to sing. They responded all together that she loved a certain folksong.

Lucy was referred to us by the General State Hospital as a patient who had a 50% chance of recovery. She was admitted to our facility quite some time after her accident, but showed some improvement after two months. She was paralyzed on the right side of her body and was unconscious. When the team discussed her, we decided we would do anything to help her to recover. We believed that she would probably wake up as the swelling of her brain became less and believed that she might even return to a normal life.

Inspiration

Lucy's history and medical condition immediately made me think of a case study in which Paul Newham described a similar patient. As I remember it, Newham was in a hospital ward and, passing a man in a wheelchair, heard the man making sounds. It struck him that, with no movement in his legs or arms and no proper breathing, there was still a voice. Newham wanted to bring out that voice. The man couldn't walk and couldn't talk, but there was a sounding voice there, so Newham asked permission to come back and work with him. He worked with the man by sitting in front of him and mirroring back the sounds he made. In doing this, the man's voice became increasingly more clear and more loud, and as he discovered the music of his own voice, he began to make his own tunes. Newham helped bring life back into that man by singing sounds together with him and, even when Newham left, the man would continue to sing his songs in his own way.

I was touched by the similarities and decided to make Lucy the subject of a case study, with the intention of getting her voice back. I proposed this to the family and to the treatment team, and they agreed to try it.

Assessment for Suitability for VMT

Despite the fact that she was unconscious, Lucy immediately struck me as the kind of person I might be able to help. From the beginning, it was clear that, as a pastoral counsellor, I would be involved with the family and leave the rest for the rehabilitation team to do. But I now felt I needed to get involved with Lucy's treatment, too. In our first interdisciplinary meeting, I asked the team's permission to work with her. They could not see any sense in it, but they allowed me to do so, requesting that they be present during the sessions. I knew it was going to be difficult since the patient was unconscious, but something about her and what I knew made me feel that with VMT I could reach her.

I. OUR SESSIONS

From the medical side, they advised that all of us needed to wait for at least a month to see her progress, but since I had to visit other patients in the same room, there was nothing to stop me from singing to her as I passed by. I would enter the room and sing the same song, her favorite. For the first months there was no reaction, but all the other patients loved my singing and soon they sang together in the ward. Then one morning I read in the nursing notes that she had moaned softly when they washed her. We were all very happy. Because there was good support from the staff, I then explained my plan of action to the family and continued on.

I took her in her own bed to my counselling room where there was less distraction. I sat next to her on the bed and sang close to her, keeping her healthy hand in mine to notice any movement; nothing happened. Lucy just lay in her bed. I asked the occupational therapist to tell me if she saw any movement and we decided to work together the next time.

Every time I entered the room, I sang and even if I didn't start, somebody else would. I started to become known as "The Singing Pastor" to the patients and the staff. This went on for many weeks and one morning the doctor was sure there was more progress. She was sure Lucy's eyes moved and the scan showed less swelling of the brain. She asked the rehab team to please report on any new signs of progress and felt there was a good chance that she might regain consciousness.

Figure 9. Anne Maarman, "The Singing Pastor," International Association for Voice Movement Therapy Biannual Conference in Australia–2013. Photo: Gertruida Dowse.

It was six weeks after admission that I reported one day during my session that I was sure Lucy could hear me singing. They all doubted it and felt that I was interfering. However, they did not ask me to stop, so I continued since it was clear that I could do no harm. One doctor, who watched me closely, was sure that I must carry on. Up to this point, I had not counted the number of sessions; whenever I had the time, I was at her bedside singing.

When the rehab team reported that she was definitely waking up, I decided to do more. The doctor felt there was some cognitive response in a routine brain scan and the whole team was surprised that she had recovered so soon. According to the usual process, it would take longer. Gradually she recovered consciousness, moving her eyes, especially, to see where my voice was coming from, but she still was not aware of what was going on around her. My sessions happened on a daily basis and sometimes the family was present.

And then came the breakthrough: she cried softly when I sang to her. Of course, her crying could also have been a natural response for a CVA patient, but I thought it was more. Then, after another scan, came the good news that there was a chance of full recovery. The doctor felt strongly that my work with the voice was contributing to her recovery.

One morning during the therapy I decided to sit behind Lucy so that her head could rest on my chest. The physiotherapist was treating her and I kept her close to me and breathed with her. She had shallow breathing even with the help of oxygen. It looked very funny to all and they wanted to know what I thought I was doing. My response was, since I couldn't do any harm, to help her breathe deeper and more rhythmically and to encourage her to use her voice by supporting her body-to-body so that she could feel the vibrations of my voice.

Beginning with breathing morning by morning and just singing her favorite folksong, I became sure that she was listening to me. Her eyes followed me wherever the sound came from. To me, it was progress. Every morning I would walk in and sing. One morning I could see she was interested and I sang and sang, and then a sound came from her side—just a sound, but progress, and we all cried.

I began to make use of VMT massage techniques, massaging her back and shoulders while continuing to encourage her to breathe. To my surprise, one day I asked her to press my hand and she pressed it every now and then. Day after day I sang softly while she was lying on my chest. I breathed deeply through my chest and put her healthy hand on her chest, remembering all the time that I must communicate by physical contact. As time went on, I showed her where the sound came from and encouraged her to sing, to make sounds, and one day the night staff reported that she was crying during the night. Where they saw distress, I saw progress. One of her sons said he was jealous because she reacted when I did something. Later, she turned her eyes if I moved to the corner of the room, following my singing. Eventually she would respond more to others, as well.

During our sessions, I would sit beside her on the bed, pulling her stiff body close to my chest, putting my hands on her ribs and breathing, and I would remind her to do the same. Weeks later she started to take deeper breaths. I then lifted her from the bed and took her to the floor on her mattress, breathing, singing and massaging. As she became more aware, she realized her condition and slipped back into a sense of "I don't want to do it." Again, with the help of her family, I explained that she was doing well and that she must keep on breathing.

PROGRESS

It was four months after admission when the family and I told her of the stroke and explained to her why she couldn't talk. She trusted the doctor and me and we gave her hope that she could recover well. Encouragingly, we told her that we would like to continue our work with her and that we were hopeful for further improvement. We believed it was possible that she could recover in due time. She understood, and we encouraged the family to be strong. Lucy became a model patient, and the team agreed on and acknowledged the effectiveness of my work. Lucy was such a loving person; although she couldn't talk, she stole our hearts.

I continued to begin my days with singing, breathing and massaging, starting with her upper body and then massaging her legs and feet, singing all the time. Then we started to make the "Haaa" sound that I taught her; her voice was coming out.

One morning when I walked in, they told me that she had made sounds during the night and that they were loud; others were sure she had cried. The team agreed that we could put her in a separate room, but I thought she needed the other patients to recover. By now she recognized her family and responded both to my work with her breathing and voicing and to the rehab team's treatment to strengthen her leg and arm. Working alongside the physio and occupational therapists, we all agreed she was becoming more wakeful and that she understood what I was doing. After months of working, she responded to VMT breathing techniques and we removed the oxygen. At this stage I also showed her my breathing by putting her hand on my chest, ribs and stomach. We would then breathe together in an attempt to help her lungs recover.

Lucy developed a strong non-verbal voice. She believed that she could sing, and in a way she could. Although it was mostly random sounds, in her mind she was singing and we left it like that. It was a huge accomplishment. Her case was unique. She recovered sooner than the average patient, even though the brain damage was severe. Others with this degree of severity often don't recover or speak, ever.

A typical day with Lucy looked like this: I would walk into the room and sing the folksong to get her attention. Then I would take my position behind her and sing softly by her ear. When I breathed, I would take her healthy hand and put it with mine on the breathing areas and breathe with her. When she got tired, she would press my hand and we would sing again. During that time, I would massage her stiff shoulders and back and the physiotherapist would work with her arm and leg. She enjoyed that and would sing with me. This would go on for half an hour or more, and I would stop and leave the room in a singing mood. The singing always went on when I was in the hospice in the other rooms. The staff told me that when Lucy heard my singing, she would look around and start singing, too, so we measured the improvement through that. She now listened, used her voice, and breathed on her own.

For me, it was really good because I was, and still am, confident that people who are unconscious can hear us, and I still practice this way with many of the patients. I am excited and want to take VMT with me wherever I go. The Non-vocal Components of breathing together in all three areas of expansion (chest, rib cage, and abdomen) to increase the amount of tidal airflow (the amount of breath available and used), and 2. The use of massage specifically to increase rhythmic breathing and encourage sound by the closeness of another person and the vibrations that can be felt, are my strengths at this work, together with singing.

Ongoing therapy enabled Lucy to continue to improve. She loved the massaging, mostly on her arms, shoulders and back, and she gained a more firm grip and could use her hand to press "Yes" and "No." She sang in her own special way, and we all shed tears as this happened. She recovered enough that we planned to discharge her into the care of her family. We also agreed that we would do home visits to support her, and we were all happy. We sent Lucy home for weekends and it went well. My singing to patients wherever and whenever I could was now familiar to all.

And then there was a call. Lucy had started coughing and was referred to the General Hospital for treatment for pneumonia. She recovered and came back to us at the hospice. This kind of relapse is common when the lungs are weak. Lucy was back on oxygen. Months of hard work had paid off, but now it did not look good. I still sang and held her tight, and sometimes she would turn to me and listen as I sat next to her on the bed.

On a Monday I walked in and they told me she was struggling for her life. It was hard for us to accept. We placed her in a private ward to protect her against any infections. Her children could not understand it; she had been doing so well. She held my hand and the doctor encouraged me to sing as she passed on. The whole staff attended. She died, but with a song in her heart.

Conclusion

My experience is that VMT can be beneficial to physically, mentally and emotionally challenged patients/clients. In this case I was very frustrated, but I knew that I had made a breakthrough and a difference in her life. I promised myself to do the same with any other patients who were suitable candidates. Allowing breathing space and the power to understand oneself better is a journey that one can only take for oneself. The job of the VMT practitioner is to go on that journey with the patient/client–to help liberate others, irrespective of religion, race or creed, in whatever way seems most suitable to the situation.

POST-SCRIPT TWO YEARS LATER: DEIRDRE BROWNELL INTERVIEWS ANNE MAARMAN ABOUT HER STROKE:

Deirdre: How did VMT help you in your own recovery? What did you do? How did you use it?

Anne: After the initial shock of my situation, I found people who could play me music, occasionally sing to me, and I imagined singing to myself. I essentially tried to find ways to use all the VMT-inspired practices I had used with my stroke patient, with myself. This is what has inspired me to create the Project: VMT with Stroke and Recovering Covid Patients. These are the people I am mainly working with now and planning to continue working with.

With the help of God, and singing to myself, I recovered from my own stroke which happened about four years after working with the patient I wrote about for my VMT thesis. VMT is for me a vehicle for all my stroke patients, mild or severe, and the first thing I do is start singing with them, even if they are in a coma. I repeat, over and over, songs that the family tells me they love, until they start opening their eyes to see what I am doing. If they are blind, I repeat to them what we have just done or are doing now. Singing, talking, and sometimes actually cradling and breathing with them, brings them back into the conscious world. I am a pastor, a spiritual counsellor, not a trained singer, but I cannot do what I am doing without the help of VMT. I use my voice to reach them when they are unconscious, creating a sphere of sound around them, breathing with them, and singing familiar songs to them. Where God is coming in is that I am an example. God preserved me for this work. The patients can see that I have had a stroke. I am still limping, and there are other things they can notice. I say, so you will recover, look at me.

I can now extend this work to people who have been very ill with Covid and they are becoming the second focus of my work. Somebody in a coma is not far away. There was a young man who could not hear or see. Often such patients just go home and babble and the medication doesn't work. I use VMT with them and the work is so fantastic because the mind is not closed, even though you are in a coma. Often from being in a coma, you remember the bad things, how you will die, or be forever impaired. But they know somehow that they're not dying and the singing reaches in, just like touch. Then, when they are conscious, you can carry them for a while emotionally, saying, "What did you do yesterday?" Sometimes it has affected their memory, but, again, repetition helps, just like pumping their hands and helping them to walk again. They may have forgotten that "This is my child or my dog," but there are many ways they can be reminded, like by making up a song. When I sing, I choose one song and sing it over and over, and I don't change the tone of my voice. Even when I am with another patient in the same room, I can take a moment to sing that song in that voice again. They hear my voice, they miss my voice when I am gone, and they begin to look forward to when I will come back.

Lucy proved to me that even if you can't talk and can't speak, you can use your voice. When she came in, it was not a good prognosis, but she regained full consciousness and spent time with her children again. The family felt it was a great gift and the medical staff came to believe in my work and that my pastoral service was enhanced by the use of VMT. And that is how I became the Singing Pastor.

SINGING FOR JOY: CREATING COMMUNITY AND SUSTAINING FUNCTION IN A CHOIR WITH PARKINSON'S DISEASE

Carol Grimes

The Sing for Joy Choir, now composed of approximately twenty-five individuals, was formed to provide people with Parkinson's disease (PD), their carers, and others with neurological and other limiting conditions, the opportunity to sing. Its further purpose has become to promote community singing as a part of the long-term treatment of chronic conditions. It has since its inception been led by Carol Grimes, an inspired soul-jazz legend who trained expressively for this purpose with a Speech-Language Pathologist to find singing exercises particularly suited to the needs of such a group in order to combine them with her own way of work. In the words of founder and choir member Nina Temple, "The choir has become a physical therapy which strengthens throat and facial muscles to help with continued clarity of speech, a creative experience, and a supportive community." According to co-founder and choir member Sarah Benton, it gives "A sense of purpose to lives often broken up by isolation, providing a quality of lively inclusiveness." Carol says, "You often hear people who work with voice saying, 'If you've got a voice, you can sing.' But people with PD have to contend with the literal withdrawal of voice, so to see them really going for it and enjoying the singing is inspirational." As Nina says, "When we are singing together at the top of our voices, I feel a release from the constraints of my disease and a connection with joy."

I was born, and many years have passed and much music have I made. I discovered one day, in a Pub in Hastings, that I could sing–a surprise, as I had had no encouragement as a child or young adult and no musical training. I perform my own curious songs and poems–Jazz, Blues, Improvisations, and Contemporary Opera–with the musicians and singers I have had the phenomenal pleasure to work with over the years and have recorded and toured extensively here in the U.K., in America, Europe (East and West), Scandinavia, Scotland, Japan and beyond.

In the early eighties, I began working with a group of young people in Poplar, near where I lived in the east end of London. This was to be the beginning of my passage towards an understanding of my own voice in order to best facilitate others, an investigation of what supports our voices in order to sing out what the heart and soul feels without strain and damage to the vocal instrument. Prior to this, I had opened my mouth and whatever sound I made was it! No thoughts of "How does it all work?" My entry into the world of singing had been more accident than design; and then it became my life. Finding my voice and singing my life has given me my life.

When invited by Nina Temple, the founder of Sing for Joy and a Parkinson's patient herself, to work with a group she was setting up for people with PD, I was immediately interested and curious. Encouraged by Nina, I spent some time at the Hospital in Queens Square with the Speech Therapist Elina Tripoliti and soon discovered that the physical and creative aspects of the singer's and vocal facilitator's life worked wonderfully well with the symptoms group members are struggling with.

Besides Parkinson's, we have people with Multiple Sclerosis, M.E. (known in the U.S. as Chronic Fatigue Syndrome), Cancer, Arthritis, Asthma and people referred by NHS with mental health difficulties, but the choir is mostly composed of people with Parkinson's. Muscle tension and rigidity; shortness of breath; loss of vocal strength and stamina; monotonic speech patterns; imprecise articulation; a closing down of facial expression; tremor in jaw, lips and tongue; disturbed swallowing patterns; a closing down of facial expression; fatigue; low self-esteem–all these symptoms seem to be helped considerably with the singing and breathwork.

Another aspect of my work with Sing for Joy began life because of a need to raise money in order to continue the group's existence after our grant expired. We organized a benefit concert using the TUC Congress Hall (a local union hall), raising enough funds to survive another year, and the group became a performing one. We have just held our fifth benefit there and have performed for the Parkinson's Disease Society Annual Carol Concert three times in such splendid venues as Southwark Cathedral, and at other events, both formal and informal.

Figure 10. Carol Grimes leads her Sing for Joy choir in performance at Salisbury Cathedral for the Parkinsons Disease Society Annual Carol Concert, UK—2010.

Performing skills require rehearsals: building bigger and bolder voices, developing stage presence, courage, commitment and the necessity to communicate, singing out to an audience while projecting not only the voice but also the whole person, working together as a team to support each other towards producing an animated and dynamic performance.

Most of the Sing for Joy members had never performed in public or even sung in a choir or group prior to joining Sing for Joy. A few people had sung with amateur choirs, but most had not sung since school days, if at all, and given the very little rehearsal time—once a week for two hours—preparing for performances was challenging and sometimes difficult.

Some struggled with pitch, others with rhythm, some with memory, harmony, phrasing, or timing. A few read music, most did not. I prefer to work from ear, employing memory, both muscular and emotional. I want people to sing out rather than singing to sheets of A4 paper with dots and words written on them. I prefer the songs to be learned aurally and enjoyed physically, rather than as an academic exercise. Word sheets are handed out, but all are encouraged to memorize.

The nature of the group, brought together with the common criterion being illness, meant that people's taste in music varied widely, unlike the Jazz Singers' classes I run at the City Literary Institute where there is a common musical thread. I brought them The American Song Book, Brecht, Joni Mitchell, Sting and Lily Allan, The Pogues and Leonard Cohen, Jazz, Blues, Folk, Pop, African and Albanian songs and more—an eclectic mix! I encouraged the participants to bring in songs they loved, adding to my own vastly growing repertoire for the group. We have an enormous list of songs. This sometimes led to difficult discussions around what songs to perform. We now have a very democratic voting process!

The rehearsals: memorizing words, melodies and arrangements; working on articulation, rhythm and phrasing; my pleas to smile, to look at each other, to sing out to the audience and to themselves—all necessary in the performer's art and in this situation were an example of the therapeutic benefits of the work, visibly bringing people into life: listening, looking, feeling and engaging.

At the beginning of each weekly session, whether rehearsing for a performance or not, we work with a warm-up, using breath for respiratory support, resonance, vocal pitch practice, harmony and rhythm, singing loud and soft and, in between, doing muscle exercises for the mouth and the face, all put together with gentle physical movement. These skills have clearly helped in soothing some of the symptoms and building vocal strength and breath control.

A tense, tightly held body resistant to the music, operating purely from the head, fighting the pulse and rhythm and denying access to the emotions, will result in a singing voice using only a fraction of its potential and a delivery that has limited dynamic range. The message will be contrived and empty, a shallow performance.

The human being carries extreme vulnerability within the vocal tract, the throat, the mouth, the lips the tongue, the voice. Well-used metaphors, such as "A lump in the throat" and "I feel choked" accurately describe physical sensations felt within the body in response to emotional disturbance or cognitive discontent and these sensations will indeed disable a voice, producing an unsupported and strained representation of the dominant means of connecting and communicating with others. A mind in torment or fear will shut down, retreat, become strained, the vocal timbres infused with the ingredients of those emotions.

A common area of tension is located in the neck and jaw. A head thrust forward from the shoulders, the jaw clamped almost shut, lending the voice a trapped and strained tonality, talking through clenched teeth—all are very noticeable in a person with Parkinson's and other neurological conditions.

A way of identifying the most basic and necessary actions needed to manifest the human voice is to tap into the primary life force, without which living would be impossible and which is expressed through breath, movement, mind and body. Engaging with hearing and sensation, tapping into the vibrations of the voice as it hums around inside the body as energy and resonance, is in itself an act of self-investigation leading to a deeper and more informed physical and cognitive awareness.

For many people, the initial work with breath while the foundations are established in order to produce a strongly supported voice, and even before a vocalized sound is raised, is enough to revive any dormant memories that inhabit the body, stirring and reactivating feelings and responses. In assisting the participant in the extrication of long held tension, releasing the neck and jaw, and working with both physical and emotional holding on, a practitioner is enabling the participant to release vocal power and fluidity, to enrich the timbre of the voice and to inhabit fully the potential to speak with a voice that is imbued with a more rounded and confident range of expression.

Working with the body in the discharge of tension through voice enables the participant to verbalize a more fully integrated delivery, giving their vocalizations–their song–freedom and flight. Allowing the body to fully accommodate the voice is the route toward resonance and support. The effects of working with voice in a physical way, thus bringing the voice into the body, are dynamic, a multi-sensory somatic experience. Working toward the attainment of a harmonious balance of physicality, breath and voice will instill in a group of like-minded people, whatever their limitations, a sense of harmony and fulfilment. This is *Singing for Joy*.

Chapter Four

TRUSTING OUR VOICE TO SUPPORT US IN TIMES OF TRANSITION AND STRESS

INTRODUCTION

Gina Holloway Mulder

Anything in you that is wounded may be silent. Voice is the medicine.
—*Gina Holloway Mulder*

In the last two decades, much has been discovered about how trauma and chronic stress affect the bodymind—that combination of mental and physical factors that we are coming to treat more and more as a whole organism—and its health. It has become ever more clear to researchers and practitioners that unexpressed emotions are a prominent factor in the development of illness, disease, and addiction. It is often the silenced, shutdown and contracted parts of us that carry our pain and hinder our flow and ease-of-being. These silenced parts are charged, loaded, and can trigger us into conflict with ourselves and others, or leave us lost and wandering alone through the barren shadowlands. As practitioners of Voice Movement Therapy, our task is to journey with clients so that we, too, may become aware of what is silenced and unexpressed and provide invitation and guidance to find expression and healing for these parts.

Giving ourselves space to discover and time to develop trust in the process of embodying our voice brings us to a grounded presence where we are able to allow our voice to lead us back to a truer sense of self and what we need to move forward in our life. From the shutdown states of contraction and stagnation, this "medicinal" voice restores the flow of life, moving our energy into expression and expansion. Through this increasingly embodied voice we make contact with both physical and emotional feelings—for experiencing the painful and the pleasurable, the old and the new, the conscious and the unconscious—and create a space for expressing these felt experiences in a deeper and broader way than words can offer. Created by the intricate and coordinated movements of hundreds of muscle fibers, ligaments and nerves throughout the body, our voice knits together body and mind, connecting heart and soul. Now when we hear ourselves, we know and feel something of our real Self.

It is through the voice that we connect with and share our inner experience with others. Our voice, if we can learn to trust it, can lead us into our own inner realms and to the outside world on our quest for meaning and connection. There is no way to prevent the journey through the shadowlands, although I think we all try. No matter who we are, we will all at some time find ourselves there, stuck in a quagmire or on sharp slippery rocks, in the darkness and alone. When we learn how to sing our songs, our soaring melodies become our soul's companions. Voice Movement Therapy shines a light into these dark places, encouraging us to discover and bring what is of value to the surface.

Well-being is not about being immune to pain, trauma, stress or hardship but rather about developing resilience and feeling resourced so that we can move through difficult experiences and not get overwhelmed by them. When we acknowledge and work with the intrinsic interplay between body and psyche through the voice, we discover how naturally resourceful we really are. We learn how engaging more meaningfully and creatively through the voice with the depths of our felt experience—with our shadows, our pain, our habitual patterns, and our ever-changing identity—and expressing our experiences fully is a way to develop resilience and create a pathway to change and wellness. In this chapter, several practitioners share how they use VMT to create such pathways so that inner feelings and experiences can find their way up and out into the world.

In "Subpersonalities and the Voice," Christine Isherwood tells how her use of John Rowan's concept of Subpersonalities begins by focusing on her clients' smallest spontaneous sounds and movements and how she gentles them along until they can grow and develop them in self-composed song, enabling them to forge new behaviors rather than continuing to live with the maladaptive ones made in order to survive.

In "Swallowed by Grief, Saved by Voice," Trish Watts writes about opening a space for the "unspeakable"—those things which we would almost rather die than reveal, for personal or societal reasons—to find her voice of lamentation. The experience of grief needs an expressive range far broader than what our Western culture allows or deems appropriate. Giving herself and others permission to feel, experience and express the depths of their grief provides sacred passage through this emotional landscape, allowing it to flow out of the body rather than remain bottled up inside. Trish shares how the use of specific Vocal Components and Timbres, as defined in our work, directly relate to grief and how working with these sounds and the medicine of song releases these terrible and overwhelming feelings so we can move on.

In "Letting the Darkness Sing Itself: Working Creatively with the Shadow to Reveal Buried Rage," Julia Norton shares how, through the use of various vocal strategies, she creates a safe therapeutic container for women to acknowledge and find expression for their often repressed, silenced, or denied anger at the ways they are still treated in their families and in the world. Through her work, Julia discovers different creative ways of expressing anger, demonstrating how a developmental approach can lead to success. She writes that when working in the realm of the toddler, for example, "It's much easier for people to accept [anger] as part of themselves." Julia's integration of VMT's Instinctual Postural Cycle, also known as the Animal Cycle encourages the embodiment and voicing of the animals, and in tandem with various Vocal Components, helps clients to discover a more expressive "language" for their rage. Her case studies show how she creates a container for the intense, uncomfortable, sometimes explosive emotions within us and how that container can both hold and transform such extremes of experience.

Many people embark on their VMT journey during times of transition when things are shifting and identity evolving. In "The Voice in Motherhood," Anna Grabner works with women transitioning into a new role, offering space for the expression of the complexity of emotions experienced during this time of changing identity. Through her nurturing work, Anna creates opportunities for prospective parents to find strength, stability, and bonding, sharing how vocal work and the voice's instinctual function provide a primal connection between parent and baby, and how the concept of the Sphere and the guided Voice Movement Journey offer meaningful ways of working through feelings. Throughout time, mothers have sung to their babies instinctively. Knowing the voice's great soothing and healing power, Anna brings the personal song to the center of this process of transition, demonstrating its potential to reconnect parents and connect the baby in utero to this ancient wisdom, helping them to transition into new ways of being.

"Soul Song Deep from the Bone: The Power of Story in Voice Movement Therapy," by Veronica Phillips, weaves together the four traditional Shamanic healing salves of storytelling, singing, dancing, and silence with her work as a VMT practitioner. She shares how bringing a story with its accompanying archetypes and symbols alive through voice and body to create personal meaning is a deeply healing process. Stories offer us a way to work through our feelings and doubts while keeping a little distance from them, providing a container for reflection and connection to an ancient healing imagination.

What is evident in the articles that follow is that by entering into a process to contact and develop a voice which is more alive, expressive, and communicative of our needs, truths, and passions, we become more alive, more well, and more able to look after ourselves.

SUBPERSONALITIES AND THE VOICE

Christine Isherwood

Voice Movement Therapy provides many opportunities for accessing, expressing, and coming to know different aspects of oneself through voice, movement, and creativity, and we use the notion of subpersonalities to further deepen and express them. Jung considered the psyche to be composed of multiple aspects, both conscious and unconscious, and John Rowan based his subpersonality work on Jung's complexes and archetypes, later coming to describe them as "Any aspect of the whole person which can be personified."[1]

Subpersonalities occur as a consequence of many different situations and occupy many different realms: some may be determined by roles assigned one in life or constellated by life events, some may manifest in certain situations or relationships, and some may appear as images or in dreams.

In our early days, in our attempts to be loved and accepted, we adapt to that which is required of us and attempt to dispense with aspects of ourselves that are not wanted, with the result that the self is partly composed of what is expected or desired by others. There are many reasons why certain aspects of ourselves come to life, perhaps to protect or defend against unsupportive environments or guard against trauma and distress. Each aspect of the self has a function and role to play and each may have its own individual stories, history, breathing patterns, movements, posture, voice, vocabulary, and self-image; also feelings, moods, beliefs, thoughts, behaviors, ways of relating, purpose and perceptions. These are not acted roles, but parts of the essence of the self which may have emerged at different stages in life and have disparate functions. Much as feelings and emotions come and go, wax and wane, so, too, subpersonalities may move in and out of the self and in and out of presence and influence over our life.

For some, it may be that early investigation of the work of subpersonalities is taken up with aspects of the self which require the greatest attention. Subconscious material emerges as people delve into the nuances of their bodies and voices. Each subpersonality also holds its opposite which may be hidden deep in the unconscious. Parts that have been discarded, assigned to the shadow, still impact greatly. Many are limited by their conceptions of themselves or the reality that they were allowed to live. Learning to allow, express, acknowledge, recognize, and know different subpersonalities allows greater flexibility in the movement and construction of self and identity, enabling relationships to be forged with feelings, needs, creative energy, and power held within particular aspects, rather than suppressed. Shame, pain, fear, confusion, and feelings of lack of congruence may be alleviated as people are able to see that perhaps one part of them that they consider shameful or worrying does not have to be the entire story about them. When we wear a mask for too long, removing it can leave us bereft, lonely, and often desperate. To claim ourselves back from the imposition of masks is crucial work.

Alfred Wolfsohn, through his own research, came to believe that it was possible to give voice not only to the many different aspects of the self but also to the collective unconscious. Through expressive, investigative voicework, he was able to lessen some of the traumas he carried and bring himself to greater emotional health. In VMT, subpersonalities can be shaped through vocal components (see page 19) to attain greater life. Voicing can help to express and manage different aspects of the self, especially material that does not fit so easily into words, and thus allow for their integration. Some people may find they are able to sing in certain aspects of themselves or certain parts of their voice, and not in others.

At times, it may become apparent that a new aspect of the self, a subpersonality, has come into being with consequent vocal changes. The voice may become higher or lower; feel or sound younger; have more or less breath, broken qualities, different melodies or timings. It may have taken on harsher or more rigid aspects, involuntary sounds may emerge, or any number of permutations and combinations of vocal components may be in play. Allowing the many different voices of the self means to be able to give expression to parts that may have been silenced or repressed.

I think of one young woman who had been part of a week-long intensive group process. She was very contained somatically and vocally, her voice barely a whisper, with an ingrained look of terror on her face. After some days, she indicated she would like to work individually. Sometimes there is a pressing need or a great clarity as to what one would like to work on; other times there is only the desire to work and we begin just where we are.

The group had formed a circle into which she entered meekly. I asked some questions as to how she was and what areas she might like to work on; she knew only that she wanted to "express" and was scared to do so. I suggested we begin by strolling together in the circle and conversing in vowel sounds without words. She wanted me to start, which I did, my sound based upon the tiny emissions of sound she was releasing on the breath. She began to join in with me and we continued to walk.

As her confidence increased, her voice opened out into a more open mid-range and louder Flute (see page 20) and I began to drop down in volume. The release of her voice began to melt away some of her somatic defenses and sobs began to emerge on the breath. In response to this, her body attempted to impose a greater rigidity in order to keep things locked in and her vocal tract tightened. To help the sound pass through a more open Vocal Tube, I encouraged her to move her arms and legs so that her focus was directed onto a greater expanse of her body, thus taking away from the tightening and holding, and this enabled her to release some of the tension. Her response to this suggestion was to enter into movement reminiscent of a tantrum, much like a two-year-old might do, alternating and thrashing with her feet and arms. It was dispersing a lot of that tension and I encouraged her to keep doing it.

The movement faded away, yet there was still a lot of feeling there. Asked how she felt, she responded that she wanted to break something. The room was a hired space, pretty sparsely laid out, and although sufficient for our needs, there were not many resources to hand. There were, however, some large sheets of paper nearby. I presented one to her, suggesting perhaps she might like to rip it up. She took it from me, and holding it in front of her, observed it for a while and then hit it, hard. It broke, and she hit it again and again, breaking it into smaller pieces. Her hands were strong and her blows direct, carrying a lot of power and energy.

I suggested that she allow her voice to express some of that energy and she began growling and yelling. In this manner she went through several large sheets of paper, the pieces of which surrounded her on the floor. She began to kick the ripped-up paper out of her Sphere (see page 21), using the force of her voice and body as she roared and wailed at the discarded fragments of unwanted material. I began to push some of the paper back at her so that she had to keep kicking it away. It would be too easy if the process was completed so efficiently and my sense was there was more to be expressed.

Her leg was kicking backwards and forwards, trying to rid the circle of the bits of paper. Picking up the scraps, she began ripping the pieces smaller and smaller and then throwing them up in the air. Surrounded by falling paper, as she gathered and then released it, the group began to cheer. Surveying the messy scene triumphantly, she paraded in the circle in the manner of a champ who has just won the fight. Her sounds became words and she sang, "I used to be a stone and now I am free." Once the song was really in her and known to her, she sang it to the group and they echoed it back to her in chorus, in her own words. She invited the group to come to their feet where, enthused by her energy and freedom, they now joined in throwing heaps of paper snow at her and each other, and then the whole group danced and sang in the tsunami of paper snow which she had created. Finally, she directed the group to photograph her as she posed triumphantly, sitting in the midst of it all as she threw the bits of paper up in the air and they came to rest around her.

Through listening to what was trying to emerge through voice and psyche, taking it one step at a time, allowing the process to unfold, she arrived in the midst of a wonderland of having expressed and torn up the old restrictions. In reflection afterwards, she said that she felt she had been having to hold herself in too much in order to be accepted and that she had become a stone, that there was no movement within her and nothing that could move out from her. The person she revealed in the session was alive, beautiful, vibrant, glowing. Everyone could see the reality of who she was, could see the difference in her as she was freed from too much repression. She called this aspect of herself "Live Freely and Beautifully."

This piece of work contained the interplay of freedom and "old story," as she balanced the antithetical desires of expression and not being judged or abandoned, walking a tightrope between what she felt was OK and stretching into a new reality: that which she could hold and that which she could let go of. At each step along the way, I ensured that she felt safe enough to express what she wanted and to move to another step. Through voice she was able to rage, destroy, express, be met, be seen for who she was, find some freedom and come to a greater self-knowing. She was able to experience the power of unleashing in a safe way that which had been suppressed, to feel what it felt like to be free and also, in song and community, to self-soothe and self-identify. She later reported that this session had a profound impact on her life.

We work with subpersonalities not to fragment, but to come closer to knowing and understanding the components that form us, rather than being bound by old patterns which exist down deep in our psyche or body, so that we may come to integration and a wholeness of being. If our behavior is inexplicable to us or makes us ashamed, if we cannot understand what our moods or responses are about, then we are not free to live or make choices. In allowing subpersonalities to become more conscious, it is possible to develop greater compassion, understanding, and new ways of expressing oneself and relating to others. This approach allows for aspects of the self that emerge through voice to be brought to awareness, heard and shaped, in order to bear witness to and reflect on them. It means that we can tend to wounded or scared parts of ourselves which may have had to adopt a facade of bravado; nurture the internal good-enough parent; or allow wise or loving aspects of the self to constellate. By not having to expend energy on keeping parts of ourselves silenced, imprisoned, and disassociated, subpersonality work can free tension held in the space between that which is known and that which is unknown.

Introjected Voices

Everybody has some parts of themselves that are based on the opinions of others. Often it is the voice of authority when we are young. For example, there may be a parent, caregiver, or teacher who tells us we are not good enough. Their voice becomes an introject, a part of us, and eventually we do to ourselves what they used to do to us. This is often, of course, unconscious.

Evelyn had become pregnant and it had been determined that the fetus had chromosomal abnormalities. Her husband had insisted that physically and emotionally she was too vulnerable and would not be able to cope, so she had an abortion which she regretted profoundly. She felt undermined constantly by him and his wishes dominated. All her life, she said, people had told her what to do and she had come to realize that even as an adult she was not able to make her own decisions. Filled with grief, she realized she had not been allowed to consider what she might like to do.

We began with the pressing issue of grief and the deep and painful feelings she wanted to express. Initially, her sounds were those of wandering, undifferentiated, helpless loss. Within the sessions, I helped her shape those sounds into a form that she could carry with her and use both to express and self-soothe. Helping her to recognize areas she had visited vocally that she could leave and return to, locating herself in time and space, and revisiting emerging melody, a tangible melodious form began to appear. Lyrics spoken or expressed became part of the structure and the song began to shape itself, carrying the wounds and the loss, yet also bringing comfort. Expressing as it did some of what she had been through allowed her to hear it and live with the reality of the loss. Shaping this loss was important, bringing her to a new relationship with what she had undergone.

In another session, weeping softly, she realized she wanted to communicate with that part of her she felt she had not allowed to live. The use of repetition is an important component of songwriting which allows us to recognize territory and become familiar with certain soundscapes, bringing comfort in this recognition. I supported her with breath and presence, and acknowledged the depth of her feelings which she had been trying, unsuccessfully, to dismiss. A song began to emerge which became a lullaby to the aborted fetus. Afterwards, she felt relief that she had been able to voice her feelings. Everyone else had dismissed these feelings and she had tried to do the same. Acknowledgment, however, was critical for her to be able to move on past the void of her grief and the old stories it had constellated. Evelyn realized that she had disowned and severed a part of herself which was not perfect.

Our work together progressed into song, poems, and artwork about nurturing her own hurt and damaged selves, claiming her voice and ownership of her own body, and having the right to make her own decisions. There were many different aspects which needed to be voiced and this took place over a period of time. The work was multifaceted and she went on to invoke and support her child-self who had always had to obey and was never allowed to think for herself. Now she began to attend to the sorrows and wounds that she had endured as a child.

In responding to her husband within our sessions, she raged at him that he did not listen to her, did not treat her as an adult, and she came to realize that was the relationship they had constructed and that she, too, had played a part in allowing that dynamic to exist. She was able to tell him of some of her struggles and work with him towards having a more equitable relationship, one between two adults rather than that of parent and child.

Voice invokes the inner world and allows for relationship and engagement with the many internal figures and images of the self, voices which may have been discarded because they could not find their place in life, or there was not room for them in a self constellated to meet the requirements of the family, the world, or one's own expectations.

Through the lens of breath, movement, sound, creation, song with or without words, invention, investigation, and story, subpersonalities can be given expression and form through the voice. The Vocal Components enable the differentiation and identification of distinct aspects of the self which can be engaged with, sculpted, shaped, and incorporated into the repertoire of self. Voice reveals its own world and its own language which can be accessed and processed through engagement. Subpersonality work allows greater knowledge of the many aspects of the self at work and also makes it possible to view these selves from a different perspective. It enables past wounds to be brought into a new environment or context, as behavior previously unconscious begins to come to consciousness, bringing about greater creativity and ways of being that often lead to new solutions. We cannot re-write the scripts of the past, but we can learn to find acceptance of ourselves, and through that, repair some of the damage wrought. For many, expressing feelings through song rather than having to translate and shape them into spoken language can be a route to self-knowledge. In my experience, everybody has a song to bring forth.

Subpersonality work allows access to the shadow in creative ways, and through expressive means can give voice to that which is literally unspeakable. In this way it is possible to locate and contain shadow material within vocalized song containers, enabling integration. Much of the burden of trauma is the inability to give expression to what has occurred; by giving voice to and hearing ourselves, we can become more aware of ourselves in our multiplicity and attend to that which needs attention. By expressing in this way, people learn to trust themselves and come to a greater understanding of the roles of subpersonalities active within them, causing a transformation of their relationship to them.

In connecting with one's inner selves, questions can aid in honing understanding. For example: who was encountered and what was their purpose? What was found or perceived? Was any information gleaned from the encounter? What qualities, movements, or characteristics were present and what vocal components or qualities were in play? Did the subpersonality have language or affective sounds? What was comfortable, or not so comfortable for you? Other questions could be: Did the subpersonality need anything, and if so, what? Did singing in that way remind you of anything and were any emotions experienced when singing from that aspect? What was felt? What was lost, what found? Where did you go? What was there, what was it there for and what did it become? What did it have to say to you; what do you want to let go of? How does the subpersonality sing or sound itself; how would it like to express? As the relationship of sound and image is expressed and investigated, then the different subpersonalities find vocal styles and characteristics specific to them which allow for nuanced differentiation in order that their voice may be heard more clearly.

Coming to know other aspects of oneself helps to expand our sense of self and agency. The vocal subpersonality work of VMT allows the audible and felt expression and embodiment of aspects of oneself, giving them vibrational life. As voice and self create in the moment, story is put into song, allowing for the telling and re-playing of the tale, enabling a re-framing of events and letting new light be shed and fresh perspectives gained, bringing emotional release.

In one group, a woman shared tales of ill treatment at the hands of others. At first, people were empathetic and sympathetic until gradually they, too, began to treat her in ways familiar to her, yet uncomfortable for them. As a child she had suffered significant abandonment, receiving only the most basic of care. Desperate to avoid encountering that again, she sought to make herself indispensable to others' lives: compulsively care-taking, proffering advice, always knowing best, and encroaching upon others. Wise, talented, and kind, she knew no boundaries in her desperation to be seen and recognized. The group individually sought to flee each tiny interaction until she was left all alone, again, with an entirely new group of people abandoning her once more. She raised in the group that people were recreating childhood classroom behaviors and seeking to isolate her. I suggested that in order to understand why an old dynamic had shown up again, she investigate this scenario through a sub-personality and express it in song and character.

In song, costume, and dance, this woman thrilled to present her goddess self which she thought loving, generous, and gorgeous; the group as a whole responded with revulsion and nausea. She was completely flabbergasted, considering that self to be one of the most important parts of her. Through the amplification of some of her characteristics into a role both part of her and at the same time more performative, she was able to see, acknowledge, and witness the impact of those cloying and overbearing aspects of herself that had not been available to her consciousness but were so obvious to others. It was the first time in her life she had ever received feedback on a part of her which turned people off and away. Engaging with it as a subpersonality, she was able to see it more clearly as a part of her, rather than retreating into the belief that all of her was unlovable. She was able to see this was a part that she had begun to play when very young in order not to be left alone, yet which had become so grotesquely out of shape that it brought about precisely what she was seeking to evade.

Subpersonalities allow for the location and expression of a wide span of feeling within an artistic framework, enabling transformation at many levels. Through giving expression to and recognizing previously obscure parts of themselves, people find new freedom and self-understanding which allows changes to occur. Denying, silencing or stifling parts of ourselves exerts a heavy price, while reclaiming disavowed parts grants some liberation.

Through coming to know ourselves, it is possible to achieve a greater understanding of which subpersonalities are present or in charge at any time. This means that it is possible to allow different outcomes to occur. In this way, communication and engagement with self and others can be enhanced.

NOTE

1. John Rowan, *Subpersonalities*: The People Inside Us. London, UK: Routledge, 2015.

SWALLOWED BY GRIEF, SAVED BY VOICE

Trish Watts

I lost my voice when Lady Death choked me. Constricting my ability to breathe and thieving my vocal cords, layer upon layer of emotion crept up as grief took hold.

In 2001 my father and mother-in-law both died, my mother was hospitalized with a stroke and my 10-year marriage collapsed, to say nothing of 9/11 and the twin towers! All I had known of my identity and stability came crashing down. It felt like a huge oak tree had been wrenched out of my body and all that was left was a gaping hole with roots protruding upside down. Gone were the loves of my life, gone were the songs of joy that ran off my tongue with ease, gone were the songs of hope that gave my life purpose. All that was left was a disconnected fearful body, a wounded broken heart, and a numb mental fog in which to move through the world. I was deeply lost out at sea, feeling exposed and vulnerable. I was terrified that if I opened my mouth, uncontrollable feelings would consume me and I would not be able to stop them. Zipping up and swallowing down the emotion seemed the only option if I was to function and keep face for the life I was leading. I became desperate for a healing medicine that could meet me holistically and give me the tools to navigate this dark, foreign experience.

Instinctively, I knew the only way forward was to find a way to voice my anguish and sing it out. Singing and listening are primary to how I navigate the world. I found Voice Movement Therapy and it resonated to my core. It became my sealskin, my breathing apparatus for swimming through the tidal waves and wild currents of grief, providing a safe container to integrate the unspeakable voices of the psyche that were aching for release. Through Voice Movement Therapy I learnt to trust my own descent into the shadowlands and be instructed by the subtle wisdom of both my body and the deep unconscious.

When I came across Alfred Wolfson's work with voicing the psyche, I identified with his notion that if he could find voice for the sounds of the monsters in his soul, he would also find relief. He did! With several vocal students he started a practice of vocal exploration delving into the primary emotions of the voice "in extremis." Encouraging his students to access their own shadow material and felt-body constrictions, he led them into uncharted waters. His work stretched the vocal range of his students into heightened sounds of hysteria, terror, anxiety and paranoia and stretched their lower registers into the moaning, disruptive sounds of agony, depression and grief. In doing so, he crossed into the androgynous voice that has both male and female aspects and accessed the instinctual voice which is both primal and animal.

When a person screams out in agony, it is hard to tell if that person is male or female; the voice crosses into an emergency language, a cry for help that we all recognize. These extremes, to an untrained ear, trigger terror; however, to Wolfsohn it was a cathartic medicine for the traumatized individual. Wolfsohn's life work was dedicated to the exploration of the connection between the human voice and the psyche, and he deeply inspired me to begin the soul work that I knew was the missing piece for my own healing and recovery.

I. VOCAL COMPONENTS USED IN GRIEF WORK (see page 19)

In Voice Movement Therapy both vocal and non-vocal components are used. Three of the vocal components that were helpful in my own grief work were: Violin, Pitch Fluctuation and Saxophone.

The Wailing Voice: Using the Vocal Components of Violin, Pitch Fluctuation, and Saxophone

Violin is a quality of voice that focuses the air into the sinuses, making it sound nasal and giving it the ability to cut through or rise above other sounds. Singers often term this as singing into the beak or mask. We also naturally use this voice when we're whining, complaining, or wanting intentionally to annoy another. It's a great way to express a hostile impulse or meanness and can act as a valve for releasing stored vindictiveness.

Pitch Fluctuation generally occurs, to a greater or lesser degree, as a fairly regular and even vibration when one is singing or speaking. When we're feeling unstable or nervous, it presents as a shaking or wobbling in the voice as well as the body. To shake up old patterns and spit out "rubbish worry," vocalizing with Pitch Fluctuation can free tightness and loosen the grip of fear.

Saxophone is the timbre that allows most access to the instinctual, primal voice. It is accessed by loosening the jaw wide as in a yawn and widening and lengthening the vocal tube to access abdominal breathing, the sound dropping deeper into the guts. When the instinctual body is accessed, the cognitive self-relaxes. Sounds emitted are often in the form of sobbing, yelling, screaming, belly laughing or wailing.

Whilst attending a beautiful meditation ritual, I experienced a disconnection and felt a desire to run out of the room screaming! I was overwhelmed with feelings. I couldn't manage. My guts were stirring and I needed a space for the messy sounds of my interior chaos to be expressed. In my panic, I caught the eye of a friend who was also visibly unsettled. We promptly fled to the ocean where we found ourselves on the top of a cliff. Both of us felt held by the crashing waves and the belly of the sea below. Taking turns, we held space for each other and witnessed the raw emergence of emotion. Using the component of Violin, I allowed vindictiveness to rise so the fierce energy of disappointment and disbelief could be expressed. For me it felt like poison was being released from my veins, so clear and direct was the pointed sound escaping my mouth and skin. My muscles started to contract and expand with my breath and I became increasingly hot. Coughing sobs and percussive gibberish poured out of my mouth as I opened into Saxophone and Pitch Fluctuation. A low-toned moaning followed as I felt my heart falling into the ocean which could hold the world's tears. I felt like a blocked drainpipe being flushed out.

The Cracking Voice: Using the Vocal Component of Register

Another vocal component I found exposing was Register which speaks to the lower and higher pitches in the voice. The lower voice is often termed Modal, or chest voice, and the higher voice is called Falsetto, or head voice. When moving between low and high voice there is a transition point known as the Register break. These registers can be blended or they can be allowed to sound the break.

As a voice moves step by step from low pitch to high pitch, a natural "crack" can be heard; I call it the "gear shift." In Classical Western music, singers are trained to remove any hint of this break and practice blending the Modal and Falsetto voices seamlessly, enabling more control and stability. The Register break is often amplified in folk music, particularly with the yodeling style heard within country music and in indigenous cultures. Here the voice is developed to carry communication across field and mountain. When we're affected by emotion, the voice can naturally break and reveal the authenticity of what we are feeling. Often people will swallow back this vulnerable, naked "breaking" sound for fear it will reveal too much.

Busting the dam of emotions held within my own register break was liberating. I was in so much denial around my marriage dysfunction, it was very difficult to acknowledge and express my anger. As a singer I was trained to iron out any cracks or weak parts in my voice. Giving myself permission to explore the "crack" in my voice revealed a whole new world. My troubled psyche poured out in the voices of many different characters, and the unknown realms within myself were acknowledged, felt and heard. It was the place of being off-balance, out of control, swinging right out to the edges of my comfort zone. I experienced this physically when literally swinging out sideways to places where I was about to fall and then swinging back. This allowed an edgy rise and fall of my voice which was full of fear and excitement. Opening to this fluctuating voice helped me express the constant tug-o-war of moving from home to home between loved ones and from gig to gig in my work as a freelancer. Playing with the register break enabled me to integrate these extremes and move from terror to welcoming the next stage of my life.

Shaking Medicine: Using the Vocal Components of Pitch Fluctuation and Loudness.

When people feel overwhelmed with life–be it an overload of information, a drowning in emotions, a numbness of body or a feeling of being "beside oneself"–then we might use shaking to ignite the body, to wake it up and release energy. Shaking is an ancient practice that is often used to release trauma, allowing the muscles to relax and unwind and to let go of the need to control. It brings the body's energetic system into alignment, creating more ease.[1] When we add the vocal components of Pitch Fluctuation and Loudness, we invite people to shake free the voice, to loosen the jaw and to play with pitch and volume. Sighing, grunting, exhaling loudly and letting sound out can shift stuck energy and take the lid off hidden sorrow.

The Projected and Intimate Voice: Using the Vocal Component of Loudness (Volume & Dynamics)

We think that to be heard and noticed we must be loud and compete for attention. Loudness takes up space and says, "I'm here, pay attention to me." Loudness in the VMT system is the sound perceived on the spectrum from loud to quiet, created by the vocal cords vibrating in response to the pressure of the breath releasing from the lungs.

There is much that can be said about the place of Loudness in our lives. We all know when a loud person enters the room; we may say they have a "big personality" or they "take up space." In grief work there are times when the loud and rageful, the "Here I am!" voice needs to be expressed, heard and validated in a safe space. It can be hugely freeing and revealing to allow the full voice to emerge without having to "get it right." Conversely, when a quiet person enters a space. their presence can be felt as being "light as a feather" or in some cases, unnoticeable, like a "wallflower." The voice echoes this sense of presence of loud or soft and every dynamic in between.

Quietness is highly underrated. Although a quiet voice can be frightening and off-putting, its opposite quality of softness is aligned with the ability to listen deeply and intimately. When children are unsettled or hurting, mothers sing in loving, caressing tones. As human beings, our nervous system responds to the intention of tenderness and softness. Sometimes this is all that is needed for comforting and healing to take place. We should never underestimate the power of reassurance that human kindness offers.

If we truly listen and observe, with the whole self, we can notice something more than just what is going on at the surface of a person's life. In my experience, sometimes a person may present with a soft, almost inaudible voice, so learning how to "wait," to be with the uncomfortable silences, the unknown, the questions that arise, without jumping in to "fix it" requires patience and is a sacred act. Often those who suffer trauma present with deep shame and unworthiness, thinking they don't have a right to speak or sing, let alone admit that they may be hurting. There can be intense pain and the fear of being punished more if they raise their voice. Taking the time to establish trust by breathing with a person first can be revolutionary, communicating that it's OK to slow down, take up breathing space, BE and recover.

The warmth and power of soft singing was fully revealed to me when I had the privilege of singing at the bedside of my own mother in the last stages of her life. Singing quietly the hymns of our faith tradition gave her, myself, and those around us great comfort. It was the song-line of our lineage, an auditory cradle, rocking on the threshold of two worlds.

It was in this context that, in 2007, I stumbled onto the humble beginnings of The Sydney Threshold Choir, a women's choir that sings at the bedsides of those in hospice and palliative care. It was the first of many women's Threshold Choirs to form in Australia and I was invited to take on the role of Musical Director. I was interested in how we could create a container for soft singing rather than performative singing, where a mix of lyrics, vowels and humming could be used for soothing and comfort.

Often the patient may be too ill for us to use words, and so we slow down the breath and breathe together first. Then we sing long sustained vowels or simple melodies to create an intimate space similar to that of a lullaby. After we sing at the bedside, the singers gather to reflect on their personal experience, allowing each member to be heard. As a group, this is a very important part of self-care and building trust between us.

II. KEY VMT APPROACHES

The Song as Container

The song is a wonderful vessel that holds us all safely on the high seas of emotion and in murky mental chaos. The repetitive pattern of melody, lyric and chord can provide essential musical structure for the nervous system to rest in, creating an internal scaffolding on which energy can reorganize itself. In grief work, songs that contain the strong feeling fabric of a person's biography can be a source of great comfort. Our cellular memory resonates and relaxes when we hear a soothing song from our past, recalling scenes of health, happiness, or peace. These songs become resources in our collective memory and can be a tremendous medicine in times of suffering. When the mind and body are saturated by stress, words can be difficult to locate. A person can be transported into a younger age of development where trauma and language may be stuck, triggering hidden aspects of the psyche. Humming the melody of a familiar song is a gentle way to reassure and calm the feelings of overwhelm while the words find their shape.

Blues and Laments are tried and true song frameworks for holding the cries of the soul. An ancient round, "Waters of Babylon," as sung by Don MacLean, is an easy lament that works beautifully for group singing: By the Waters, the Waters of Babylon, we lay down and wept for thee, Zion. We remember, we remember, we remember thee, Zion.

We can set the song up and repeat it to take people into a gentle dreamtime space. The rocking lilt of rhythm and melody becomes a cradle for holding the unprocessed, raw feelings that arise. By using repetition, returning to the song over and over, the structure of the song becomes a steady vessel from which one can sing and release the murmurings and howls of the heart. Repetition of a phrase or a drone is important; it becomes an anchor for the participant to move off and onto at any time. We give the mind a musical ostinato, a hook, a pattern to focus on, creating a meditative zone in which the voice can wander and ride the emotional waves. By using simple lyrics, humming and vowels of oooo and ahhh,'we can set free the improvisational spirit to play with a phrase, uninhibited and yet held safely by the song. Accessing collective song memory helps a person join the dots in their cultural and personal landscape, reminding them of where and to whom they belong.

Songwriting and Poetry

Another powerful approach is creating songs in the moment, using improvisation and written poetry. Returning to songwriting and poetry was a coming home process for me. It is one of the reasons I decided to train in Voice Movement Therapy. It's a strong meaning-making vehicle that allows space for reflection, exploration and expression: catching the melodies as they rise in the moment, feeling into the soul and listening for what it wants to say or sing, noticing the movement of the body, its rhythm and sway, and calling forth the imagery that accompanies each impulse... Herein lies the unsung song waiting for birth.

Within dark poetry, I could pour out my frankness and irrationality onto a page, speak or sing it, and then look at it and say "Here I am today. This is my truth and a part of my life story." It felt a relief to have a safe place to put these words and not have to hide the feelings in myself and pretend I was OK. If others asked me how I was, instead of shutting down, I could read them a poem! Surrendering to the cycle of a song, as in a lament, enables the fast mind to slow down and assist the languid heart to "feel" into the beat, melody and lyrics, and cradle that heart. I wrote a song for my Mother after she died, titled "My Belly Weeps." In it I was able to express the deep love and sorrow I felt for her as her daughter, woman to woman. I felt very close to her when I sang it and it brought much healing and peace at a cellular level of my being.

Vocal Improvisation: Spit out the "Rubbish Worry:" Gibberish and Nonsense Words.

Generally, from the time we can utter sound, we're conditioned to hold our bodies and voices in certain ways, to be measured in what we say, and to edit the back-story. Social conditioning, appropriateness and the rules for what is acceptable play out. There are not many public spaces where one is given the permission to be "unkept, messy, ugly or unpredictable." Grief can be a messy, out of control business emotionally, and trying to hold it all together to look like we're OK takes enormous energy. The holding in, the tightening of the muscles, the obsessive mind that wants to control or deny what's going on, can be exhausting for the body. There is usually a tipping point where one needs to let go and release the pain of the tension, to soothe the heart and integrate a different, new way of being. VMT uses vocal improvisation as much as possible to assist with this opening. It also values every sound humankind can utter, including the instinctual moaning or rageful sounds of sorrow that are rarely heard in everyday life.

When I work with individuals or with groups, I create a safe container for the grotesque, impolite self to be expressed. If it is an individual, I will work in a duet form of call and response. If it is a group, I limit the time frame for this experience to one or two minutes. I invite people to play with their voices, changing their facial expressions, contorting the mouth and jaw, inviting jerky movements. For those who feel self-conscious about "having to sound right," it can be hugely liberating. When they see others being foolish and having fun, pulling faces with wild sounds, it gives the whole group permission to go for it in an environment of non-judgment. I then invite them to get in touch with what is overwhelming and "spit the rubbish out"—the excess information or energy—using gibberish and percussive staccato sounds.

Breathwork: A Felt Sense

When exploring grief I invite participants to scan their body, to notice if they are breathing shallowly or deeply, gasping for air or feeling short of breath. The breath is primary in processing emotion. Our deepest fears are amplified if we're unable to breathe and attend to what we feel. When we're scared, our heart rate accelerates and our breathing becomes short. A feeling of panic or anxiety may rise up. We start to hyperventilate and clavicular breathing, using just the top part of the lungs, takes over. Through conscious breathing opening into thoracic and abdominal breathing where a full breath of air is hosted, we can return to the body and wrap awareness around the felt sense of emotion that may be present. Breath awareness can also assist with coming home to the self, moving focus from the busy monkey-mind to the simplicity of breathing in and out.

I invite clients and groups to drop into soft abdominal breathing by placing their hands on their belly and taking a deep breath into them. The rise and fall of the belly is a beautiful quietening rhythm which can calm the emotions and the mind. Breathwork enables us to befriend the tides of emotion during loss, helping us to stay with difficult feelings and giving them internal space to reside, to be heard, witnessed and accepted.

Active Imagination

As developed by Carl Jung, Active Imagination offers images, narratives, and/or personified entities that can serve as a bridge between the ego and the unconscious. In VMT, Active Imagination opens a vista to perceive what is already present through embodying the felt image and bringing it to life through voice and movement. Here follows a case study using Active Imagination with grief:

Valerie was a 50-year-old massage therapist. She presented with a huge desire to sing and to find her creative voice. Although she had studied piano and loved performing when given the chance, she had been totally denied this opportunity and was vocally suppressed in an abusive family environment. During one of our sessions, I noticed she was holding her solar plexus in pain. The muscles were contracting downwards. She spoke about a "fallout" with her sister, and I noticed her stomach extended. I invited her to hold her solar plexus and to breathe into her hands. A tiny voice emerged on the outbreath, a child's high voice with pitch fluctuation. She began to speak tentatively: "I'm scared, something bad has happened, I have to run away to be safe."

In her imagination a baby elephant showed up, trumpeting towards her, wanting to play. The elephant was a friend. She then felt the elephant inside her... Silence descended. I asked her how she felt, she replied, "I feel covered, buried alive." I invited her to engage more fully with the vision of the elephant, using active imagination. This enabled more access to unprocessed material and creativity. The elephant within began to trumpet through the mud, using long sustained notes. Her vocal cords tightened in anguish and then released, using saxophone and loudness. She started to stand up and sway like an elephant. As she moved out into a bigger space in the room, she spoke strongly: "I'm here . . . Back off!" I stepped back and gave her full space to claim her strength vocally as she embodied the power of the elephant. This demanded a lot of her energy and at the end, she was exhausted.

Catching her breath, her body started to shake naturally and her voice began wobbling with pitch fluctuation as if she was going to sob, howl or throw up! I could hear the raw sorrow in her voice as she remembered the lost years of being denied her full voice. I encouraged her to continue shaking everything out and around, then to stop, soften, and shake again, moving the energy out. Pitch Fluctuation continued and tears fell. She started to lift her legs out of the mud and they became the center of attention. Her feet began to stomp and her legs started moving freely. A vibrant energy filled her entire body, and then she began to dance.

To finish, we sat quietly resting. She told me stories of the women in her lineage, about how her powerful grandmother pushed back and rebelled against the abuse of her mother, and about how her own mother did the same. It was time for her to kick back the shackles of a controlling mother who denied creative expression for herself in any form. It was time for her to grieve the loss of her voice and to claim its rebirth for her own health and well-being. Valerie's experience of using the modality of Voice Movement Therapy demonstrates the transformative nature of the work, especially when a person experiences suppression and verbal abuse from others. Naming and releasing her deep sorrow for the loss of her voice created space for compassion and freedom to rise.

The experience of loss and grief is unique to each person. I have found that Voice Movement Therapy has given me a wide and deep lens to meet people where they're at—to listen, enable, and facilitate safe passage from distress to self-knowledge, from anguish to inner peace. With the fracturing of society and the deconstruction of systems that once held us, the need for an internal scaffolding to help navigate radical and profound change is immense. Loss and sorrow are evident at every turn, particularly with the bombardment of news and views via TV and social media. The immediacy of having a front row seat to everyone's personal experiences, pain, opinions and challenges leaves us vulnerable to disconnection with the Self. Voice Movement Therapy is a powerful and compassionate modality that honors and respects each person's soul journey. It helps people integrate the myriad of voices felt when experiencing loss and grief and resurrects the internal resources that nurture and restore wholeness.

NOTE

Bradford Keeney, *Shaking Medicine: The Healing Power of Ecstatic Movement.* Inner Traditions, Bear and Company, Rochester, VT 2007, p. 14.

BIBLIOGRAPHY

Gordon, James, S. *The Transformation: Discovering Wholeness and Healing After Trauma.* New York, NY: Harper Collins Publishers, 2019.

Keeney, Bradford. *Shaking Medicine: The Healing Power of Ecstatic Movement.* Rochester, VT: Inner Traditions Bear and Company, 2007.

Weller, Francis and Michael Lerner. (2015) *The Wild Edge of Sorrow: Rituals of Renewal and the Sacred Work of Grief.* Berkeley, CA: North Atlantic Books, 2007.

LETTING THE DARKNESS SING ITSELF: WORKING CREATIVELY WITH THE SHADOW TO REVEAL BURIED RAGE

Julia Norton

The following article began its life in my thesis: "Breaking Down the Walls of Anger" (Voice Movement Therapy Training, London: 2000). In this study, I examined various ways in which the Expressive Arts Therapies in general and Voice Movement Therapy in particular could be used to unlock and integrate anger. My interest was in working with women who found it either difficult to express their anger or who were in denial of feeling any at all. This extract deals with uncovering and somatizing shadow material. For those who find the acknowledgement of angry feelings impossible, a thorough investigation of the shadow is essential:

> The shadow acts like a psychic immune system, defining what is self and what is not-self. For different people, in different families and cultures, what falls into ego and what falls into shadow can vary. For instance, some permit anger or aggression to be expressed; most do not. Some permit sexuality, vulnerability, or strong emotions; many do not. Some permit financial ambition, or artistic expression, or intellectual development, while some do not.[1]

Simply put, our shadow is often the part of us we want to deny. For example, "I don't get jealous/ill/angry," etc. For the purpose of drawing out repressed angry expression, I often encourage my clients to begin to consider the possibility of having a shadow side. What is more difficult, however, is persuading people to try to open up to the creative possibilities of the shadow and look specifically at their own contribution to, as Robert Bly puts it, the world's "shadow bag." An obvious reason for this difficulty is, of course, because the shadow is by definition, "Unseeable, buried in our unconscious, to all intents and purposes out of harm's way."[2] But it isn't; it leaks out in the form of hostility, angry impulses, or unpleasant physical conditions like muscular tension, rashes and digestive disorders. There are, however, ways of bringing that unconscious material to the surface, one of which is to work physically and vocally on developmental material.

When shadow work is approached more developmentally, at toddler age, it is much easier for people to accept it as a part of themselves which can be selfish or persecutory, jealous or terrified—remembering, of course, that trust and love can also be found in the shadow. A group exercise I learned from Anne Brownell on the 1998 training is very powerful in terms of directly accessing shadow material:

Having worked developmentally for the beginning part of the session, we are now at the stage of crawling. At this stage, each participant is asked to put a non-valuable object into the center of the circle. They are then asked to focus on another object that they want to play with. When the facilitator calls "go," all have to crawl as fast as they can into the center to grab the object of their choice. Inevitably, some people will have chosen the same object as others and whilst the "lucky ones" withdraw to begin a sensory exploration of their new acquisition, mini-confrontations may occur between the others.

Some will scream right into the face of their opponent, Loudness (see page 19) being a significant tool in claiming space through self-assertive aggression; others will try to succeed by the use of physical force, and still others will quickly shuffle away when they suspect confrontation and either find something that has been left over or steal something from a less challenging participant. So much is to be learned about our shadow and consequently often our relationship to aggression, in its various manifestations, forms from these encounters.

A similar exercise, still in the realm of play and imagination, is working with animal images. Working with animal imagery can have a very liberating effect. All the moral constraints of being a person are lifted and the being is able to "be" once more. By this I mean to suggest that when we take on animal form, we are once again in a position to react immediately and freely to others, within the full gamut of our primal emotions, as Erik Fromm said, "without undue hesitation, doubt or fear."[3] We do this vocally and with our bodies. Joan Chodorow, Dance Therapist and author of *Dance Therapy and Depth Psychology*, quotes Darwin when writing of this phenomenon: "The young and old of widely different races, both with man and animals, express the same state of mind by the same movements."[4] She goes on to point out that, of the many different names we give our emotions, they are mostly drawn from one of the main affects. For example, weeping, sobbing and mourning all come from grief.

During my VMT training, we did a considerable amount of work with animal imagery through a thorough exploration of the Instinctual Postural, or Animal, Cycle, taught by Paul Newham (see page 22). This was a perfect opportunity for those with unacknowledged feelings of anger and rage to be fierce jungle cats or gorillas. One thing I have noticed in my work, which isn't part of the VMT system, has been another predominant animal taking space: the bear. The bear seems to sit in that position between Feline/Canine and Primate (see page 23). To be more precise, it is both. When relaxed or playful, she can remain on all fours, incorporating Disruption with the Saxophone configuration of that position. If angered she can come onto her back legs and roar with more force than a lion could ever hope to match. Once her foe has been challenged, she drops back down onto all fours, probably still growling with Disruption, knowing she is one of the strongest animals in the wild. She doesn't have the speed or high pitch-cutting quality of the big cat's voice, but in terms of physical strength, vocal depth and volume, she is unsurpassed.

TWO CASE STUDIES

"Jackie"

"Jackie" had been coming to see me for ten weeks. She was in her late twenties and dividing her time between living in a Buddhist monastery in the countryside and at her sister's apartment in the city. She was an actress by profession, but had never really been able to sustain her career. Her mother had been put into a psychiatric hospital when Jackie was only eight years old. Her father and his second wife had fought, to the extent that Jackie had been forced to telephone the police on a number of occasions because she really feared someone was going to get killed. I had taken what I thought was a thorough history, but she chose not to disclose any of this information until we were eight weeks into the work together. This is the shadow at work.

Having spent the prior two weeks working quite high in her pitch range and focusing on the neglect she had felt as a child, I suggested we focus on her low pitch range. There was a moderate amount of natural Disruption (see page 19) in this lower range which I told her to keep and use. We had used Disruption quite a lot in our time together and she manifested it easily without any vocal strain. In addition to Loudness, Disruption is a significant VMT technique to use when working with anger. As Paul Newham says, "We tend to use Disruption when we are extremely angry and when we are scolding someone with a warning; and those with naturally disrupted voices are often host to a backlog of rage."[5]

When Jackie paused for a moment, I asked her what image she had to go with the sound she was making and she replied, "grizzly bear." That had been exactly what I had perceived in my counter-transference, so I encouraged her to use that image and embody the bear, to feel her weight, fur and claws. She vocalized again, increasing in Loudness and with more Disruption. The pitch was still at the low end of her range. After another four or five minutes, I stepped in as another bear to challenge her territory. She became ferocious and pushed me back with enormous volume and power in her voice. There was no tension in her throat as there had been on previous occasions. When she stopped, she was quite flushed and laughed, saying "I have never made a sound like that in my life!" She had tapped into and begun to express the magnitude of her rage. This work was really important for Jackie's journey. When she first came to see me, she had been so fixated on being good, happy and whole, yet her past had been filled with her mother's mental illness and depression which Jackie had spent most of her life trying to deny.

Three sessions later, we were working on a song that Jackie had brought to express an aspect of herself, a subpersonality she called "Kirsty Rage" whom she described as "angry, fiery, vengeful and demonic." The song was "Sister" from the film *The Color Purple.* It was bitter, vengeful and celebratory all at the same time. She started singing in Modal (see page 20), but the effort still seemed to be from the neck up and she was having trouble getting high notes. I did something I learnt from my training which was to increase the physical effort to the extent that the voice and body connection becomes much clearer. I have a trunk in my studio which is filled with blankets. I asked Jackie to push it around the room as she sang. At first, she didn't seem to have much trouble doing this, so making sure she kept her knees bent and her center of gravity low, I piled a few heavy books on top of the trunk, to make her breathe harder.

As Jackie sang and pushed the trunk, her breath became more located in her belly and her voice became louder and louder, her whole body engaged in singing the song. The high notes started to come through a little easier and the lyrics were powerfully sung: "Oh Twister, hope you think that you're something too, 'cos Honey, herself is feeling fine." When she had done this several times and was quite exhausted, I told her to pile lots of cushions against the trunk and lie back into them. This time I asked her to sing it through again, but completely effortlessly, not attempting any techniques whatsoever. She sang, still in Modal but much more quietly; there were traces of Disruption in her voice and she was employing sub-oral Clarinet with mild Free Air. (see page 19) The song was quite transformed. Afterwards, she looked delighted and said, "That felt so easy, it was as if the song sang itself." We worked in the shadow for a further three months and when she came out on the other side, she said that she experienced more depth of feelings in her life and less anxiety.

When we begin to work with the manifestation of the shadow, we come to a major difference between Freud and Jung. Freud's work was based on acoustics; he listened intently to what was actually said. Jung, on the other hand, was much more concerned with pictures, visioning and envisioning. In VMT, when the voice is engaged non-verbally, shadow material takes the easiest route to the light which is through the vocal tube, from the lungs to the mouth and out.

"Jenny"

"Jenny" was fifty years old when she first came to see me. She had taken the decision at forty to "sort herself out." When I first encountered her in a weekend voice workshop I was facilitating, she was overwhelmed by a breathing exercise at the beginning of the day and quickly found herself in tears. After attending an eight-week VMT group of mine, she saw me individually on a weekly basis for nine months. One of her overwhelming concerns for the first half of our work together was her desire to be seen as being "respectable" and "good," yet at the same time she had a sense that inside she was "very bad indeed and not worth loving."

Six months into our work together, Jenny came to see me complaining of having difficulty with a colleague. As she described her adversary and detailed her side of the argument, I became acutely aware of what I felt to be Jenny's extreme disgust and revulsion for this other woman. A dispute had been going on for some time but had escalated into a full-blown argument a few days earlier. Jenny was deeply troubled by this and felt under the other woman's power. I suggested we begin the session with this issue and asked Jenny to enter her Sphere (see page 21), taking on the physical body of the other woman. It was only a short while before her body was contorted and twisted in a way that was unrecognizable as the graceful and "upright" figure I was used to seeing. She hunched over and her arm became useless (the other woman had a withered arm), the rest of her body cowering over it to protect it. Her breathing became irregular and limited to the upper chest, the tension in her shoulders and back culminating in a face so contorted and full of pain that I found it difficult to maintain my gaze. Incidentally, it transpired that Jenny couldn't look this woman in the eye. A high-pitched Flute voice, with maximum Glottal attack (see page 19), and Violin came forth, full of anger and resentment: "Couldn't you have been friendly? You're never friendly." I was suddenly reminded of two of Jenny's shadow subpersonalities that we had worked on the previous month: an all-devouring spider and a deformed girl with spikes in her back.

Afterwards, I disclosed this counter-transference and a look of deep understanding came across her face. I am cautious about disclosing my counter-transferences because of the obvious difficulty in untangling how much of my reaction is my issue and not that of my client, but on this occasion it seemed to have been the right thing to do. After a short break in our work, she came back saying she felt that session had really helped her relationship with this woman; she was more able to accept her revulsion as revulsion not so much at the other person, but at a part of herself that she finds very challenging. The friction between them, as she said now, "Has the energy taken out of it."

The shadow is a very powerful aspect of ourselves and one is never free from its influence. For everything that we aspire to, the opposite is in our shadow "bag." It isn't only negative things which we keep in the "bag," but also positive attributes that have been denied somewhere along the way. "In a family that frowns upon athletic ability, a natural athlete may feel forced to go to law school, thus banishing his giftedness into the shadow."[6] In short, shadow is anything we may recognize in some way but which we don't associate with our self. Since it is a very powerful aspect our psyche, we need to learn how to live with it, or even better, how to utilize the energy it holds. In a lecture in 1998, Paul Newham, the founder of VMT, said of the shadow, "To take the volatility out of the manifestation of the shadow, we need to give it room to express itself."[7]

A final thought: Since moving to California in 2000, I have continued to work with the shadow individually and in groups and am constantly excited by how much relief and growth people find in finally shining a light onto the shadowy parts of themselves. When I use VMT to work with the shadow, the possibilities seem endless and this article only touches the surface. I would, however, like to add a simple group exercise that I have recently incorporated into my work because it has proved really useful for those who find initial engagement with their own shadow confusing.

Start by covering the floor in pictures cut from magazines and invite the group to choose six for which they have the strongest negative feelings. Then invite them to go off on their own and each attach their pictures to a large sheet of paper. When they have done this, I ask them to write down an adjective next to each one. They come together into two groups of four or five (I don't run shadow workshops with groups larger than 10) and show their pictures stating "I am. . . ." This exercise works on the assumption that much of our shadow material can be drawn out by identifying the things we hate most in others. It's uncomfortable and not all of it is going to feel right, so I then invite the participants to engage in a short Voice Movement Journey where they move and vocalize in the safety of their Spherical Space, exploring the noises and movements that might go with these different possible shadow selves. Afterward, we engage with art materials, or journal, and then join together as a larger group and share. Whilst not all the shadow selves they initially chose will ring true, some will be more clearly identified and, in doing so, move forward a little into the light. On the journey of revealing the shadow, a little light goes a long way.

NOTES

1. Connie Zweig and Jeremiah Abrams, eds, *Meeting the Shadow: The Hidden Power of the Dark Side of the Self,* (New York: Ballantine, 1991), xxv.
2. Robert Bly, "The long bag we drag behind us," *Meeting the Shadow: The Hidden Power of the Dark Side of the Self.* Human Nature, eds. Connie Zweig and Jeremiah Abrams (New York: Jeremy P. Tarcher, Putnam Books, 1991), xvii.
3. Eric Fromm, *The Anatomy of Human Destructiveness,* (Leicestershire: Pimlico Publishers Ltd.,1997), p. 83.
4. Charles Darwin, quoted in *Dance Therapy & Depth Psychology,* Joan Chodorow (London: Routledge, 2011), p. 62.
5. Paul Newham, *The Healing Voice,* (London: Element Books, 1999), p.70.
6. Connie Zweig and Steve Wolf, eds, *Romancing the Shadow: Illuminating the Dark Side of the Soul.* (New York, NY: Ballantine Books, 1991.), p. 17.
7. Newham, p. 70.

BIBLIOGRAPHY

Bly, Robert. Meeting the Shadow: *The Hidden Power of the Dark Side of Human Nature,* ed. by Connie Zweig and Jeremiah Abrams, 6-12. New York: Jeremy P. Tarcher, Putnam Book,1991.

Chodorow, Joan. *Dance Therapy & Depth Psychology,* London: Routledge, 1991.

Fromm, Eric. *The Anatomy of Human Destructiveness.* Leicestershire, UK: Pimlico Publishers Ltd.,1997.

Newham, Paul. *The Healing Voice.* London: Element Books, 1999.

Zweig, Connie & Steve Wolf, eds. *Romancing the Shadow: Illuminating the Dark Side of the Soul.* New York: Ballantine, 1991.

THE VOICE IN MOTHERHOOD: HOW I USE VMT TO SUPPORT WOMEN IN THEIR TRANSITIONAL JOURNEY

Anna Grabner

It is through sound that a mother and child first connect with each other. While in the womb, the sounds of a mother's heartbeat, her tummy rumblings, and especially her voice are the baby's first connection to the external world. The maternal voice creates a resonant sound massage for the baby and the vocal vibrations reverberate through the baby's bones from early on. Babies begin to feel these vibrations at around 16 weeks and begin to hear their mother's voice from around 24 weeks. While the baby begins to react to different environmental sounds with movements and changes in heart rate, it is the mother's voice that the fetus responds to profoundly. As the baby grows, it connects to and recognizes its mother's voice above all others. Research shows that singing and speaking to one's baby will deepen the mother-child connection both in utero and post-partum, and will also pave the way for the child's development of language skills.

Similarly, the mother's senses are heightened as she listens intently for her baby's voice in the first seconds after giving birth. The silence that a mother acutely tunes in to as she is waiting for her newborn's first cry is possibly one of the most focused listening experiences that a woman will have in her life. Women often describe a deeply visceral reaction when they hear their newborn's first cry. An instinct that they have never felt before—the need to protect their little one—awakens in them. In the first hours and days, the mother's body responds to the cry of her baby by producing milk. Later, a mother can distinguish her baby's cry from that of other babies and understand what her child needs by different variations of crying, for example: tiredness, hunger and pain. It seems almost obvious, then, that voice could offer a most powerful medium for supporting women in the transition to becoming a mother because voice is naturally such an instinctual part of the process for both adult and child.

Before I became a mother myself, a lullaby was just a lullaby. I didn't fully understand the deep connection a person was capable of creating by singing a simple song to another human being. I would hear mothers share how having children is both the most rewarding and most challenging life experience. I would notice how friends went through hormonal changes which showed in sudden outbursts of irritation and sadness. However, the reality of sleep deprivation, identity crisis, and both overwhelming joy and anxiety only sank in when I became pregnant myself and realized how my training in Voice Movement Therapy could support me on my transitional journey into motherhood. I actively investigated and observed the effects of embodied singing during pregnancy and how the maternal voice and mother-baby communication can be explored and deepened with specific Voice Movement Therapy Techniques. I became fascinated by the possibilities of therapeutic and emotional support for mothers-to-be and saddened and increasingly aware of their lack.

Figure 11. Anna Grabner uses VMT to connect to her unborn child. Costa da Caparica, Portugal – 2019. Photo: Simon Griesser.

Preparing for motherhood can be a beautiful and sensitive journey, and for many, embodied voicework has been hugely beneficial and empowering. Over the years I have guided many first and second-time mothers on their journey, in both individual and group contexts, as well as accompanied couples in birth preparation workshops. I have been moved to see women beautifully support each other during my prenatal singing and birth preparation sessions, have witnessed mothers who felt their first in-depth connection with their babies, and have supported women and families in writing a welcoming song for their child, accompanying couples in really acknowledging their needs as individuals and as parents-to-be.

The techniques of VMT that I have found most helpful in supporting a woman on this transitional journey are embedded in therapeutic, emotional, physical, creative and vocal support techniques. Through these techniques my work aims to create a space for engaging with a changing body, a changing identity, and for healing. Importantly, I create space for a mother-to-be to give voice to her doubts and anxieties; there is a need to give voice to the unspeakable aspects of this journey and to be held in a safe transition from being a woman to becoming a mother.

The 4 Pillars of my VMT work with mothers here are:

1. The Sphere as Conceptualized in VMT (see page 21).
2. Supporting the Identity Shift. The Guided Voice Movement Journey: Embodying the Emotional Journey.
3. The Lullaby: Song: Medicine for Mother and Baby.
4. Embodying the Maternal Voice: Breath, Voice and the Pelvic Floor.

The Sphere: Supporting the Identity Shift

The therapeutic significance of the Sphere in working through the experience of a shifting identity is present in every session from prenatal singing sessions to supporting mothers in need of postnatal care. The role of the mother as the nurturing archetype takes on a new dimension when women are transitioning into becoming mothers themselves. Independent of their connection to the notion of "Mother," when a baby grows inside a woman's body, she becomes both attached and also momentarily detached from the being that she was before. The notion that the energetic sphere around her female body melts with another sphere inside of her pregnant self may feel overwhelming when a mother does not know how to give voice to and embody this process. The natural, and sometimes traumatic, feeling of interconnectedness followed by separation of these two energetic worlds is a journey and transition that VMT practitioners emphasize in therapeutic voicework with mothers.

I introduce the Sphere in prenatal care to help support a woman in the emotional process of her identity shift. One of the mothers-to-be whom I worked with shared that the only thing she really knew how to do was take care of herself. Moreover, she described that the idea of becoming a mother felt as if parts of herself—the woman she knew best—were "going to die." To support her in her transition, I introduced the VMT technique of the Sphere as a valuable practice for her to explore, marrying the worlds of womanhood and motherhood in sound. I invited her to imaginatively paint a colorful world using voice and movement, enabling her to give voice to the body space she was most familiar with.

We left this space untouched for a moment as I invited her consciously to step into a space that felt unknown and to give voice to this Sphere. Out of the palette of imaginary colors she chose various shades of dark blue, giving form to the void that she did not know how to fill with bright colors. Her sound contained a lot of Free Air (breathiness) with, at times a disrupted vocal quality (Disruption: see page 19) She shared that the idea of becoming a mother and tuning in to her changing body was not easy for her. I gave her time to imagine another energetic space in which she could mourn the parts that she felt were dying. As she felt safer, deep sorrowful tones rang through her body into what she named the "grieving space." I encouraged her to give all her mourning and weeping thoughts a voice and to fill the space with melodies of lament, and anger, if need be.

In another session, a nurturing melody emerged as she connected with her "grieving space." I asked if she could bring this sound into the "unknown" motherly space, sensing a possible lullaby that she could also bring in to soothe herself and the baby in her womb. Over the course of the sessions, we took time to honor each of her Spheres: "The Woman I Know," "The Grieving Space," and "The Unknown Mother." She slowly began to weave one energetic world with the other, expressing sounds and movement that enabled her to accept all as part of her journey. In the final session, she gave sound to these three Sphere worlds as one, wrapping her grief into arms of compassion, sending sounds of lament towards the earth, then moving into a cradling dance and sounding softly, as if embracing the idea of her Woman Self becoming a Mother. She did this by leaning into the back of her Sphere and strengthening her voice in a concave position before she opened her arms and sounded in alternating free-flowing and long sustained, more joyful tones, moving in convex into the unknown space at the front of her Sphere. She described later that it felt as if she was imagining communicating from the new place of motherhood into the world. There was a tangible shift in the moment, noticed by both of us, as she was reclaiming her womanhood and integrating it into the knowledge that she felt ready to embrace equally the new journey of motherhood.

Voicing this transitional journey in a group postnatal session is similarly vital and very moving. As we address the sense of lost identity, we help mothers to integrate rather than separate "mother" and "woman," while still honoring the change. At the beginning of every session, I create a safe place of confidentiality and ensure that every woman understands how being held and witnessed in the vulnerable sharing process encourages others to share their journey, too. This helps mothers feel that they are not alone and that, in fact, many women have similar doubts and anxieties

To arrive in the present moment, I then guide them through a breath meditation to help quiet the mind and deepen their connection to the body. I gently invite them to create a safe space by breathing and sounding into their energetic Sphere. The mothers are encouraged to give voice and compassion to the memory of a time when they were taking care only of their own needs as a woman. As they connect with vocal improvisation, intuitively moving and sounding their process, they may express pain and grief to help the body-mind acknowledge the transition that has happened. Finally, we name the emotional shifts along this process together and I invite the mothers consciously to step into their newly found role in the world. This is an essential part of the therapeutic journey.

The Guided Voice Movement Journey: Embodying the Emotional Process

In individual as well as group sessions, a mother may be invited consciously to embody the whole journey from pregnancy into the present moment, connecting with herself through the VMT technique, adapted from Jung's practice of Active Imagination, of a Guided Voice Movement Journey. For this journey, I often introduce the ocean drum to create a calming drone over which the mothers can freely improvise. Often mothers feel safer to explore this practice together with other women, tuning into the mesmerizing sound of the sea and imagining "the beginning" when their babies were being held safely in the amniotic fluid. The flow of water helps the mothers to travel, emotionally and vocally, from pregnancy through birth to the first moment when they held their babies. I invite them to intuitively voice and sing through a Voice Movement Journey, alternating between quiet and loud tones of voice, while they express the different dynamics of significant moments in the journey. In this healing space, they are invited to express the full spectrum of joy and anxiety that accompanies the transition from being a woman to becoming a woman with a baby: a mother. Being held and seen by other mothers helps them to give voice to their own journey, each in her own rhythm.

For every woman the journey into motherhood is different. It can be beautiful and empowering as well as challenging and overwhelming. Some mothers feel an intuitive sense of connectedness with their baby. For others, this instinct may not be so vivid, the bonding may not come as naturally, and they may need postnatal support to help in connecting with their newborn. The sleepless nights and overwhelming responsibility to suddenly fulfill the needs of a little being, with the constant fear of doing something wrong, can take a toll on a mother's body and psyche. Mothers often experience a lack of emotional support which may mount into moments where they cannot find the strength to get out of bed. They feel deeply that they are not good enough and sometimes regret having become a mother at all. As awful as these thoughts appear to be, they are very real to most mothers, as the lack of sleep shakes their fragile stability.

Women doubting themselves to their core, feeling guilty for having such unspeakable thoughts, need to be held in a safe space. Allowing women to give voice to these dark aspects of motherhood is therefore an important element in this work with mothers. Both individual and group sessions provide a safe container for healing, thus helping mothers who are wandering these shadowlands to find a moment of rest. In the safe space of a session, a mother may experience her doubts as being part of the "normal" continuum of emotional expression. The reality is that society conditions women to think that pregnancy, birth and motherhood must be "magical." New mothers feel ashamed to speak of the lack of such "magical" hormones and the lack of connection to their baby. As the mother begins to feel safe enough to voice her overwhelming concerns, she can feel supported and find a moment to recharge her energy. Using voice, movement and song to express her personal story, she can feel seen and heard in her journey into motherhood.

The Lullaby: Medicine for Mother and Baby

One of my intentions in accompanying women through pregnancy is to encourage them to listen closely to their body and voice and thereby begin to create a deep musical connection with their baby before birth. One of the benefits of doing this is that it provides the mum and baby with a transitional focus that feels comforting, familiar, and tangible enough to help them through the transition. Songwriting is an important part of VMT and practitioners work with lullabies across the client spectrum. A lullaby, as a distinct song, holds a very specific medicine, the potency of which seems further amplified when working with mothers and babies. I have found that facilitating the creation of a personalized lullaby is a particularly powerful way to support and accompany a woman on her journey into motherhood. Giving space to the creating, singing and revisiting of personal lullabies, and "practicing purposeful singing" to the baby, helps to deepen the mother-child connection and can provide great comfort for both mother and baby in moments of distress. Purposeful singing is a form of improvised singing that evolves in the moment between mother and baby.[1] It has a similar quality to the lullaby. A mother responds to her baby's cooing sounds, by imitating and reflecting back what she hears in the baby's "melody." Often this purposeful singing involves vowel sounds such as "uuh," "ooh" and "aah" and sometimes can involve words invented in the moment. It is very much a musical conversation between mother and baby, created in the present moment in response to different situations and feelings. A second-time mother shared the following:

> My second pregnancy passed by so quickly. I was working full time and didn't really feel connected to the baby like I felt the first time when I was

> pregnant. So at the very end of that second pregnancy, I decided to join the pregnancy group with Anna, hoping to be able to take a moment just for me and my son. And it was the most wonderful experience! Listening to Anna's voice and singing myself, moving and being in a group of women on a similar journey helped me to relax, open up and feel true happiness. Even today, when I sing a lullaby to my son that I learned with Anna, he calms down immediately. I guess there was a true connection between us that first day in the pregnancy group and we still profit from that prenatal bond.

Lullabies are one of the most naturally powerful song types because of their simplicity and repetitive nature. Carvalho et al. have investigated the positive neurological effects of repetition in singing lullabies.[2] These benefits extend into the postnatal context, too, as the lullaby provides a safe framework for transitioning from pregnancy into motherhood, allowing the mother to continue to deepen this new bond by singing her special song to her newborn. When asked to create a song, a mother will often first say she cannot because she feels she can't sing. However, mothers spontaneously create lullabies for their babies on the spot when they forget about the need to impress. Baker and MacKinlay have found that it is a mother's instinct to create nurturing melodies in the moment so as to communicate with her baby.[3] Often as the baby grows, he or she begins to be able to sing their lullaby, too, both with the mother and on their own. This is a real gift to the child who can use the song as a positive coping strategy when they need to soothe themselves, for example, when their mother is not around.

During both of my pregnancies, I created a welcoming song for my baby. I tuned in to the melody and words of the first lullaby, "Two Hearts," as I was walking in the mountains, feeling my heartbeat and realizing that there were now two hearts beating inside my body. The journey of this song is beautiful, from pregnancy through birth. I sang it to her a few minutes after she was born to watching her grow with this song at her side. I can distinctly remember the moment that she began to sing her own song back to me, and it is so rewarding to sing it together with her now all these years later. For the lullaby of my younger one, I asked my older daughter to tune in to a song together with me and it was a beautiful collaborative song creation process. She now sings her little sister's lullaby to comfort her, sometimes together with me and often alone.

When accompanying a mother and family in the songwriting process, it often helps to begin with an existing melody that they like and to create words that are specifically tailored to what they envision their child may be like. Or if the family wishes to create an original lullaby, I may play the piano or guitar to help give ideas for a melody that they can improvise over. Moreover, since lullabies are nourishing and repetitive in nature, it helps to connect with its rocking rhythm in the body to find the tune that will become the gentle current of the personal lullaby. Suggesting simple body percussion exercises helps the parents-to-be to bond with the idea of an original melody that is born through them. I guide them through various creative practices and encourage them to continue this song creation in their own time and to bring a song script to the following session.

All the couples I have worked with highlighted the significance of the creation of their personal welcoming song for their baby. I remember one couple in particular that had tuned into the name for their child through improvising in a couple's birth preparation session. I had encouraged them to improvise together, nudging them to look into each other's eyes while feeling into a rocking rhythm for their song, and in this moment the name of their baby was born.

Every moment that embraces a healthy transition into motherhood is sacred. I have witnessed many women purposefully communicating with their babies in the womb, deepening the bond through the presence of their voice and through the song they specifically created to sing at that moment in time.

I had one client who was very anxious about becoming a mother. In our private sessions, she shared, "I do not know how to take care of myself, so how can I take care of a little being? How will I be able to give birth, if I am afraid of becoming a mother?" Her anxiety showed; she was very disconnected, unable to be present or to communicate with the baby in her womb.

The act of breathing together with her baby was the first step. It began with understanding how she could breathe in a healthy way for herself first by connecting with her abdominal, thoracic and clavicular breathing areas in full breaths. A second step was to invite her to add humming sounds on her outbreath to consciously send a nurturing vibration into both her own body and that of her baby. I then encouraged her to envision her fetus being cradled in her womb, as she moved from intentional humming towards long sustained sounds and eventually into "sending a loving melody into her womb."

When she was ready to create a lullaby for her son, the creation process came quite naturally to her. I encouraged her to sing it many times throughout the day, especially to comfort herself when feelings of doubt arose, and to communicate and deepen her bond with her baby. As she was transitioning into motherhood, I noticed a shift in her from overwhelming anxiety to feeling more confident and joyful with the prospect of becoming a mother. After her son was born she shared with me: "When I sing his lullaby he instantly calms down. It is as if he recognizes his song and then his little body relaxes, and he drinks more easily and I can finally relax, too."

Embodying the Maternal Voice: Breath and the Pelvic Floor

Embodiment practices, such as breathing, toning, sounding and pelvic core exercises support women during their journey and highlight the importance of body awareness for labor and postpartum recovery. Developing a deeper sensitivity to their voice, body, sound, and expression and assisting mothers-to-be in dropping down from their headspace into their body are two of my main aims in VMT-focused birth preparation sessions. In these sessions women are guided to tap more easily into their instinctual voice, enabling them to draw from a primal power that will help them give birth naturally. Another mother recalls:

> I was afraid of giving birth again. As a second-time mother I knew of the pain and I did not know how to express my fears. The VMT sessions gave me a safe way to connect within. I could connect with my body, voice and emotions in a way that was so direct and safe. I felt alive in my body in a way I had never felt before.

When I began working with this mother, I felt her body as a soft timid space that wrapped around her so snugly that she did not know how to unwrap her voice. She had been tucking her self-expression away safely for such a long time and needed a slow process to carefully open herself to the voice she had dismissed. She had been meaning to work with me for a long time, feeling the need to give voice in a more open and relaxed way. She felt that her second pregnancy was the right time to reconnect with her voice and to empower herself; she anticipated that this transition was going to be an "emotional rollercoaster."

In the first sessions, we took time for her to really embody the notion of giving herself permission to open up through sound and to allow her emotions a resonant space. I guided her in sounding into and from her vocal skull, her throat, her chest, her thoracic and diaphragm areas, her womb, and her pelvic floor. Using the bones and open spaces of the face and sinus areas (her "vocal skull") as resonating chambers in order to amplify the sound and the feeling of and connection with vocal vibration helps to open up other body spaces, as well.[3] I further invited her to strengthen her sense of grounding and of "having her own back" by sounding while lying on her back, comfortably supported by cushions. We gradually moved our focus to preparing for her ideal natural birth scenario in which she wished to be able to "naturally open up with the help of loud, relaxed, primal sounds." I guided her through exploring the contraction and release of her pelvic floor muscles with the help of both staccato and sustained sounds. This felt unnatural to her at first; she felt disconnected from her pelvic floor and resistant.

Over time, she gradually felt more connected to her pelvis through the work we did. She found guided embodiment as well as free voicing and tuning into the Vocal Components of Pitch (in low range) and Loudness (in high volume) most valuable. Her posture changed, her voice sounded more free, and there was more vocal variety. The timid body that I encountered in the first session seemed to awaken into a grounded, calm and connected body-voice. I so distinctly remember when she was close to her due date and she joyfully shared that she was looking forward to connecting with all the techniques that we had embodied in the sessions.

Most women know of the importance of the pelvic floor as part of building core strength. In my experience, it is most valuable to ensure that the mother fully understands the physicality and the use of the pelvic floor-voice connection. Via the vagus nerve, there is a physiological and emotional connection between the pelvic floor and the vocal folds. In the work of VMT, we often observe that tension in the pelvis is accompanied by vocal tension and that this disconnection with the pelvic floor limits breath support and vocal production. Therefore, practicing specific exercises such as short repetitive movements of contracting and releasing pelvic floor muscles along with singing staccato sounds and then the more contrasting long sustained notes to open up wide are vocal self-care practices that have proven to be valuable tools that VMT can offer both during labor and postpartum. Such an embodied understanding of contraction and expansion is beneficial for the postpartum recovery process and for regaining muscle tone.

Working with the imagery and metaphor of the Vocal Tube and especially understanding the shape and resonant quality of the Saxophone timbre—a fully lengthened and dilated tract—can prove to be most valuable in being able to drop into the body for labor. Using these techniques whereby the client integrates movement and voice during guided imagery to connect with the womb, as well as embracing the relationship between the vocal folds and the pelvic floor, helps in understanding and gives meaning to the physical process of contraction, expansion, and relaxation. In addition, learning to visualize and connect with the cervix through sound vibration facilitates the opening process during labor.

In VMT there are no wrong sounds and every sound is welcome. This is a very important message for expectant mothers as it allows them to fully embrace their empowering and expressive voice. Practicing diverse vocal expressions in the prenatal and birth preparation sessions through techniques such as call and response, and embodying a healthy production of disruptive sounds, helps the mother to explore and understand the quality and use of these sounds. Mothers are also guided to experience other VMT techniques aimed at developing healthy breathing practices, enabling them to envision helping the baby move more easily through the birth canal.

Many midwives hold that the ease of birthing is related to the extent to which a woman is willing to open herself up. This is a theme that is given voice to in our individual sessions. Besides discovering and opening up into the wide dilated configuration of Saxophone, the component of Loudness provides us with another opportunity to explore and experience expanding and opening up. As one mother expressed it:

> The seemingly dynamical dialogue throughout my labor process—between stillness and silence, patiently listening to my body and breath and trusting in the capacity of being loud when the moment felt right—was powerful. I have never heard myself make such deep primal sounds.

As the mother becomes more comfortable with the diversity of sounds available to her, her body relaxes and opens up. As she is able to move through and express her fears and anxieties, there is less holding in her body, more flow in her movement, and her breathing expands and relaxes. There is a deeper connection between voice, body and mind. This alignment provides the mother-to-be with a sense of grounding, vital energy and empowerment. The increased confidence in her own body is tangible to her and clearly evident to me.

The more active the expectant mother is allowed to be during birth, the greater the probability of her having a positive experience all around. Singing and moving facilitate the preparation for birth and the labor process itself. Couple preparation sessions are important so that the partner can embody all these practices, too, and in doing so fully support the mother-to-be in opening up for birth. Moreover, applying massage which is integrated with specific sounding techniques is explored to help the mother release intense feelings and pain during labor.

As I am also a qualified Thai Yoga Massage therapist, with the client's permission I often create moments for the mother to feel more at ease through touch. In these sessions, I invite the mother to find a comfortable position and then provide supportive touch to enhance her notion of her breath capacity. I find that mothers particularly enjoy and are comforted when I create the gentle sensations of rocking and cradling her body, a practice also used in VMT work. I then invite the mother to connect with open vowel sounds on the outbreath. Sometimes a melody emerges from the body in these moments which may even evolve into a unique song. These are wonderful times to witness, for both the mother and for me as a facilitator.

In postnatal sessions, I guide women to connect consciously with their womb and to acknowledge the physical journey it has taken to bring their child into the world. I invite the mothers to breathe into and visualize the connection of the earth's womb and their own womb in order to release any tensions connected to their womb's journey. Through toning into their womb space they bring a sense of belonging and compassion back into their bodies. As I accompany them in a process of free sounding, I encourage creating a song for their womb, honoring the individual journey of motherhood that is intertwined with the story of their womb. Sometimes I may work with mothers who gave birth decades ago, as they, too, feel the need to reflect on and nourish their physical, energetic and emotional womb space. It is such an honor to witness mothers of all ages giving voice to their womb journey in song.

Conclusion

A singing mother is doing something healthy for both herself and her baby. When in the womb, the baby and mother benefit from the increased flow of oxygen that singing induces. Singing also stimulates the hormone oxytocin, which deepens the sense of belonging and creates a feeling of love and compassion (Keeler et al.).[4] Especially in times of sleep deprivation and overwhelm, singing can energize the mother and help awaken a sense of joy that may otherwise be lacking. Moreover, such intentional singing invites calm, helping the mother to ground and nourish herself and the baby to feel soothed.

As we guide mothers-to-be to tune into their body wisdom, we intrinsically support their experience of pregnancy and labor emotionally and mentally as well as physically. As we provide them with empowering practices, they may awaken an inner sense of knowing that they have deepened their capacity to transition into motherhood. The essence of supporting a mother in embodying her Maternal Voice as she transitions into motherhood is wrapped up in this mother's sharing after birth:

"Feeling her on my tummy after the strenuous work of labor, feeling her breathe while singing to her, is a moment I will never forget. It's been such a long journey and I am ready now. I am her mother."

Remarks:

As I write "woman/she/her" I do this to facilitate the reader's flow. I acknowledge everyone experiencing themselves as women on this journey.

The mothers I work with choose births in hospitals, natural and caesarean, as well as home births. In this insight into my work I focused on the process of natural birth preparation.

Postnatal Depression is serious, though very sadly often overlooked or misunderstood. Every woman I work with in need of special care receives my guidance as well as support from other help systems that I recommend.

NOTES

1. Felicity Baker and Elizabeth MacKinlay,"Sing, Soothe and Sleep: A Lullaby Education Programme for First-time Mothers," *British Journal of Music Education 23*, (2006), p. 14.
2. Maria E Carvalho, et al. "The Impact of the Maternal Voice on the Fetus: A Systematic Review," *Current Women's Health Reviews 15*, 3 (October 2018): pp. 196-206.

BIBLIOGRAPHY

Baker, Felicity and Elizabeth Mackinlay. "Sing, Soothe and Sleep: A Lullaby Education Programme for First-time Mothers." *British Journal of Music Education 23*, (2006):147-160.

Carvalho, Maria E, et al. "The Impact of Maternal Voice on the Fetus: A Systematic Review" *Current Women's Health Reviews 15*, 3 (October 2018): 196-206.

Keeler, J. R., et al. "The Neurochemistry and Social Flow of Singing: Bonding and Oxytocin." *Frontiers in Human Neuroscience 9* (23 September 2015): 518.

SOUL SONG DEEP FROM THE BONE: THE POWER OF STORY IN VMT

Veronica Phillips

Listening to or reading a story can bring a frisson of excitement, anticipation and the possibility of a deep connection. In my experience, embodied involvement with the depth of a story through the creative possibilities of the other three healing salves of shamanic practice—singing, dancing and silence—offers a full and expansive experience. Shamanic societies believe that when we stop singing, dancing, and are no longer enchanted by stories, we experience a loss of soul. Voice Movement Therapy embraces all four healing salves and offers a way of maintaining and retrieving them that can restore and expand our soul's capacity.

I. THE ALCHEMY OF STORY

For an individual, exploring a personal issue through story can ease the unnerving discomfort that may accompany direct self-focus. A less direct approach can warm the healing process; it can help a person to reverse or even find gratitude for protective trauma symptoms, engendering a grateful space and compassion for even one's most troublesome subpersonalities.

Through engaging with a story and often turning it into a song, the focus can be on the imaginative, metaphorical aspects of that story, rather than the actual historical events of a life. Characters, landscapes, and symbols bring their own depth and intriguing compass, and VMT principles offer a clear, felt acoustic connection with such elements. An acoustic connection with one's active, embodied voice within the containing structure of song offers a measure of safety of expression for the traumatized, exiled, ignored parts of one's being, as well as for gloriously enhanced expression and communication for the marvelous magnificence of those parts that are ready to soar.

In my VMT work with story and song, I focus on the life-force energy and the relationship with Self and Soul that is embodied in an individual in all their aspects. In addition, through experiencing the veracity of imaginal landscapes, characters, and narratives, we can bring forward our interdependence with all that is.

I incorporate different types of stories in my one-to-one and group work. Particularly potent, ageless, and coming from who knows exactly where or when are Myths. "One thing that comes out in myths is that at the bottom of the abyss comes the voice of salvation...at the darkest moment comes the light."[1] Myths show us how to live and guide travelers through tough times. Myths hint at the vastness that lies beyond our understanding. A myth is always imbued with clear, powerful archetypal energy, whereas fairy tales offer access to subpersonalities through earth-bound and magical characters who inhabit the world on which we stand but are often not completely of it. The third kind of story emerges from within: an individual's story which evolves and develops during one-to-one sessions and finds form through personification, metaphor, and relationship in the practicing of Voice Movement Therapy core principles.

Just about any story from any time or place carries with it layers of alchemy not far from the surface. Stories as metaphor for the human struggle often take the protagonist on a journey, skirting or entering physical or psychic death and emerging to renew and transform. Such universal plots always lead to the heart of what stories are and why they exist: to open paths to show us who we really are, individually and collectively. In tandem with Voice Movement Therapy, this can lead to the embodied heart of each of us, offering a deep, moving, resonant vocal connection with any story: a portal to our inner world, the world outside, and the world beyond our immediate reality.

Experiencing Story through the Salves of Singing, Dancing and Silence

Singing and voicing, particularly as explored within the extended parameters and depth of VMT, draw from the body and its felt sense rather than from cognition, thus offering a rich palate that surprises and excites in the expression of the many different elements of a story. Vocal resonance comes to be felt, affecting, and connecting with both the physical and subtle body, thereby enhancing vitality. The energy of vocal sound and song sheds light onto inner shadows through the resonating instrument of the body, inviting extension beyond and below the personal Sphere (see page 21).

Dance and movement bring connection with and embodiment of characters and elements of the story; internally felt, externally visible, and defined in space, expressive movement stirs the unknown. The elements of body shape, effort, contraction and expansion are visceral and often unexpected. In explorations, movement can flow from vocal sound, though somehow, more frequently with story, movement comes first. Perhaps movement feels safer, although it often gives rise to wilder, freer, hitherto suppressed vocalizing and communicating.

The healing salve of Silence offers opportunity for mindful reflection, distillation, and deep inner sensing after activity. From silence, one's felt sense, intuition, imagery, self-witnessing, and transpersonal connections can emerge along with a heightened sense of palpable resonance with others.

My Singing Soul Emerged from Deep Within My Bones

This piece is entitled "Soul Song Deep from the Bone." I find the juxtaposition of "Song" and "Bone" intriguing. For me, it highlights the containing frame that bone provides in contrast to the intangible fluidity of sound and song. I hear the echo and resonance of sound within a cathedral or cave, in the call from a hollow ram's horn or the sound from a bone-carved flute. Adding and nurturing an ever-deepening vocal resonance reproduces a vibration that one can feel in one's bones. In sound drawn from bone there is something that intimates profound interconnectedness between matter and spirit, calling us to foster a remembering deep within our souls. We can begin to hear and unearth a greater conscious truth of ourselves when we sing our song from our bones. Both tangible and metaphorical, they encompass the stories of our lives, offering amplification, exploration and hope for both our personal and our ancestral selves, and global stories.

Oriental medicine considers the energy contained within the bones as the most powerful energy of all. As the most fundamental element of the physical body, they give a basic structure and support, offering an enduring relationship with earth and gravity. Thus, bones offer a balance between tension and relaxation which can maximize body spaciousness both physically and psychically. Metaphorically, bones represent indestructibility and tenacity and suggest the kind of durability of psyche and soul that can lead us to a transformation of being.

There is a story that tells of this creative transformational interdependence. Clarissa Pinkola Estes tells the story of La Loba in her book, *Women Who Run with the Wolves,* and offers us great encouragement to bring our own stories to life.[2] She tells of a fat, animalistic older woman: a Crone, La Loba, the Wolf Woman who crawls around in desert or forest grunting, cackling, snorting, and collecting bones, principally wolf bones. Wolves sing to the moon, queen of the feminine, and are intuitive pathfinders who guide and lead, especially, those who are lost. Having gathered sufficient bones, La Loba shapes them into a coherent form. Then she begins to sing the life back into the skeletal remains, often with beautiful tone and melody. When fully re-birthed and with soul re-embodied, the creatures rise up and dance away with re-born vivacity and joy.

My immediate response on reading this story was to feel La Loba's sound echoing way down in my physical being. Secondly, I had a joyous, hopeful sense that, with compassion and time, my regrets and past "mistakes" might be understood and transformed, including my ancestral legacy and, in some way, my ancestral suffering. Stories of many kinds offer a dynamic and profound link from past through to future. They open wide a doorway to the playfulness and profundity of Active Imagination, imaginal discovery and creative connection from the realms of the unconscious. Active imagination is a concept and practice introduced by Jung. It invites one to enter a state of conscious fantasy; to enhance and encourage the unfolding of internal, imaginal elements that are out of focus or hidden. Associating with and exploring the arising imaginal world with consciousness is intended to lead one to expanded meaning, understanding, felt sense and attitude. This is a very rich and creative transformational practice to which VMT practitioners add a more conscious use of the voice.

As I delved into becoming La Loba, I let my body become immersed in her image, sinking to the floor, moving through the fluidity and gravitational pull downwards. VMT offers a fluid cycle of animalistic embodiment through the Animal Postural Cycle (see page 22) which is intended to offer an experience of malleable, embodied movement starting from human upright standing, to animalistic primate, and down to earth to connect with a cat- or wolf-like being. Body malleability allows the voice to open out and encourages a multiplicity of sounds emotively, archetypally, imaginally and shamanically. Simultaneously, this evolutionary cycle offers an experience of individual human development, baby to adult, as well as the wider compass of evolution.

Engaging with this cycle carried me toward what felt like the essential kernel of life and psyche which found expression in expansive non-verbal sound. It was so good to feel Earth's strong, warm support. Becoming La

Loba eased the egocentric, repressed focus on myself. Clearly, diving into stories, living the stories, embodying the beings and elements therein, offered me the opportunity for a deep letting go, taking me away from inhibition and introspection, calling forth and releasing hidden and blocked aspects of my own being. Layered on my low belly breath, I felt and heard my voice resonate with deep-toned growls, groans, moans, and screeches, exhilarating, satisfying sounds disallowed in the "civilized" world, that had been waiting to emerge. This fuller embodied aspect of myself came through, allowing my Vocal Tube to lengthen and expand and freeing up various vocal qualities just right for La Loba and her ancient, heavy Croneness. Travelling inward with my mind's eye, I experienced a tangible connection with the strength and vibrancy of my physical skeletal structure. I worked with muscle and bodily organs to sound the subterranean vital Saxophone tones loved by this La Loba (see page 20). As I mingled with vocal sound and movement, active imagination took me further into the being and terrain of La Loba. She gave me great strength so that I was able to revive the metaphorical bones of my life in an extremely profound personal revelation.

La Loba inspired me to embark on a series of Voice Movement Journeys that brought forth a transformational compassionate recognition of the many years of pain endured by my forebears and through my own trauma legacy. This alchemy at last pushed open the flow of love for my antecedents, both near and far, initiating conscious, tangible healing of unaddressed trauma in the family, which still unfolds.

Truth surfaces. Each of these Voice Movement Journeys inspired me to make a drawing These speak of an intense longing for communion and transformation in my family lineage and have a profound and sacred purpose for me. Through my vocal embodiment of La Loba, I recognized expansive human elements and rich threads of archetypal energy. She encompasses all stages of my human development, including my becoming an ancestor myself, bringing forth a clear connection with the Triple Goddess, the Maiden, Mother and Crone who is such a pivotal character in most mythologies. As I grow nearer in age to my Crone self, I feel increasingly suffused with the keen, perceptive, strong and freeing energy of La Loba. I love her as the earthbound archetype who lives in the canyons of primitive being and draws out the deepest wisdom embracing past, present, and future.

Emerging from my gorgeous, freeing sound and movement improvisation came songs inspired from the depths of my soul, echoing through the hollow bones of my life and lineage. These songs have allowed me to sing out the strength of hidden vulnerability, the repressed vitality of my child-soul and creative core, re-membered in the adult through the alchemy offered by La Loba. Each song tends toward a particular VMT core vocal quality, interweaving with others, but mostly Modal: Flute with Free Air; Saxophone with deep Pitch and Free Air; and Clarinet with Vocal Fry (see page 20). These core principles have given me confidence to love and expand my voice as a non-trained singer. They have offered a rich palette for improvisation, from which these songs have emerged and guided me to find the timbres and colors to enhance the spirit of each song:

> Give me a bone and I will sing a diamond,
> Show me the bones and I will sing their light,
> Hand me the bones, I'll give voice to their spirit,
> Believe in the bones and trust them to me now.

This is the chorus of my La Loba song. I sing it with a deep Modal belly resonance which can be loud and sonorous, or with some Disruption that stirs urgency and motivation, or I sing it with the same whole vocal tube expansion plus a softer Free Air quality to offer a more gentle encouragement of hope for change. Moving through a rising arpeggio, the pitch and musical shape anticipate a stepping up to discovery and renewal. The words and music of the verses tend toward a quieter dynamic with a somewhat less expanded vocal tube. Phrases such as "valleys of despair," and "grief held deep in the ocean" evoke compassion and a sense of resonance with the difficulties and suffering of people. This song enables me to enter fully into the imaginal landscape of La Loba in a contained, clearly accessible way. I make use of it for myself and in working with others. It has been a gift for opening workshops that explore the depth and strength that La Loba has to offer. The story of La Loba is, likewise, a gift to Voice Movement Therapy, as many elements experienced in this practice fit so well with the story: the sensing of physicality and the safety that is offered to the self in Sphere work; the flexible evolutionary movements experienced in the Animal Cycle of postures; the malleability available when working with the metaphorical Vocal Tube, and the Timbres and the amazing range of vocal qualities that is encouraged.

II. SINGING THE BONES ALIVE WITH OTHERS IN WORKSHOPS

I have offered several workshops to different groups, mostly attracting, as one might expect, women both young and older. Whatever our chronological age, the three different aspects of our selves (Maiden, Mother, and Crone) dance together waiting, whispering or taking the floor. This story's great attraction is the opportunity for vocal sounding that is free, wild and un-judged. It allows one to dive deeply into the body and bones of the psyche, allowing self-unfolding, witnessing, and validation that is spaciously and freely expressed. The planned progressive structure of my workshops with La Loba is intended to bring participants, layer by layer, to the deepest experience of liberation and creativity in the shadowlands of their psyches. The flow of a workshop depends, of course, on the emotional strength and needs of the group and on participants' experience of VMT. There is always flexibility for embellishment or a change of plan.

One group, previously unknown to me and unfamiliar with Voice Movement Therapy, manifested a powerful shared experience of loss around a particular, very real and immediate life issue. This deep need gathered impetus and found enough safety from the connection with La Loba energy, the formation and containment of both the individual and the group Sphere, the felt sense of the Vocal Tube, and freeing the voice with movement. The shamanic energy of La Loba nurtured and nourished courage, impelling an urge to journey together with and through the sharing of pain and grief. Groans, moans, screeches and sobs intermingled with and were fostered by the vocal components: particularly Saxophone, Clarinet, Free Air, Disruption, Glottal Onset and Pitch Fluctuation.

Together we planned a ritual. Gathering together in the medicine Sphere, a bowl of water was carefully placed at the center with reflective vocal toning. Water was the element chosen to absorb, receive, and cleanse. Short word phrases invoking healing were sung freely, followed by a reflective space and time for non-verbal release of painful feelings, once again directed to the sacred water. Then came a time of quiet and gentle toning as we carried the water to a chosen place in nature, returning it to the earth, to the natural domain of La Loba. Thus, some shared inner flow was restored which opened space for cleansing, nurturing strength, and for the next step to be firmly taken.

An Alchemical Encounter With La Loba

Another workshop illustrates the healing power of working with the La Loba story. This workshop was with a group who were well versed in Voice Movement Therapy. It began by everyone gathering into a medicine Sphere smoothly and reflectively. The boundary of the Sphere immediately became a sacred threshold to step into the alchemical encounter with La Loba. She was called into being through the song, "Give me a bone," first heard and then absorbed through a deepening breath and awareness of the felt sense in heart and belly, and then through an invitation to join in the sounding and the song.

Figure 12. Veronica Philips (UK) and Petra Rudolf (AT) singing together at the 2019 IAVMT Conference. Port Elizabeth, Eastern Cape, South Africa–2019. Photo: Rian Trosee.

The song itself, within and between phrases, gave room for a wide variety of non-verbal improvisation. This offered a warm, generous anticipation to listen to the story of La Loba, to visualize and sense a meeting in the half-light of evening. I led the group:

> You see a form . . . or do you hear something before you see?. . . A figure moving slowly, humpily, lumpily . . . a grunting, cackling, bursts of beautiful melody. . .. As your eyes get better used to the gloom you see and hear each "trophy" as she fills the basket she drags. . ..

Encountering the La Loba of the story as part of the internal psyche, I offered an invitation to "Let her strength and courage be yours." To enhance the potency of energy stirred and bring it even more fully into the present, we attended to the current moon phase, waxing at the first quarter which highlights nurturing self-love, self-focus and renewal. Particularly as a Wolf Woman, La Loba is archetypally connected to the Moon. Moon energy affects our psychic state and female biology as well as bringing connection with the Triple Goddess. We drew down cosmic energy with words offered by the group: "fullness," "inspire," "heal," singing gently or freely sounding vowels.

Moving nearer to the heart of this workshop, we took time for reflection: to consider a need, desire or intention, whether clear or unclear, for which to ask for clarity. Some chose to write or draw, some to rest in not knowing.

Thus, we came to the nub of the workshop: the Voice Movement Journey. A brief grounding of one's body on earth brought a mind's eye awareness of bone gravity, the space within for breath, and the Vocal Tube (see page 18). I prompted:

> She lives here within you, she spreads her energy through you; allow it to resonate within your being, deep in the wild spaces. Let La Loba touch the shadows with sound, leading you towards healing.

Thus into the Voice Movement Journey: an imaginal interweaving of breath, body, voice, and psyche unfolding spontaneously from the depths of inner vitality, kindling new awarenesses, stirring hopes and new possibilities. Being experienced in VMT, this group wove all the VMT components together seamlessly, delving deep with strength and courage, giving full voice to inner longings, regrets, sadness, memories and hope, journeying through dark places with all the extremes and beauty of expressive sound.

Coming to quietness and stillness, the women took time to write, draw, rest, reflect, and emerge, becoming more aware of glimmers of change. Then came an intense and beautiful ritual, almost a rite of passage for some. As the group toned gently and with great compassion, each woman, taking her time, moved to the center of the medicine Sphere, speaking or singing words of truth that La Loba had tilled and toned in her. This compassionate communion of sound and silence brought gentle tending and shared nourishment.

Every group that has experienced the story and embodiment of La Loba within the context of Voice Movement Therapy has spoken of finding a deepening sense of self, emerging strength and determination, and not infrequently of a clear next step towards internal and/or external change. Some, new to experiencing their expressive voice, have found delight and beauty exploring VMT in the company of La Loba. Others, more accustomed to full expressive voicing, dive into the depths of the story without hesitation. Always the embodied voice, nourished by this story, has illuminated individual inner life and purpose, often looking to past generations and future global life. Participants have shared:

"You couldn't go much deeper than that."

"La Loba's wisdom helped me step onto my path more boldly."

People were hungry to drop into the bones of their ancestors and see what needed to be sung; the skeletons started to rattle in each of us and what poured forth, individually and collectively, was akin to Ezekiel's sacred message: "The spirit breathed into the valley of dry bones and the bones took shape and started to dance and sing."

I am full of inspiration and ideas, with a sense of acceptance and joy in my own voice and being:

> In the pit of the earth's core
> In the hollows of your bones
> Where no one sees
> My song echoes.
> Seek me out and
> I will call you
> We will travel through the darkness
> Then sing and fly towards the light
>
> The dark night is rose colored,
> Cradling truth and joy.
>
> Hold fast,
> Delve down.
>
> You are the diamond
> With many mirrors
> Trust yourself–sound with your whole voice–unearth your richest Self.

Conclusion

Stories, an integral part of human activity, invite universal, perhaps eternal connection with humanity and an unfolding consciousness. We are taken to a space between the worlds; we swim into the waters of inter-being both within our own psyche and towards that which we deem outside of ourselves. Stories bring together personal and collective life journeys and cultural ways of being and seeing. They nourish us by drawing us in, enlivening and inspiring our active imagination, sharpening insight, sparking "aha" moments and synchronicities. As Susan Perrow writes, stories are "important to our soul-life as water is to our being."[3] They can excite a profound inner shimmering of soul. Voice Movement Therapy offers a very rich, expansive and deep aliveness, both inner and outer, through the embodiment and envoicement of story.

In this piece I have shared my work with one particular story and how I have used it personally and within the group context. No less valuable are other stories, including those written by clients and working though story with an individual client in one-to-one sessions no less potent. The philosophy, concepts and practice of Voice Movement Therapy can immensely enhance the rich alchemy offered by stories of all kinds, guiding participants to "The moment when the breath hits the bones and the story has its way with us"[4]

Practitioners of VMT travel with and witness clients on their journey through the shadowlands, offering tools and containers, awarenesses and alternatives to habitual expressions and experiences of self which challenge the images clients hold of themselves, and their lives, opening up their body, breath, and imagination to other more creative rather than destructive possibilities: grounding, being in the moment, connecting, relating, meeting; being present with what is, not wiping or cleaning things up so they are presentable and acceptable, non-threatening and comfortable, but rather, singing with, playing with, creating with, weaving with, sculpting with . . . and thereby transforming what is.

NOTES

1. Joseph Campbell, "On The Shaman," Disk 3, Joseph Campbell and the Power of Myth with Bill Moyers, vol. 1-6, DVD, Interviewed by Bill Moyers (New York, NY: Apostrophe Production, Inc., 2007).
2. Clarissa Pinkola Estes, *Women Who Run with the Wolves* (London, UK: Rider, 2008).Newham 2005:381)
3. Susan Perrow, Forward in Healing Storytelling: The Art of Storytelling for Personal Growth, by Nancy Mellon (Gloucestershire, UK: Hawthrone Press, 2019).
4. Martin Shaw, in Essays on-line, Small Gods. https://dr.martinshaw.com/essays/ accessed April 5th 2021.

BIBLIOGRAPHY

Campbell, Joseph. "On Shaman," Disk 3, *Joseph Campbell and the Power of Myth with Bill Moyers.* Vol. 1-6. DVD. Interviewed by Bill Moyers. New York, NY: Apostrophe Production, Inc., 2007.

Estes, C. Pinkola. *Women Who Run with the Wolves.* London UK: Rider, 2008.

Perrow Susan, Foreward in *Healing Storytelling: The Art of Imagination and Storytelling for Personal Growth.* Foreword by Nancy Mellon. Gloucestershire: Hawthorn Press, 2019.

Shaw, Martin. Essays online. Small Gods. https://dr.martinshaw.com/essays. Accessed April 5th 2021

Chapter Five

NURTURING THE SOUL IN THE PERFORMING ARTS

INTRODUCTION

Gina Holloway Mulder

Liberating the performer's voice and attaining a voice that can, in the words of Paul Newham, "animate the depths of the soul" has been a primary aspiration of Western theatre practitioners for centuries.[1] People such as Roy Hart, Antonin Artaud, Peter Brook and Jerzy Growtowski, all of whom searched for ways to develop the performer's vocal expression into a range that could authentically and powerfully communicate the depth and breadth of human emotion and experience, greatly inspired Newham's creation of Voice Movement Therapy (VMT). Interestingly, both Grotowski and Brook were influenced by Alfred Wolfsohn whose work predates them all, except for Artaud who was a contemporary.

Performance is a realm where extremes are allowed, even encouraged, and the normal sociocultural rules can be put on hold while a deeper truth is expressed. Practitioners can experiment and take risks in researching and developing new avenues of expression. Since theatre lies in the realm of imagination, abstraction, fantasy, archetype, mythology and the symbolic, it offers a vast space for vocal play and discovery since the voice of the performer need not conform to any established norm. In this liminal space, we are not limited to verbal or rational expression; all manner of sounds can be used to express emotion, connect to the audience and transport them–and us–into a different world.

Theatre demands embodiment from the performer, and a certain courage is required to animate a voice and body. Over the years, the context of theatre and performance has allowed the development of many vocal techniques, and also, as Newham points out in relation to Artaud, Brook and Grotowski, some have been instrumental in returning "the notion of therapy to the arts from which it has been extracted."[2]

Voice Movement Therapy is an Expressive Arts Therapy, a modality founded on the notion of the therapeutic value of creative embodied expression. It provides performers with two supportive containers, both of which are embedded in the notion of the embodied voice: 1) It can be regarded as a vocal pedagogy, that is, a way of training or educating the performer's voice as an embodied instrument, developing all its many facets to be as versatile, flexible and durable as possible, using the categories of the 10 Vocal Components and the metaphor of the flexible Vocal Tube, and 2) It offers the artist a safe way of exploring and examining their own material as a way of creating new work.

Voice Movement Therapy provides a spectrum of creative options for the artist to explore, a versatile toolbox that can always offer an alternative, an idea or an amplification to investigate. We can follow narratives, feelings, relationships, symbols, and impulses. We can play with subpersonalities and archetypes. Concepts like the Sphere, the Postural Cycle, and the metaphor of the continuous flexible vocal tube (see page 18) offer ways of making meaning and connecting more directly to our tangible physical self through voice and sound, or we can go in through the image, exploring what the imagination actively offers in combination with voice and movement. There is a natural fluidity between the voice, the body and the psyche that seems to enable us to lubricate all manner of "stuckness" and offers us a mirror or sounding board for making meaningful art.

In this chapter, we share how VMT practitioners in the performing arts integrate Voice Movement Therapy into their work as artists, voice and drama teachers, choir directors, and professional performers, and the impact this work has had on their own relationship with their voice both on and off the stage. Many of us struggle with the pressure of getting it right, "hitting" the note and always producing a "good" and "beautiful" sound. VMT supports us in releasing ourselves from this expectation, thereby discovering that there is something more. All the authors in this chapter write about how the non-judgmental framework of VMT is key to the vocal liberation it offers.

In "The Artist-Practitioner: How VMT Informed me as a Singer, Songwriter and Performer," Mali Sastri of Massachusetts shares how VMT has had a great impact on how she both creates and performs material. She also speaks of how important her explorations of the Shadow have been in her vocal development.

UK-based VMT practitioner and Body-Psychotherapist Melanie Harrold, in "Singing the Breathing Body: Being Present to Your Own Performance," explains how she believes that breathing and an ever-increasing conscious connection to breath and the felt experience is key to staying connected to yourself and to the moment when singing and performing. Melanie holds that such breathing brings forth a deep and meaningful relationship with the song, opening us up to a deeper understanding of what the song is asking of us and our voice. Melanie shares her specific approach to working with the breath and the voice in a way that is embodied, compassionate and sensitive to the history held in the performer's body.

South African practitioner and vocal coach Lerina van Rensburg takes us deeper into the Ten Vocal Components, a central part of her work with singers, both novice and professional. In "Developing the Singer's Vocal Creativity," she shares the value of using the Components as both a technical framework to develop vocal range and expression and as a way of exploring the performer's emotional landscape. She highlights how the performer's life circumstances affect the voice and how various VMT principles and practices offer integration and liberation.

In "Experiencing the Joy of Singing Through the Container of Song," Austrian performer, vocal coach and singing teacher Eva Haidl shares with us her gentle approach and the healing benefits of helping the client to discover the deep pleasure of singing. Central to her work is the concept of the Song as a Container which offers the client an experience of being held in safety and joy.

In "Voice as Archive in Devised Theatre," I have written about how VMT and taking a voice-led creative process changed the way I make and perform theatre. The well-being of the performer during the creative process is important to me and here I share an example of how VMT as a therapy has become my pedagogy in the university context. I also describe my work with a professional musician who was able to shift both his relationship with his voice and his approach to making music by creating a VMT-informed devised theatre piece.

THE ARTIST-PRACTITIONER: HOW VMT INFORMED ME AS A SINGER, SONGWRITER AND PERFORMER

Mali Sastri

When I look back over the past twenty years of my journey as a vocal artist, it's hard for me to overstate just how much the study and practice of Voice Movement Therapy impacted and continues to impact the way I sing, write songs, and approach performance. My experience with VMT greatly and profoundly shaped me as a performing artist and continues to do so.

I trained in VMT in London in 1999 with founder Paul Newham, assisted by Anne Brownell and Christine Isherwood. Over an intense seven-month period involving no-nonsense self-reflection, stark self-honesty, concentrated group interaction, and hours and hours of rigorous vocal exploration, experimentation, work and play, I experienced what I like to describe as my voice "bursting wide open." It became something more than what it had been until then: a part of myself I thought I needed to exert control over in order to tame, train, and prettify. Instead, it became an instrument that was powerful, flexible and dexterous, with tremendous expressive and artistic potential. It also became a part of myself I could trust.

Many of us go into the performing arts because we are moved, consoled, inflamed or otherwise *made to feel* through artistic expression, whether by witnessing the art of others or through our own creative process, or both. We find an understanding, a validation, a knowing beyond words and the mundane of the everyday. We find meaning that we can't get enough of and that is worth dedicating our lives to. Yet in the pursuit of artistic excellence—with its tendency towards perfection of technique and the demands of an arts career with its fierce competition, fickle audiences, and financial uncertainty—it is common for artists to lose our original love for and connection to our treasured art form and its potential to tell our unique story.

Voice Movement Therapy was, for me, a way to study deeply voice and singing—and by "study" what I really mean is *embody*—on a journey that was physical, psychological, emotional, even spiritual. This journey was one of self-discovery and self-knowledge, and the voice was the vehicle through which it was taken. My voice was stretched and strengthened, my songwriting encouraged and challenged, my performances questioned and celebrated, and my ego provoked and laid bare. The process was simultaneously artistic and therapeutic, at times, excruciatingly so.

One of the main tenets of VMT is the radical and liberating view that *all* vocal sounds—not just what we or others might consider the "beautiful" sounds—are not only acceptable but valuable, psychologically and artistically. This philosophy views the groans of displeasure, shrieks of terror, wails of grief—even ragged, crumbly, broken-edged vocalizations—as all part of the human voice's enormous palette, carrying with them their own emotional and artistic merit. VMT instilled in me a fascination with and awe of all that the voice can express and showed me how to appreciate, both as a singer and a listener, a much wider range of vocal sounds than I had done previously. It was tremendously freeing. I was released from the fear of hitting a "wrong" note; there were no wrong notes. Instead of avoiding the "weak" places in my voice, I was encouraged to spend time with and get to know them. And I discovered that by allowing and exploring such a variety of sounds, especially the "ugly" ones—the caterwaul, the scream, the whine, the register break (not always a smooth "passaggio")—my singing voice was growing fuller, richer, and more expressive. When I went to make the "beautiful" sounds, they had increased in depth and fluency.

Figure 13. Mali Sastri in performance Boston, MA USA–2008. Photo: John Dogherty.

A part of this process in VMT–of allowing, exploring, and valuing the whole spectrum of human vocal sound–involves the concept of Jung's Shadow archetype. As Newham described it, the shadow is where we relegate the disowned parts of ourselves, the parts that we are ashamed and afraid of. These aspects of the Self go "underground" into the unconscious where they can wreak havoc on our lives and relationships, out of reach of our conscious control.

Training under Paul, my fellow students and I often heard the refrain, "With light comes shadow." We explored the idea of how our individual and collective focus on the "good" and "positive" aspects of ourselves and our society (i.e. what is "lit," or in our consciousness) can leave us vulnerable to unexpected, uncontrollable darkness (i.e. what is in the shadow or out of our consciousness). The more we emphasize and focus our attention on the "light," the more powerful and unwieldy the shadow grows because, as Newham said, "Where there is so much light there must also be a good deal of shadow." However, we can work with and perhaps even balance out this effect by consciously bringing the shadow into our awareness and embodying it in our conscious life.

A significant part of my VMT Training experience involved actively uncovering the shadow, in myself and beyond, in an effort to heal and balance the opposing energies of light and dark. I was encouraged not just to face but trust the dark in myself–not to fear it, but to discover its treasures.

This process of shadow work had a far-reaching impact on me artistically. It influenced not only what vocal sounds I accepted, but also my understanding of what I was allowed to sing *about*. It gave me permission as a songwriter to go into unexpected, unexplored territories that I would not even have considered before. For me, shadow work always felt as artistic as it felt therapeutic, if not more so. It was not about drowning in the muck and mire of one's own personal darkness, but about mining that darkness and hauling it up into the light to transform it.

This process of transforming aspects of one's psyche and story through the making of art is inherent in all the Expressive Arts Therapies, and in VMT that transformation involves voice, movement, *and song.* During my VMT Training, I was shown ways of taking parts of myself and my narrative and making art of them through an embodied process that could potentially reshape my relationship to the troubled parts of myself and my story.

The concept of *rewriting one's story* plays an important role in VMT which views this process as more effective when fully engaging the body, the breath, and the voice–what I believe most people who enter therapy are actually looking for. Talking about one's problems and looking for solutions from the head alone is not always enough. Many of us need to dive deeper into the various parts of ourselves–what we call *subpersonalities*–and name them, embody them, give them voice, song, even costume. In essence, VMT encourages us to create our own kind of psychological theatre, but with an approach more like autobiographical method-acting than role-playing. We go into ourselves and amplify–through breath, movement, vocalization, and songwriting–our shadow and our light. The art we make is both a by-product of that journey and a container for it.

The Expressive Arts Therapy concept of art-as-container, which in VMT terms translates into song-as-container, was a crucial way that VMT artistically informed and influenced me. Songs could be structures for supporting intense emotions and experiences. I could "pour out" emotional contents, be it vocal sounds and/or lyrics, and contain them through the act of song-making. And in singing the song, I could revisit those emotions and experiences, but from the perspective of an artist/performer.

Many of us who are drawn to the performing arts know instinctively, if not consciously, of the healing and transformative nature of these disciplines. And it is not just the art-making process that is gratifying and meaningful; most artists want to communicate and connect with an audience. It is through the experience of sharing the work–of performing, being witnessed and received–that the personal has a chance to expand into something larger than the individual self towards something like communal elevation.

On my VMT Training we had many conversations about the intensity of emotion that can be brought up by performance, particularly performance involving the human voice. The voice, being something we all share, can elicit a more universal and immediate empathetic response than any other instrument, with the drum perhaps coming next. As vocalists and singers, we are working with a tool that has a unique capacity to connect with, possibly overwhelm, and even provoke an emotional "deliverance" to an audience.

A frequent topic of discussion on my Training was the concept of *catharsis*—the therapeutic release of intense or repressed emotions—and its roots in Greek theatre and later use in psychology. The artist/performer, by singing and dancing her story, especially when at the height of her craft, may bring about a cathartic release or purging in the audience. VMT observes in the role of the performer a distant echo of the shaman who, for thousands of years in indigenous cultures around the world, was, and remains, an integral part of human tribal society, performing climactic healing ceremonies using dance, chant, and song.

But what happens if the source material of one's song, or other art form, is so raw, so full, so fraught with autobiographical significance that the artist herself is swallowed up by it? How much of an emotional journey or catharsis "should" a performer experience onstage and could that interfere with an audience's experience of her performance? Is there a line between the therapeutic and the artistic, and if so, how does an artist/practitioner navigate it?

This was also a rich topic for discussion within my VMT Training. Paul spoke of the importance of a performer to maintain what he called an "artistic distance" from their material during the act of performing. This distance—often hard-won through the therapeutic process of embodying, transforming, and containing one's story—is needed to stay connected to the audience and true to the song. The heightened emotion that inspired its creation—the trauma, outrage, loss, or even ecstasy—has been contained and transformed by the song. The job of the performer now is to give the audience a *trace* of that original emotion or experience without being subsumed by it herself.

This trace is something about which Paul waxed poetic and which stuck with me. To my ears, it spoke of the ineffable connection I as an audience member have felt when taking in art that has really grabbed me by the throat and heart. Whether or not I feel or experience the distinct, specific emotion that inspired the artist to create the work in question, I know I am at the very least experiencing a trace of it, however big or small that trace may be. The idea of the trace made me feel part of the artistic continuum: I was just another artist trying to make musical gold from life's dross, and maybe I, too, could share a knowing, meaning and connection beyond conscious thought with those who would hear it.

One of the most valuable artistic tools I learned from VMT was a practical one: how to approach "problem" songs, the ones that seemed a little bit out of my range, with lines or phrases that tensed me up and had me reaching, contorting my face, or neck, or tongue; or that gave me some other specific challenge. VMT taught me to approach those songs with a "take it to the floor" attitude, to pull the experience of singing the song out of a practice or performance mode and take it on a voice and movement journey. I could move with the song, give it physical form, stretch out the phrasing, vocalize using different vocal components, speed it up, lie down and roll around with it, and/or amplify what the trouble spot was eliciting in me emotionally, vocally, in breath, or in movement. Sometimes simply removing the song from the "space" where it was causing trouble (i.e. traditional practice or performance) could lead to the difficulty resolving itself organically. The active relaxation that can result from the slow, exploratory, experimental Voice Movement Therapy headspace and approach, with its release of a perfectionist's agenda, becomes embodied wisdom, the riches of which can be gently coaxed back into rehearsal or onto the stage.

One of VMT's most fundamental concepts, the Sphere (see page 21), is particularly applicable and valuable to performers experiencing performance anxiety, or stage fright. Creating one's sphere is a spatial exercise in which one's sense of personal space and self are imagined and "located" as a bubble, or kinesphere that extends into the space around one's body. Those of us who practice VMT have spent considerable time physically establishing our Sphere and ourself in the center of it, exploring its many sides and where in the space we feel safest, or most vulnerable, or relaxed, or confident, or any of a host of feelings and sensations. As performers, we may get thrown off, lose our center, become ungrounded, untethered, tense, fearful, distracted by the audience or the lighting or technical difficulties or lack of preparation or any number of anxiety-triggering situations. This practice teaches the importance of "gathering oneself" before going onstage, of taking a moment to physically and mentally ground, center and place ourselves in body, mind, and spirit where we have the best chance of accessing our courage, confidence, and ability to stay loose.

We are encouraged and reminded, to the best of our nervous and excited ability, to engage in and use movement and breath that support a relaxed state before and during performance. To this day, if I find myself feeling particularly nervous, out of breath, or disembodied while on stage, I'll place a hand on my lower abdomen to check in with my body and my breathing, reminding myself to release and expand my belly on the inhale. Belly breathing, expanding the lower belly while inhaling and gently contracting it while exhaling. and the concept of placing oneself in one's Sphere, when used together before or during performance can provide a direct way back into the body.

I use these tools with my VMT clients regularly, whether they are performers or not. I've had the privilege of watching clients surprise themselves with what may come out of them when allowed and encouraged by a non-judgmental witness to take up their space and give voice.

During a first foray into Sphere work, one client who had previously trained in classical voice was so surprised at the unplanned sounds he found himself making in conjunction with his movements that he exclaimed, bewilderedly and delightedly, "What's going on here?!" Even lifelong professional singers may access a very different emotional relationship to their voice and their material when encouraged to look within for direction and intention or to express in movement old lyrics they have sung for years.

If I were to distill down to a maxim what I learned about singing and voicework through Voice Movement Therapy, it would be this: with enough relaxation and confidence, anything is possible. When I believe I can do it—and my whole body believes it, too, and remains supple, loose and open—I can do it. Much of VMT is about letting go, allowing, *being* with oneself, one's body, and one's story. That process requires trust, or at least daring: trust in the creative, therapeutic, and artistic process and one's ability to come through it, and daring if the trust isn't quite there yet. The journey towards embodied ease and self-belief, however, is not quick, easy, predictable, or even necessarily lasting. It is an ongoing process that takes time, attention, commitment, energy, patience, and a willingness to make "mistakes"—just like the process of learning any art form.

BIBLIOGRAPHY

Jung, C.G. *The Collected Works of C.G.Jung*, vol. 9, pt. 6 (Bollingen Series XX). Princeton, NJ: Princeton University Press. 1953.
Newham, Paul. *Therapeutic Voicework*. London, UK: Jessica Kingsley Publishers. 1998.

SINGING THE BREATHING BODY: BEING PRESENT TO YOUR OWN PERFORMANCE

Melanie Harrold

The existential moment of meeting our embodied self in the midst of a performance is both desired and feared. In my experience, as much as we long to be heard, we are also terrified that our voice may "count;" for what may be the cost? Those first live performances of a song hold the edge between surrendering to the breath, allowing our voice to bring emotional resonance to our singing, or succumbing to the old holding patterns that seek to edit us and shut our voice down. Am I enough? Am I too much? Can I dare to be seen and heard?

A song just wants to be sung, to sing through us, asking only for our emotional commitment and the willingness to stay present. We can, through the process of anchoring our voice's resonances within our muscles and bones, serve the song with heartfelt compassion, unspoken sadness, our deepest fury and our ineffable joy. Songwriting itself is a transformational act, drawing this mix of feelings up from the darkness into the light of our shared humanity through word, melody and rhythm. Singing the song can liberate, challenge, and lead us forward in our vocal journey, but the song itself is the container, rooting us in verse, chorus, narrative, melody and rhythm. So where do we begin?

The Body Breathes

Everything starts with the breath. From a new life's first intake of oxygen to our last ending sigh, we are breathing on waves of inspiration and expiration and our voice rides on these waves. Breath is the conduit of our emotions: we can shallow breathe and deep breathe, we can panic breathe and hold our breath, we can sigh and pant, and love can take our breath away. Our voice is activated by the flow of breath emerging up from our lungs, stimulating our vocal folds and causing them to vibrate. The true potential of our voice is not found in our head or even in the larynx itself but within our conscious connection to the muscular ebb and flow of breath.

In VMT we work with three primary areas of respiratory expansion and contraction. The Clavicular area refers to the space in the upper chest; the Thoracic area refers to the Ribs, Diaphragm and Solar Plexus; and the Abdominal area refers to the lower torso from just above the navel down to the pubic bone. By naming and focusing on the expanding and contracting movements in these areas, we can develop a conscious awareness of the connection between body, breath, voice and feeling.

We begin by loosening the jaw, opening the mouth and allowing the muscles of our face to drop and our eyes to become soft as we experience the cold air coming into the mouth and travelling down to the lungs. Placing our hands on our chest, we can feel how it rises and falls as our upper lungs fill and empty. Moving our hands down to the sides of our ribs, we feel the intercostal muscles relaxing and contracting as the air goes down deeper into our lungs. Then, placing the front of one hand on our abdomen and the back of the other hand on our lower back, we feel the front and back expansion and contraction of our lower torso as the diaphragm flattens and the lowest part of our lungs fill and empty, while our belly bulges and hollows as various internal organs move to accommodate this action.

Learning new breathing patterns takes time and patience, but every time we place our hands on one of these breathing areas, we are establishing a sense of connection: this is my body breathing …here…and here... slowly building trust in the connection of our muscle and bone, surrendering to the ebb and flow of breath. Over time we can experience the body breathing us, releasing the need to control the breath with our will. This surrender is pivotal in managing performance anxiety and provides a secure platform in the process of recovery from the many kinds of muscular and emotional constrictions that inhibit breathing and hold back the expression of feeling.

Convex and Concave

All movement is on a spectrum from convex to concave (see page 21) and one can get caught at one end or the other in reaction to life circumstances. Two examples:

A significant part of my childhood story was of an elder sister who died after a long illness. Grieving was "not done" in our family and so there was no way of resolving the long-term impact of suffering and early death; we all just had to be very brave and carry on. When I arrived at the VMT Training in my 40s, years of being brave with nowhere to grieve had fixed my body into an over-expanded and raised "shield of honor," convex in front and no support at the back, relentlessly forward-facing to defend against heartbreak and collapse.

At the other end of the spectrum, I had a client whose father was killed in the Second World War and whose young mother could not cope, pushing her daughters away as she threw herself into the war effort. My client was sent to a boarding school at the age of three and remained there until she finally persuaded her mother to let her come home when she was eleven. When she arrived at my studio in her sixties, her upper chest had collapsed into a concave position while her larynx was high and her throat narrow as if she was just keeping her head above water, surviving despair through her will.

Both of these habitual holding patterns, hers and mine, had formed in reaction to loss and abandonment, but had settled in each of us at different ends of the spectrum, influencing our relationship to ourselves and to the outer world. Putting myself "out there," I started writing and performing songs at age fifteen, embarking on a lifelong journey of recovery through my singing and performance, meeting and re-meeting the emotional chaos in which I was bound by my survival defenses.

My client had married, had two children, and as the good wife, had become the holder and container for her family, rarely tending to her own needs for self-expression. She came to me "backed up against herself" with little space to breathe and a tight suppressed sound. I, on the other hand, had ended up exhausted, bellowing in Irish bars with a powerful modal chest voice and little access to a light and tender falsetto.

Breathing and sounding the timbres while moving through the convex/concave continuum has become the cornerstone of my work. Over the years I have been able to drop my fixed raised shield of bravery which protected me in front and reposition it at my lower back, thus supporting my voice of anguish and effectively reversing the position of convex from defensive to supportive. The relaxing of the convex in the chest, in tandem with the loosening of the contracted muscles of my lower back which had formerly held it in concave, released my diaphragm. This enabled me to deepen my breathing and drop further into the pelvic floor, giving me a felt sense of groundedness and self-support.

The Convex/Concave Cycle

Standing with your feet hip-width apart, breathe in; then, breathing out, take one step forward with both arms in front of you; then opening your arms wide while grounding the back heel, raise your chest into convex, turn your head up to the ceiling in front of you and breathe, opening into the belly. Then, contracting the belly muscles on the next outbreath, initiate stepping back while rolling your upper body over into a concave position and feel your back opening, your arms hanging loose; breathe in, letting your belly drop open. Then, on the next outbreath, contracting your abdominal muscles slowly, unroll to standing. Then, taking a step forward and grounding the back heel again, continue breathing out as you open into a convex position while raising your chest and opening your arms wide, allowing your head to follow your eyes up to the ceiling; then breathe in before starting the cycle again.

This system loosens the diaphragm, opens the chest, and releases the muscles in the back, lower abdomen and pelvic floor, integrating the upper and middle torso with the pelvis. Stepping forward and back anchors these releasing muscles through the three iliopsoas muscles: the Psoas Major, The Psoas Minor and the Iliacus. Together they establish a diagonal connection from the middle and lower back down across the front of the pubic bone and to the inside of the top of the femur.

This diagonal connection aligns with the vertical and circular expansion and contraction of the abdominal breathing that cradles the pelvis, rooting the breathing that supports the voice. Carefully grounding the back foot brings energy down into the legs, completing the vertical alliance of ground and sky.

I came to understand the value of grounding through reading the work of Alexander Lowen[1] who had been a student and client of Wilhelm Reich.[2] Reich's work had been about releasing the bound horizontal layers of muscular defenses of his clients with a forthright approach to releasing bound muscles. However, this work was carried out on a table and there was a notable return to these defenses when Reich's clients went back into their upright lives. It was the athlete Alexander Lowen with his work in "Bioenergetics" who highlighted the importance of energetic grounding within the process of the Sympathetic and Parasympathetic cycle of startle and release. He understood clearly how the explosive nature of trauma needed a strong connection to the ground/sky flow of energy to support the transformative process of integration.

My client, through this same exercise, has slowly released the muscles contracting her chest and throat, bringing the breath of life back into her body and enlivening her voice. In both her case and mine, through moving between these two expressive points of convex and concave, we have found a space to breathe that lies between the outwardly focused over-giver and the one who neglected her personal need for expression while serving others. Standing in this grounded center, we have the possibility of choice: choice of expression, of how and where we can breathe, and from where within us we source our voice.

The Singing Body

Our voices are led and supported by our breath and our breath is supported by muscle. The tone and character of our voices–shaped by the internal spaces of our throat, diaphragm and pelvic floor–are defined by our habitual muscular holding patterns known as Character Armoring and described and named by Reich. The mouth, throat, chest, ribs, belly and sinus bones are all engaged in the actual shifting of tone and resonance. The emotional nuances of our voice come from the layering of this resonance in the body. It is our awareness of and ability to play and give space to these elements that give our vocal delivery flexibility and variety.

Singing is the journey of grounding time and space in the present resonant moment. If it is to be effective and authentic in the way we desire, we must risk the energetic and emotional involvement of ourselves in order to move others.

I had been a professional singer/songwriter for over 20 years when I trained with Paul Newham. I had had an exquisitely frustrating career of success and self-sabotage, reaching out and retreating, falling and picking myself up again, as I sought for this edge of authenticity and presence in my singing and in my life. By the time I took the training in Voice Movement Therapy, I was using my will to find this edge. I became a taskmistress of my voice and breathing technique; binding and repressing this cycle of chaos, I had reached a dead end.

One of my first sessions with Paul Newham was a journey where we lifted off the repressive willed perfection of the Modal Clarinet voice (see page 20) and out came this floating free-air Falsetto enhanced by the forward pharyngeal resonance, bringing the experience of a limitless ceiling!

My concept of The Singing Body developed organically over the next 20 years as I continued with my own recovery alongside seeing therapy clients and teaching singing students. I had discovered that, like craters on the moon, there were indentations in my heart, solar plexus and belly, and I came to recognize that the origin of these wounds came from the cataclysmic impact of my confrontation with death at such a young age. So I consciously embarked on a journey of recovery, breathing and singing through the cycle of convex and concave while shifting through the transitions connecting the timbres: ground to sky, reach and retreat. Over the years I laid down layers of knowledge that settled into my body as I touched, felt, sang and dreamed these "empty craters" back into life, filling them with song.

In sharing this knowledge with my students, I was able to move between the mundane and the epic, between a recognizable understanding of movement, sound and breath into transformational moments of heartbreak, cracking through muscular defenses and pouring through voices that shone with resonance and emotion.

Resonance

Sound itself can be imagined as spherical, with each note shaped like an egg and vibrating with harmonics that can be teased out as we shift through the timbres. The Singing Body anchors these shifts of tone, emphasizing harmonics and vibration while connecting with this resonant experience in our bones and muscles, our physical being.

For example, lifting the roof of the mouth and opening it wide while intentionally "singing through our eyes" engages the sinus bones and brings out the cut of the upper harmonics which adds shine and presence to our voice. Stretching and releasing the muscles of the face to make space for this shimmering, easily projected quality challenges us to risk letting go of our masks, our personas held in the cognitive fixing of our eyes. Releasing the facial muscles into a deep yawn emphasizes the lower harmonics, opening the vocal tube to its full length while releasing the sphincteral muscles of the throat, the diaphragm, and the pelvic floor. In these ways, we can shift the acoustic space in our mouth and throat.

When we drop our jaw and let our yawning belly voice ride up and out of us on the breath, the vibration from the vocal folds travels down via the vocal tube through muscle and bone, giving us a resonant experience of our voice rooted inside of us as we sing. So the act of singing becomes an "in the moment" internal and external experience of vocal presence, both an anatomical and an energetic resonant reality of breath, muscle and bone vibrating within us and between each other.

By placing our hands on our chest while singing an open "Ah," we can feel the vibrations of the vocal folds on our sternum, connecting us with the emotional presence of our heart. As we move our hands downward, following the breath into the solar plexus, we change the vowel to "Oh" which encourages the larynx to drop, deepening the tone of our voice with the lower middle harmonics of the Clarinet Timbre. These deeper harmonics can call deeper feelings up to the surface, igniting our singing with recovered life force as our thoracic area expands and contracts with the breath.

The staging posts of the vocal timbral resonances presented in VMT through the facial and mouth configurations and physical postures of Homo Erectus, Primate, Feline/Canine, and Bird (see page 22) enable us to rest in these harmonics and experience how we feel there. These are the places of transition where the light of consciousness mixes with the underworld of the raw, non-verbal evolutionary base of our gut animal instincts where loss and laughter, rage and voracious hunger all co-exist.

Once we start connecting our voices to the resonant harmonics below the diaphragm, we encounter the interface between the verbal and the non-verbal where deeper, darker, not quite yet distinguished emotions can fire up and be used in our singing. This is often the place of greatest inhibition because we don't know if we have what it takes to encounter what is truly primal and render it satisfactorily in performance.

So often a singing student, while working on this timbre, will ask with a voice of incredulity, "You are not going to make me sing in public with this sound, are you?" "No," I reply, "This is about increasing the flexibility of your voice in order to bring emotional access to the resonance of this primal timbre into your singing, should you choose such a song."

I remember preparing a song called "The Last Leviathan," by Andy Barnes. It was the imagined song of the last living whale. I remember my first performance where my head began to stop my breath, telling me I was "not enough" to sing this song. Who was I to give voice to this creature's final hours, to the screams as the harpoon went in? Using my understanding and ability to release the diaphragm in order to achieve a deeper breath enabled me to release the grip of anxiety and touch the darker depths in myself so that this song of death and the annihilation of a species could come through me when I reached the whale's last impassioned cry:

> My heart it has been rent and I am screaming
> I am the last of the great whales and I am dying.

Conscious Surrender

When we start to breathe deeply, releasing the muscles of our jaw and throat, the response from our bodies is often to yawn. Yawning is a reflex action that releases the diaphragm and the pelvic floor, drawing in more breath. Vocalizing our yawns asks for a conscious intent to come into alignment with a reflex action. This is where we really meet the uniqueness of the diaphragm in that it is both a conscious and an unconscious muscle. This muscle is the threshold where we transition between consciously singing the song and where we can surrender to the song singing us. From the lowest harmonic deep in our guts to the blinding sun of consciousness found within the forward pharyngeal resonance, the more we can surrender to these sounds moving through us, the more present we can become.

In that early session with Paul Newham, breaking through modal clarinet into Falsetto/free air/Forward Resonance (referred to most often in VMT as Violin) took the lid off psychological material which had lain dormant in me for so many years. It took time to find a way of surrendering without re-experiencing a loss of self. Experiencing my voice soaring free was utterly liberating and totally terrifying! At first, I bathed in the glory of accessing for the first time the opera voice found in the Clarinet vibrato (Pitch Fluctuation), but it was the forward pharyngeal resonance that kept calling me (see page 19).

I found that the story of Alfred Wolfsohn being haunted by the screams of those dying boys in the trenches of the First World War drew me like a magnet. I have come to understand that I myself have been haunted by my own screams that were never voiced, causing me to rise up and out of my body in shock and terror at the vanishing of my sister and then losing my ground in the absence of the holding process of grieving.

My conception of The Singing Body is a map that I have shared with my colleagues, my students, and my younger self that traces and retraces this road to recovery. Ground to sky, heart to heart, it brings back to life the resonant expressive highway of our embodied souls.

Retrieval of Consciousness

In this system, the practice of Forward Resonance applies to all three timbres. It asks that we raise the roof of the mouth while opening and stretching the muscles of our face and throat. The reach of the roof of the mouth with an open throat stretches the pharynx and esophagus, signaling down through the vagus nerve to the diaphragm, gut and perineum and so exercising the felt experience of a wide, long Vocal Tube (see page 18). The rectus abdominis connects the pubic bone to the sternum and acts as a set of bellows containing and supporting the flow of breath. From our belly to our heart, muscle sustains our connection to the rooted breath, anchoring the movements of our mouth, throat and larynx as the shifting harmonics of our voice play through our body. The emotional centers running along this muscle from pubic bone to sternum awaken our relationship to the shifting vibrant resonances of the embodied vocal timbres of VMT, laying the foundation for the flow of breath and sound and the practice of "getting out of the way" while staying present.

Forward Resonance highlights the upper harmonics of our sound, giving our voices brightness and power. You can hear this quality of resonance in singers such as the Vaudeville performer Al Jolson and later in musical theatre in singers such as Ethel Merman. Not having microphones, they trained to add this harmonic presence to project their voices over the live band and out into the auditorium. They learned to be loud without effort, using the freedom of the Forward Resonance anchored in the breath and muscular vertical support. Forward Resonance brings not only presence and effortless projection to our voices, but also an awareness of space. It is the great wake-up call for our embodied conscious breathing and singing.

This is very useful in working with amateur singers. I get my choirs to think of the space above their head and consciously engage with this as they sing. When they do, their voices come alive as they become more present in the room. So many times when I have introduced this awareness of space and presence of sound to my choirs, the results have been startling in that I witness 40 people suddenly "coming into the room" and the song coming to life in articulation and projection.

Because of the resonant potency of the Forward Resonance/Violin sound and the climactic stretch of the tube, the voices of extremis become available to us. However, there is no point in expressing the outer edges of our rage and despair without knowing how to breathe and ground the existential impact of this expression back into muscle and bone. Breathing and voicing the timbres through the Convex/Concave movement spectrum creates a fluid resonant pathway along the Vertical Plane from ground to sky. This provides the platform from where we can begin the journey of safely releasing the defensive grip our stories have on our voice and breath.

Working with Forward Resonance in VMT is a journey of letting go and learning how to ground and trust our embodied voice. The muscles of our mouth, throat, diaphragm and pelvic floor are the guardians of the stories that protect and shape us. Thus, our facial and throat muscles may become a defensive mask or persona through which we face the world. As we gain more flexibility of these muscles through working through Convex/Concave and the Forward Resonance/Violin component, we begin to dissolve the muscular hold our story has on our voice. We can indeed sing our way through this mask of who we think we should be and how we should sound. We can risk challenging the perfect voice, the edited voice, the beautiful voice, the quiet voice. We can affirm the vulnerable and dissolve the shame of getting it wrong. It means that one has to let go of the persona that fixes how we see and hear ourselves. We change the way we can be present both to ourselves and to others by risking the unimagined voice. This is at the heart of vocal change and of letting go: to hear the beauty and the despair, the courage and the compassion in our voices while rooted in the potency of our "ground." In Forward Resonance we dare to let the fullness of our power and loudness ride out, bringing forth the presence and magic of the joy of aliveness.

Performing the Song

In my experience, songs tend to choose themselves, arriving to meet the emotional desire for vocal exploration. By increasing the inner flexibility of the Vocal Tube and releasing the muscular and emotional rigidities of "old stories" along the way, we open more and more to the Vertical grounding, the flow of breath, and the fluidity of vocal resonance. We can stand present and rooted to the ground and open to the stars as we sing of deep tragedy or of great joy. We facilitate singing a song by bringing the adult and the child, and the primitive and instinctive, into alignment with breath, vibration, and muscle. We play with both the verbal and nonverbal aspects of ourselves as we invite the song to flow through us.

The breathwork which anchors the Timbres in the body, the movement work along the spectrum of Convex and Concave, and the concentration on feeling and creating the different harmonic resonances all come together when we sing a song in performance. A song's essence is both a verbal and a non-verbal experience where text, tone and feeling flow with sound, rhythm and breath. The exertion of muscle and the resonance of sound against bone plays through our feeling centers. The melodic arc is facilitated by a flexible throat and access to harmonic coloring. Our moment-by-moment connection to our breath helps us phrase the lines and grounds us in the emotional pulse of the song. The more we participate, immersing ourselves in the song, the more the song gives back to us. The energy ripples through our bodies, lighting us up like Christmas Trees.

Figure 14. Melanie Harrold in performance, London, UK—1994.

Our voices are the doorway between our concept of ourselves (cognitive) and the felt sense of our own presence (affective), and songs call both of these aspects into their service (see page 19). Within the performance, as in life, we are continually challenging ourselves to stay in the present moment, breathing into the emotional peaks and troughs as the tale unfolds, not letting it run away from us or rush ahead and lose the drift of meaning. The song asks to be sung through us both proactively and as an act of surrender, and while in its embrace, to be shared as honestly and with as much presence as we can muster. It may indeed take a lifetime, but the payoff is that both the soul of the singer and the soul of the song can be heard, nourished, experienced, touched and loved.

BIBLIOGRAPHY

Lowen, Alexander. *Bioenergetics.* New York, N.Y; Coward, McCann and Geoghegan Publishers, 1975.

Reich, Wilhelm. *Character Analysis,* trans. by Vincent Carfagno. New York, N.Y; Simon Schuster, 1974.

DEVELOPING THE SINGER'S VOCAL CREATIVITY

Lerina Van Rensburg

As a vocal coach, I find that VMT offers a broad spectrum of applications to develop a singer's vocal creativity. It is an embodied way of working with the voice which brings a deep understanding of the emotional, creative, and therapeutic aspects of embodied singing. VMT facilitates a broad exploration of the creative process, of how to develop meaningful interpretations of songs, and how to bring emotions through into the singing voice during performance. I find that this deep understanding supports musical collaborations on and off the stage.

Singing and song writing has always been my refuge. As a child, it was singing that grounded and calmed me. When I sang, I was never alone. Singing became my escape from the outside world, a place where I could regain my reason to smile! I started formal singing lessons at the age of 14, but it was not until I was 18 that I found a vocal coach whose focus was on the creativity and musicianship of singing and song writing, not just technique. A whole new world opened up for me as I learned about the creative process, about trying things out and not being perfect all the time. I gained confidence in my singing and was encouraged to become a musician and to collaborate with other musicians.

The events that led me to VMT are deeply personal. In my twenties I would create improvised songs while driving. At this time, I was also experiencing change in my personal life. I had been in a verbally abusive relationship, and after a year of marriage, one day I found myself singing: "I'm a used cloth, just step on me...." I was shocked at the words that I sang. It was the first time I acknowledged how I really felt about how my husband treated me. This song became the road pointing me to my inner truth. During my divorce, my vocal coach looked me straight in the eye and said: "Lerina, stop being the victim!" This brought me to the decision that, going forward, nobody would tell me how to feel or what I am worth. So, I wrote another song: "'Done!'–I'm done feeling this way, I'm done allowing you to make me feel this way!" With both these songs I felt the healing power of song writing; song became the container for everything I wanted to say but couldn't or didn't want to admit.

Then my vocal coach, who had had such a major influence on my life, moved away. I felt stuck. Driving home one evening after teaching, I broke down crying. I knew I needed something to support my singing and teaching, but also I needed something to help me work through my trauma. In a moment of synchronicity, I opened my e-mail that evening and there was an invitation to the VMT Training. It felt unreal because it looked like everything I was searching for in one course. In three weeks, I was on my way. I had no idea what to expect; I just knew I had to do it and that it was going to change my life in one way or another!

VMT gave me the opportunity to expand my vocal range, embody my sound, and add a new depth to my singing, teaching, and performing. I also had the opportunity to work through my trauma for the first time and I left the Training in a completely different state. During the process, I reclaimed everything my ex-husband had taken from me and I wrote the song "'Claiming'–I'm not mad, just claiming it back, This is me, who I am, It's mine and it's a fact!" VMT changed my life in so many ways; I felt more confident about myself as a person and as a singer! A very important lesson I learned through VMT is to always be in the moment and trust the process. My new search started the last day of my training: the search for singers who needed this amazing work in their personal and professional life! I now have a music school, Ovie-Vibz (Vibrance), with over 240 students and 14 other music teachers.

VMT offers the singer a unique vocal lesson. In a traditional singing lesson, you only focus on the sound and making sure that everything is perfect, and you work until it is perfect. In singing lessons with a VMT practitioner, there is no such thing as being perfect. The focus here is on being true to yourself. Through Voice Movement Journeys I encourage my students to explore the different sounds and possibilities in their voice. Then we take a moment to experience what those different sounds and possibilities feel like, not only as a singer, but also as a person, and what impact these sounds can have on one's life. Lastly, we express those feelings through song and in doing so become a more expressive person and performer.

Figure 15. Lerina van Rensburg performing with San-Marie Booyse, Hoerskool Overkruin, Pretoria, S. Africa–2019. Photo: Henri Grobler.

I find the Voice Movement Therapy 10 Vocal Components a valuable structure for expanding the singer's vocal range and creativity. Using these components, we can hone in on aspects of the voice and the embodied experience of the sound. The Components of Articulation, Disruption, Free Air, Loudness, Pitch, Register, Glottal Attack, Timbres, Pitch Fluctuation and Violin (see page 19), as well as the Sphere work (see page 21) are prominent in my lessons. As a vocal coach I feel it is important to be equipped with at least five different approaches to help the client. The same Component can help two different clients with different challenges, and the same challenge–for example, throat restriction–can be resolved through different approaches and working with different Components. I'd like to share a few case studies that illustrate the value of working through the VMT lens and specifically with the 10 Vocal Components.

Mandy was a novice singer in her thirties who had moved from the UK to the USA when she was nine years old. When she arrived in the USA, she was forced to unlearn her English accent through speech therapy; her parents had wanted to protect her against being bullied. In the end, though, it took away a big part of her identity and created in her a very unhealthy relationship with her voice. She came to me for voice lessons as an adult; she spoke and sang mainly in Flute and used a lot of Violin to make sure everyone could hear her.

During her early sessions we worked on relaxing the muscles in her throat. Breathing exercises had helped a lot, but the tension in her jaw was still there.

We also worked with Free Air (often referred to as breathiness) which she managed to hold for a few seconds, but not for long. During our sixth session I suggested we remove all the consonants in the words of the song we were working with; that way she would not need to articulate and could focus more on the free-flowing melody.

She couldn't do it. She completely froze and could not make any sound without the consonants. I reassured her that it was ok and invited her to experiment with the idea at home, suggesting she try out different spaces, perhaps in the car, or maybe when she was taking a bath. One evening she sent me this message: "I got it!!! I took a bath and when I went under the water I tried to sing and form words, but you cannot do that under water." For the first time, she could relax her jaw. From this point on she was able to use the different timbres in her voice, could sustain Free Air for longer periods of time, and developed a love for Disruption and Glottal Attack! The release of the muscular holding of the jaw and throat that was facilitated by removing the demands of articulation provided her with a doorway to other aspects of her voice and creative expression. Her range expanded by at least half an octave after this experience; Violin and Flute became some of the components she could utilize, and now she had access to so much more! This was only the beginning of her journey. Within the next month, it took her on a creative song writing path. She came full circle; her journey started with taking away the words and continued on to using words to express herself and using the song as a safe container.

Estelle was an intermediate singer, 38 years old, who also had a lot of tension in her throat when singing. It took about five months for our relationship to develop to a point where she could trust me enough to try a different approach. She struggled a lot with her self-image and didn't want anyone to know her real name; she used another name when it came to anything music-related.

Over a period of three weeks, we tried different things like VMT breathing, using the Timbres and the Registers of Modal and Falsetto to help her relax and bring the sound more into the body. It was, however, our playful exploration of Disruption that made the difference. We started with sighing and ended with a tired Disrupted low-pitched sound. Then we became doors that had a high-pitched Disrupted "cre-e-ek" when opening. She then came forward suggesting that we make the sound as if we were picking up a very heavy object. We ended the exploration with a free vocalizing journey focusing on Disruption. After this lesson, she understood where her vocal cords were and how they worked and that helped her to relax her throat and her voice became more embodied.

One of the non-vocal aspects of VMT I find extremely helpful when working with boundaries and stage presence is the Sphere work. Mellie, an advanced singer and 40-year-old mother of four who had been taking lessons every second week for about two years, found herself in a place of utter exhaustion. She loved her kids, but found them to be very demanding of her attention. Her children took up all her energy and all her time and she felt unsupported by her husband. She felt that everyone expected her to give everything of herself all the time and she never received anything in return.

I noticed that she naturally inhabited the front of her Sphere, but withdrew to the back as she started to sing. She had no problem with singing on pitch, but she struggled to project with confidence. This is often the case with singers who have sung in choirs because most choirs aim for unison; one person projecting above the rest is not ideal. After a few sessions where we worked consciously with the Sphere–singing in different parts of it and exploring what she felt in the different areas, moving around the Sphere while singing, incorporating breath, and working on owning this physical and energetic space around her–she mentioned that this was the first time she felt there was a healthy boundary and that while she was in her Sphere she could find time for self-care.

At this point I introduced the vocal component of Free Air. Free Air is a component that can really help to soothe and hold us. I invited Mellie to imagine the air around the sound to be like a comforting blanket for her voice. Over time, we worked with a few lullabies and she even wrote one for herself which gave her the opportunity to comfort herself by using her voice, incorporating Free Air from within her Sphere. This experience of clarifying boundaries while integrating self-care allowed Mellie to set boundaries in her life and with her children. Her "me time" became her "Lullaby Sphere," a private space where she could practice self-care and sing her lullabies. Over the next couple of months, the boundaries between performer, mother, and self became clearer for her. She started to come forward in her Sphere when she sang and her songwriting developed, expanding past lullabies to other songs that she was confident enough to perform in front of an audience.

Loudness is another important vocal element for performers to master. It's a lot about self-confidence and taking up space as well as understanding how to physically support the voice. I worked with a 14-year-old novice singer, Wilma, who had grown up with an abusive and dismissive adopted brother. Although I could barely hear what she said when she spoke, a beautiful voice hid behind the soft volume of her singing. We had worked on breathing, mostly to improve her volume, and slowly it had made a difference, but there were two breakthrough points that changed everything.

I take my students to the recording studio once a year to experience being a "recording artist." Wilma's first breakthrough was when she heard herself in the studio. It was the first time she really listened to her own voice and it was amazing to see the look on her face when she realized that she liked it! With this realization and acknowledgement of herself, she could take ownership of her voice and her volume naturally started increasing! The second breakthrough came when we worked with the Jazz classic "Cry Me A River." Prior to her experience of her voice in the studio, she would never have even considered singing a Jazz song, but it was in singing this song that won't work without the component of Loudness that she was able to completely open up and connect with her voice and herself. As Wilma allowed herself to embody her sound more, her breathing improved and her song choices became bolder. When she was on stage she enjoyed being there and everyone could see that in her performance. Wilma went on to achieve a Merit for her performance in her Grade 6 International Rockschool exam. It was such a privilege to witness the growth of this student!

Singers regard pitch and vocal range as important areas of development. The following case study shows the progress made by a novice singer over a period of about a year by using the structure provided by the Vocal Components.

Growing up, many people had told Amanda that she was flat and that she should rather keep quiet. This had greatly diminished her confidence and her vocal range which was only half an octave when she started lessons with me. Our journey started with the introduction of breathing exercises and I focused on building relational trust for the first three weeks. We included such exercises as: breathing in, holding the breath, and then breathing out, activating the diaphragm by exploring F, T, F, T consonant exercises. We would explore taking the focus to all three different areas of expansion—chest, ribcage and abdomen—and by doing a body scan using only breathing while I would prompt different focus points throughout the exercise. These exercises immediately expanded Amanda's range to an octave. For the next four months, I highlighted her improvement and complimented her on that, always focusing on developing a positive teacher-student relationship. Just these compliments and knowing that someone thought she *could* sing expanded her range to two octaves.

In the 6th month, we started to add the other Vocal Components. The first was Free Air. This was great fun for Amanda because she naturally had Free Air in her voice and so embracing this quality felt familiar and was a positive experience for her. Then we added some Glottal Attack and Disruption. At first, she felt uncomfortable with these components, but after one session of exploring Disruption she could feel how her voice was starting to relax and she was encouraged to continue. We explored these three components for about two months.

In month eight, I introduced Amanda to Pitch Fluctuation. When she tried it, she was overwhelmed with fear. I told her to slow it down and just sing the two separate notes. This was more manageable for her. We ended the lesson with a song, as always; she didn't realize it, but she had used Pitch Fluctuation at least four times in the song. When I mentioned it afterwards, she was so excited that she wanted to do it again. Trust the process...."

In Month Nine of her lessons with me, we added the Timbres, but only focusing on moving between Flute and Clarinet. She felt that when she went into Clarinet, she was more grounded and secure in her voice and as a person. For the next couple of weeks, we focused on embodying the sound by using active imagination, vocal journeys, and body scans using humming. After a few weeks, her range had developed to two and a half octaves!

At this time, I asked Amanda if she was ready to go on stage and she was enthusiastic about the idea. Once a year I give my students the opportunity to perform with a full band. She was excited to take the opportunity with both hands, but equally scared. I reminded her about how far she had come and that I believed in her and knew she was ready. She stood on stage and sang a song with a live band! Performing with professional musicians gave Amanda the support she needed and in the end she got great applause from the audience! She said she would remember that feeling forever! Amanda had been working for her mom when she started lessons with me, but had always dreamt of starting her own business. After her performance she came to me and said that if she could do *that* and have everybody cheer her on, she knew she could also start that business by herself. Shortly after her live band performance, she moved away and did just that.

The following case study also demonstrates how range can be developed and expanded. I have found that it is often a fear of certain sounds not only sounding different but also feeling different, or unfamiliar, that limits vocal development. I find this most often with the Pitch-related Registers. For example, transitioning from mixed register–also called middle register and referred to as Modal register in VMT and where the speaking voice lies for many people–feels quite unusual for most people. Singers often consider such unfamiliar feelings during sound production to be wrong or harmful, at which point they stop their explorations in this part of their range.

I worked with Anna, an experienced musician and intermediate singer, who had come to me convinced that she could not sing high notes. She reported that the moment she sang in her higher register, it felt weird and she stopped. I explained and demonstrated to her that one *can* develop this register. In our sessions we made different sounds, funny sounds, within the higher register. We played with yodeling so that she could feel the difference between the registers. We used the breath and spent time free vocalizing to explore them. Lastly, we chose to work with songs that were specifically placed in the higher register. During our work I had also noticed that her posture began to open up the more comfortable she got with singing in the higher register. A few weeks later when she came out of the recording studio, she shared with delight, "I can sing high!" Now she chooses to sing songs with high notes.

A singer can have a perfectly trained voice, but if everything is still stuck in the head, it won't be an embodied sound or an expressive voice. The VMT Timbres—Flute, Clarinet, and Saxophone—and the associated body postures are so valuable in vocal development, even with experienced singers.

Sandy was an experienced singer who studied music, with voice as her first instrument, at university. She had come to me because she felt stuck and wanted to expand it. During our third lesson I introduced her to the VMT Timbres. We started by finding the posture of each Timbre, feeling the shape in the body. Then we incorporated only breathing and feeling the Timbre shape in the vocal tract and lastly,s we vocalized each Timbre. Giving Sandy permission to not have the "perfect posture" or the "perfect voice," and to explore the possibilities within that, was completely new and freeing for her. For the first time she really embodied her voice. We've become good friends and today she is one of the teachers at my music school.

Witnessing people who arrive inhibited and withdrawn, who battle with projection and confidence, and then become confident singers and performers with good vocal range and an ability to communicate the emotion of a song is extremely satisfying for me. The vocal and personal transformations I see because of what singing and the VMT tools have to offer confirm every day why I love what I do. These and other transformations would not have been possible without the VMT principles and the 10 Vocal Components that I use daily in my lessons. VMT opened up a whole new box of tools for me as a vocal coach and, most importantly, I learned to trust the process and to meet the students where they are.

EXPERIENCING THE JOY OF SINGING THROUGH THE CONTAINER OF SONG

Eva Haidl

I am originally from a small town in Austria and was born, as I believe most children are, with a natural sense of musicality, rhythm and a love for singing. I started playing piano when I was ten and after graduating from a high school for Music, I studied Jazz singing at the Music University in Graz and then completed a postgraduate course in Jazz and Studio Music at the Guildhall School for Music and Drama in London. After being immersed in working as a singer for some years, I became more and more drawn to exploring my own deep inner journey as a human being and developed a real passion for accompanying people in finding their own voice. I had been teaching for a few years when Voice Movement Therapy came into my life, opening up a whole new world of possibilities for combining inner process work with voice, movement and music. For more than 24 years now, I have worked in private practice with clients who have a professional singing background as choir singers or actors, including as Senior Lecturer in the Max Reinhardt Seminar teaching singing in the Drama department of the Vienna Music University for five years, and also with those who have never sung before. I have also been leading workshops in group singing for over 15 years. Central to my work is helping people find a tangible experience of joy through singing.

Most of us have experienced moments when we naturally feel happy and a song just bubbles up, making its way from our lower belly into our heart, into our voice, and out into the world. I believe the impulse to sing is part of our human nature. It's as organic as any other bodily function. I also believe that we're all born, to a greater or lesser extent, with an inherent sense of musicality. Developing our ability to sing, however, hinges on whether or not this impulse is fostered, be it by our parents, teachers, other members of the community around us, or even just by our very own nurturing.

I remember times in my own childhood when the natural impulse to sing was invited to unfold. My dad always used to sing, and he knew many songs that had some relevance to various day-to-day situations, so singing was not so much a separate activity that happened rarely but was part of our daily life. As a family, we sometimes went on holiday to Greece and took a tiny boat to find and explore beautiful, deserted bays. On our way back in the evenings, traveling across the water, we used to sing a round which at the same time expressed and anchored a sense of happiness and fulfilment, along with a sense of safety, family love and having had a great day by the sea.

I also remember learning a simple song in kindergarten which triggered a feeling of the mystic, spiritual dimension in me. I was once invited to sing it for the other kids, while I accompanied myself on my little glockenspiel. It was very well received and therefore mirrored to me that this was valuable.

Of course, another classic example in Austria is sitting on a ski lift, singing folk songs and yodeling together while enjoying a sense of freedom and adventure, breathing cold fresh air and having fun. So, singing for me was often associated with feeling happy and well and thus this experience has been the very base of my gift to many people who didn't have such luck.

We experience a deep sensitivity around how our voice is perceived by the outside world. Many of the people I've worked with have experienced one single negative comment about their singing or the sound of their voice and have not used their singing voice ever since. A great amount of joy is lost in such moments. Thankfully, though, this intersection between singing and experiencing a joyful, true connection with oneself also works the other way around. We can nurture the joy that was once naturally flowing from the inside out; it can be experienced again through the beauty of music, the artistry of melody, the magic of imagery called forth by the power of words, and of course by the grand support of rhythm and the glory and safety of harmony. If only one person truly believes in us again, we can regain our sense of confidence in our singing, and with gentleness and patience, our relationship with our voice can heal and our love for singing and our joy can be reclaimed.

In essence, my work is all about using the medium of body, voice, expression, sound and music to access our power, our joy, and to enhance our level of awareness and consciousness. Every session unfolds within the field of deeply getting to know ourselves: feeling and embracing every aspect of ourselves, becoming friends with ourselves, and looking for and eventually finding ways of being happy with and within ourselves.

The Song as Container

As soon as we move away from the spoken word in expressing ourselves, we step into the waters of emotion. This step alone is very challenging for many people, especially for those who haven't sung much in their lives. Singing immediately connects us with our own authentic emotional selves. The body remembers and energetically calls up every experience we have ever had in terms of expressing ourselves in this way. Depending on our current inner state and our history, this can be wonderful, terrifying, both at the same time or somewhere in between. Using the song as a container is a beneficial approach that sits at the heart of Voice Movement Therapy. The song provides a structure to hold the emotional experience and at the same time offers both a flexible platform for vocal play and experimentation and something of a home base, or anchor, for us to come back to. In whatever way we choose to work during a session, be it sounding freely and allowing the song to emerge organically or using songs to help people to find their vocal expression, there are both gifts and challenges along the way.

Free Sounding as a Way of Sculpting the Spontaneous Song

No doubt, expressing emotion freely without a specific structure is sometimes just what we need. It can be deeply transformational, truly empowering and freeing. In fact, sounding freely is really our first song as a baby. We express our inner moods in the most varied ways and everybody around us knows just how we feel. We must reconnect, to some degree, with this very direct emotional resonance if we want to find our authentic expression while singing songs. It is the vibrational aspect that makes us truly *feel* what we sing and immediately communicates this feeling-content to those who listen, if we choose to perform. This can be accessed by either letting the body lead in improvisational movement and allowing the voice to follow, or by allowing the voice to lead and the body follow. A natural flowing improvisation of sound and movement based on organic impulses occurs, free from any outside influence. Hence there's no need to fit into any given structure, and there's no expectation to fulfil. This way of sounding can offer a great sense of freedom, joy, play and authentic emotional expression through being in the moment, and for some people this is the best way of entering their vocal journey.

I once worked with a young doctor, an unusual character. He found it quite stressful to sing in tune and to hit notes. So, we would often spend a long time in the session sounding freely together, using breath and movement as our base of connecting with musical and emotional impulses. He was very comfortable with this approach and was quick to follow his own instincts. Loving exploring, he enjoyed checking out his range and feeling the energy and vibration of sometimes gentle, sometimes intense emotion. He was also courageous in experimenting with vocal extremes, and following these sound journeys his range soon opened up. He needed this sense of freedom in order to feel comfortable and could soon sing from very low up to tenor and even found his high falsetto voice.

This free-flowing approach is not for everybody and what makes one person feel comfortable and free can be too undefined and uncomfortable for another.

The Song Within a Musical Frame

Many of my clients have a desire to find their own authentic voice in singing songs, to lose their fear of singing in front of others, and to grow in confidence. The challenge of using the musical frame of a song is that there are more rules to play by. Various musical, physical, cognitive and emotional activities need to be coordinated at the same time. There are harmonies that underlie the melodies—we assume that we must get the melodies right—there are rhythms to be kept, words to be remembered, and there's imagery to be played with that sets the inner scene for the relevant emotions to be felt and expressed. Feeling that we need to fulfil all these expectations can bring up a lot of stress around making mistakes, getting it wrong, being judged, and since we so identify with our voices, potentially feeling humiliated.

So how do we use the song as a safe container when it has the potential to evoke such a negative charge? Below I share a general outline of how a developing process with someone who has not sung for a long time or has a fear of singing songs tends to unfold. This is no set recipe but a loose framework that has worked well for me in accompanying people towards finding their authentic vocal expression within song and performance.

I usually begin by checking in with the person. Finding out about what's happening in their life helps me to understand how their inner journey is unfolding and where to start the session. It also gives me an idea of what songs I could suggest later on, songs that might reflect an aspect of their life situation or could be an easily accessible frame for them and a natural doorway to their authentic vocal expression.

The practitioner being wholly present in the moment with the client, receiving the client and their stories with an open mind and heart nurtures trust within the therapeutic relationship. When trust is established, we gently look at how the client's life situations impact the body. They learn to feel their sense of expansion and contraction and how this is connected to their thoughts and feelings. They become aware of areas of tension and how their challenges impact their physical instrument, aware of the opening and closing feeling in the throat, and most important of all, their breathing patterns. Allowing the breath to flow is intricately linked to trust. First trust needs to flow into the very basis of life and into vocal expression. When our awareness and connection is felt in our breathing, we can move on to sounding.

There is a manageable process in learning to anchor oneself authentically in a song. Many people need to learn to hold this connection mindfully, step by step. It's helpful for beginners if I sound with them. I let them hear my voice first; this provides a sense of safety until they can start to sound with me. Often, I start with just one note and invite them to join me with a focus on feeling the resonance.

Finding pitch has nothing to do with any structure we can find in our thinking mind. It's a way of tuning in, feeling vibration, listening with the body, and trusting our innate musical instinct and ourselves. When this sense of felt concentration is activated in the client, we move into little chunks of melodies using call and response. Even this exercise of using a little melody is using song to make people feel safe. Most people love call and response; it's playful, like a light-hearted game, and, as in so many aspects of voicework, I find that it very much speaks to the inner child who wants to play, sing, be heard, and yes, feel loved and accepted as she/he is. The child is also our ally in finding the joy and fun in it all—which is by far the fastest way to learn.

In my work with actors I've observed that, although they all have great creative energy and expressive gifts, many are terrified of singing and find it difficult to hold a tune. One of my students at the Vienna Music University totally froze when it came to trying to sing even a short melody, due to past teaching experiences. As already mentioned, we cannot grasp the right notes with the control of our thinking mind; we can't think the resonance of music and match it with our voices.

To help my student establish the feeling of resonance, we took a lot of time in the beginning of our sessions to connect her with her body through breathing. By placing her own hands on her chest and belly she could, through touch and resonant vibration, begin to feel safe and held. For ages we would just stay singing one note together, rocking the body gently and feeling the resonance of both our voices together, thus letting her feel that she was not alone in this. Step by step we would build it up: two notes, then three, then four. The mind needs to calm down and forget itself sometimes if we are to open the door to the music within. When I felt she was stable enough, I added fitting harmonies on the piano to stabilize her even further, and once she could feel her own anchoring and trust in her ability to hold the little melody, she was totally overjoyed and moved to tears.

Once the sense of trust around holding a little melody has developed and the person is beginning to accept their own individual sound, I often invite them to sing while I accompany them on the piano. This allows them to feel the magic of music and of being held in harmony. This is a crucial step that needs more care and attention than many singing teachers tend to think. It can bring up a strong fear of singing out of key, of having to get it right, and often causes the gently established connection to break. Many people get in touch with images of unpleasant school memories or other scenarios that blocked their musical flow in the past. When I start working in this way with a client, I describe the piano as a dear friend that supports and holds us on many different levels. It provides the harmonic landscape for us to vocally dance to, and if we so choose, a rhythmic pulse that can ground and hold us safe. Then, nurturing an ever-deepening connection with the body, I encourage people to place their hands on their body, to find some gentle organic movement, and to stay connected with their flow of breath and the felt sense of their own natural sound. Such physical connection with the self anchors the voice in the body. This focus on the embodiment of their voice, my reassurance that we will do it together and that it's okay to get it wrong, usually opens doors quickly for beginners to find and connect with their innate musicality again. Once they've accepted the sound of the piano and found a simple melody that I have first sung for and then with them, which is then repeated for quite some time or slowly taken up step by step, people often experience a great sense of happiness.

Figure 16. Eva Haidl (*center*), Trish Watts (*right*) and Melanie Harrold (*left*) leading group singing at the public open day IAVMT Conference, Sydney Australia—2013. Photo: Gina Holloway Mulder.

I once worked with a psychotherapist who had a very difficult relationship to her voice. Since childhood, she hadn't sung much but had a real longing to rediscover her voice. Almost every time we started to sing she got so moved that she burst into tears, feeling a mix of shame and gratefulness at the same time. She felt shame in her voice for not being good enough and grateful that someone was guiding her and showing kindness in this matter. After many sessions of working through and releasing old childhood traumas—like having to sing in front of her class in preschool with a very hostile teacher—and with a lot of gentleness and patience, she was able to slowly reclaim and accept the natural sound and beauty of her voice. Becoming increasingly familiar with simple melodies and exercises and repeating them over and over again, she became secure in her ability to hold a tune, and so the relationship to her voice changed. As her musical ability became more anchored in her body, she began to trust her voice and expanded into believing she had the right to enjoy it along with the amazingly enlivening flow of energy it provides.

As she told me, this process had a strong ripple effect throughout her life. She became less critical and more kind with herself in general, which also expanded into dealings with her family. She felt that she didn't have to push her way through situations so much anymore and give her very all in order to be liked and accepted. Her trust in her own ability to guide people in her profession deepened. I find this is true for almost everybody. The voice is such a core aspect, like a clear mirror in which we are able to monitor the relationship to our self so beautifully. When we make changes in our relationship to our voice—and reclaim the joy in it—we change our life.

Not to have to focus on singing correctly, but rather on experiencing harmony and being able to tune in to the music, and indeed ourselves, makes us feel great. I believe that this feeling of joy is further amplified when we can locate ourselves within the music; being part of something wonderful and vibrational like the structural magic of music reminds us of our true nature, of being held and of not being separate. I find this amazing sense of belonging and happiness is especially strong in group singing where I teach songs by ear, using the body as a teaching tool, showing pitch with hand movements and rhythms in a form of spontaneous dance. Once melodies, harmonies, and rhythms are established in the group, the sense of togetherness and musical connection through our voices and the felt trust in our individual and collective abilities can be truly liberating and is usually a great joy. It naturally helps us to become totally present and grounds us deeply in the body at the same time.

Coming Back to the Individual Session...

Another great way of exploring one's own musicality and the freedom it can provide is to improvise over a simple chord sequence. The chords provide "holding" for the singer, while at the same time the improvisation invites vocal freedom. In such an exploration a series of two to three chords gets repeated on the piano, and depending on the singer's confidence, he or she can start off freely or with a little line that I give them which then can be left in order to start improvising by themselves through the musical landscape provided–or they might just want to stay with a few notes and play with them.

Once a high-flying manager of human resources working for big companies wanted to find her emotional connection to herself again. Her musicality and love for music was apparent but seemed deeply buried underneath the very cognitively based life she had been living for a long time. At school, she had been a popular singer in the classical field and had always gained a lot of sometimes wanted, sometimes unwanted attention this way. Yet what was most prominent in her emotional memory when she started to sing was the feeling of having to please others and get it right, a common phenomenon with performers who have been trained classically by rather unconscious teachers. For her, improvising over a series of chords on vowels, gibberish or fragments of words that just showed up was the key to liberate herself from past restrictions and to reclaim her lost feeling connection to the joy of singing. Once she started, she didn't want to stop and just loved exploring various vocal components whilst feeling the support of groove and harmony beneath her. Breaking through the barrier of having to produce a specific sound and playing with various vocal colors that spontaneously painted her emotional landscape was her way of telling her story and she didn't need any words.

Having felt and grasped the relationship of a natural and inborn musical structure and the ability to move within it, the next step could be to try to sing a song. Sometimes people then just want to keep exploring the musical aspect within the frame of a song. Sometimes they are ready to jump in and try a song that resonates with their inner emotional landscape.

There are a number of aspects of a song that could resonate with an individual. It could be the content of a song, the lyrics, the mood, the groove, the intensity or gentleness, or the tempo. Yet all of these parameters can also be pulled and changed in order to better fit a person's mood or singing ability. We can sing a song without lyrics and take away the more cognitive aspect, using vowels or gibberish instead. We can change the lyrics partly or all together in order to empower ourselves right now or express current feelings more accurately. A fast song can be sung as a ballad, a pop song can become a Latin or swing groove, dynamics can be used freely by impulse; in this way, all vocal components can be explored. The possibilities and creative combinations offered to help people to grow into singing and expressing themselves through song are endless.

A man once came to me with a history of abuse. He found it difficult to connect with his emotions and was often very much lost in his cognitive mind. He found that when he did connect to his feelings, they would often be very strong and occasionally overwhelming. After many years of working together, we found a way into singing songs beautifully and connecting to their emotional content. It was a revelation to him that he could choose to access emotion on his own terms and not feel that the emotion had control over him. Occasionally, however, he would dive in too deeply and start to get swept away again, especially in slow ballads. For him, a great way of adjusting the level of intensity was through lighting up the mood by shifting the frame into a swing or Latin rhythm. This way he could cool the emotional intensity back to a manageable, more playful and even enjoyable degree.

The Container of the Self-Written Song

Improvisational songwriting is another route we can take if someone wants to move more freely, yet still wants to play within musical structures. Again, using the harmonic frame of a simple chord sequence on the piano as a base, people can explore their musical, emotional, and vocal impulses while still being musically held. To create such a song together we might listen out for reoccurring melodies and then invite the words of the singer to spontaneously occur on the inside and then flow out into the open. Or, we can write the words of the song and then, through improvisation, find the melody.

A speech therapist came to me in search of her singing voice. In the beginning, she was very much stuck in getting it right and doing everything by the book, so we stayed with her desire for structure and worked with simple songs she knew. Her real longing, however, was to find her own natural musicality and to connect with her creative self.

After some time of building trust, she slowly opened up to the possibility of improvising over a simple chord sequence. In this process, I encouraged her to allow trial and error and reassured her that it was ok to sing off-key. She was courageous and jumped in and to her amazement was able to accept and enjoy notes of disharmony as part of the musical landscape; she also found some lovely melodies. We kept repeating this approach in many sessions and she experienced more and more ease in finding her intuitive way through music. One day she came feeling quite low, dealing with a feeling of never being enough. Having found some true connection with herself, along with a sense of freedom and comfort in improvising, we again chose to work this way, this time really calling up the nurturing quality of singing and turning it towards herself.

I asked her to listen out for a little line that might want to come to support her. After a while it showed up and in due course words naturally came, as well. She opened up to a space of self-soothing, and short phrases of encouragement and self-love appeared that turned into her own personal mantra. We recorded it and it accompanied and supported her for a long time.

The wonderful underlying principles of Voice Movement Therapy support us in discovering and expressing the various shades and textures of our voices and our emotions. In my experience, when we use the song as a container, almost all deep processes can be explored in a joyful and playful way; even very difficult emotions can be tasted, accepted, and transformed with greater ease into something enjoyable. Songs open doors that free our voices in a powerfully positive way.

VOICE AS ARCHIVE IN DEVISING THEATRE

Gina Holloway Mulder

We cannot separate the performer from the person performing. The one in front of us is performing themselves and their journey through the underworld. We all have an innate desire to express ourselves, but as artists we make a career of transporting inner experience to the outside world. Devised theatre practitioners make meaning of our emotional landscapes through body, voice and image and translate our personal story so that audiences can have some understanding of our journey. We offer our stories as invitations for them to reflect on how a theme or moment may relate to them in terms of themselves in particular and the human condition in general. On some level, I think we also seek to evoke some deeper archetypal resonance and a personal and perhaps communal shift in the process. The act of performance is intricately and inextricably connected to the performer. In devised theatre they are the same; the performer is the embodied archive from which the performance is created and shared.

I am defining 'devised theatre' as a performance work that is not preconceived but evolves through a process of engaging with the self and whatever issue is most pressing. It is, in short, autobiographical theatre created out of the desire to express one's experience or some crucial aspect of one's self in order to share, to be witnessed, and to be heard. The creation process employs improvisation, deep listening, and reflection. Such works may be political, social, or purely personal, bringing that which is not voiced, not seen, silenced and hidden, out from the shadows in order to shine a light on it. The creator has only herself as a resource, using her bodymind as the primary impulse from which to draw her material in order to elicit a creative response. A devised theatre practitioner needs courage to share her vulnerable self with witnessing others. This is not about entertainment, but about changing something, opening something up: an idea, a situation, a dialogue. It's about revealing the "messy bits" of one's personal experience to some meaningful degree. It aims to move the audience by telling a truth, pulling up the strands of experience from the deep inner heart-cave and exposing them, often painfully, to the fresh air.

Before I trained in Voice Movement Therapy, my devised performance works were primarily movement and image based: 'performance art' and 'physical theatre' as it emerged in the 1990s. I sometimes included text, drawing on avant-garde theatre voicework and ideas. As I evolved as an artist, my work became more provocative and political, steeped in feminist theory, gender inequality issues, and body politics. I was protesting about society and culture's expectations of women to conform to a constructed female ideal, against the objectification of the female body and against woman and child abuse. My work confronted the audience with shadow aspects of being female. For me it was a process of researching my relationship with my body and my felt sense of self and an attempt to understand and make meaning of it all.

When choregraphing others I was always physically involved in unearthing, discovering and creating the movement and images from my own body and actively helping others do the same. A pivotal point came when I worked with patients in a mental health rehabilitation facility who had no previous performance or dance experience. It started as a weekly creative movement class for anyone who wanted to join in. We would generally have between eight and 12 people in a class. The group loved the music and the movement sequences I shared with them to develop their flexibility, rhythm and flow. But even more so, they enjoyed the part of the class where I offered an idea, an image or a question with which to create their own movement work which they could then show the group. About four months into my work there, I was able to secure funding from the South African National Arts Council to facilitate a five-month creative process that would lead to a public performance. At this stage, there were no other such expressive therapy programs in South Africa and perhaps only one or two expressive arts therapists in the country.

Five patients and I created a beautiful production, *On The Black Hill*, in which we integrated movement, image, and vocal expression to tell their stories. Their therapeutic value and the transformations I witnessed in these performers as a result of a process that helped them to find their voice and gave them a platform to tell their story, was a profound and decisive moment for me and was part of what gave me the impulse to train as a Voice Movement Therapy Practitioner. I knew that creating work in this way had been a kind of therapy for me and now I had been involved and witnessed that same result with others. *On the Black Hill* had a week-long run to a paying audience at Johannesburg's premier dance theatre venue, The Dance Factory, and was well received by the audience and critics, many of whom did not realize that these people were not professional performers.

Embracing Kerberos was the first professional performance piece I created after my VMT Training, an exploration with my long-time artistic collaborator Rayzelle Joy Sham. It was a devised theatre piece seeking to find the merging point between VMT and physical theatre in both the creative process and in performance. Previously, we would work through either the impulses of the body; taking improvised movement explorations, often to music, to inform or inspire the choreography. Alternatively, we would work through the embodiment of, or the physical reflections on, art, photographs or images evoked by myths, poetry or self-written text. Sometimes I would have an installation idea or a specific site would inspire a piece. This time, it was by nurturing a strong vocal impetus through the techniques I had recently learned and the resulting emergence of subpersonalities and songs (a new addition to my creative toolbox), combined with the development of envoiced choreographic sequences, that we evolved the work.

I'd like to share one example of the process. In rehearsal, the subpersonality *Anxious Annie* and her song emerged during a Voice Movement Journey. After some improvised vocal exploration, I arrived at a gesture of cradling my tummy; the little finger side of my hand making curving movements along the bottom of my belly while I was kneeling and rocking ever so slightly backwards and forwards. I went back to silence to clarify the movement, and after some time of being only with breath and this gesture, I began to re-introduce my voice. Through the voicework, a tune emerged which I nurtured and felt into while continuing to gesture, rock, and connect to my emotional waters. Then the words came out: "Anxious Annie has a hole in her tummy. She's cried a pool of tears that nobody hears." These first two unexpected lines contained images and feelings that were repeated, worked with and nurtured for some time: an endless hole in my belly that never felt full and a young girl kneeling in a massive pool of her own tears, her image reflecting back to her off its dark surface. Through repetition and by allowing the words and song deeper into bodily connection with my belly and breath, and being with the feeling of the vocal resonance, the second two lines arrived: "Anxious Annie, can't tell of her fears. They've been there now, for so many years . . . a truth had emerged.

I continued to work in that way, combining all four lines and allowing the song to evolve and deepen in connection and resonance. I listened to my voice and what it was telling me and felt into my body, its movement and experience of sound and energy. The song echoed a kind of playground singsong, especially on the "Anxious Annie," only slower and more somber; it also held a hollow crying quality, a Clarinet sound that dipped deeper into my body on words like 'hole' and 'so many.' It was then that I realized the connection between overeating and anxiety and was able to explore a childhood experience of being bullied in the playground because I was chubby. Furthermore, I could acknowledge other anxiety- provoking events in my life which had exacerbated this behavior. I understood that even in adulthood there was an enmeshing of anxiety, sadness and loneliness which I was trying to manage by overeating. This coping strategy is not uncommon; the link between such emotions and disordered eating is well researched. The difference, however, was that this understanding emerged from within myself through my body and voice and was therefore far more potent than reading it in a book or having someone point it out, both of which I had previously experienced. In addition, creating with this wounded subpersonality and sharing her with an audience afforded me greater self-awareness and ultimately enabled me to make positive changes to my life.

Figure 17. Gina Holloway Mulder performing in Embracing Kerberos at the Detours Dance Festival, Johannesburg, Jauteng, S. Africa, 2012. Photo: Lisa Skinner.

This is the power of the VMT Journey: one will simply "stay with" the voice and open oneself to listening and hearing what emerges from the unconscious. In a dreamlike way, images and symbols float to consciousness through the voice. And then, very often, a deep truth comes trickling, sometimes gushing out, till finally the silenced parts of our psyche are given voice and heard. A deep sense of relief is experienced when silence is broken and some energetic flow has been restored.

In allowing the voice to take the lead in the rehearsal process, I noticed that I had a deeper and quicker connection to myself and a rich archive from which to create. Doorways were opened to what really *needed* to be expressed and crafted, and through the integration of VMT and embodied creative process arose a new way of exploring my story and of understanding my self. This way of working resulted in a dynamic and powerful performance during which I felt completely different as a performer. I experienced myself as having increased performance energy and being particularly grounded and better able to "hold" the audience. I felt my performance was more honest and vulnerable, and at the same time, the work was able to contain the intensity of emotion expressed. As a performer, I don't only want to tell my story; I want to provide an invitation to the audience to come on a deep inner journey with me and to be open to feeling the echoes of their own stories. What's more, I'd like to encourage them to voice the silenced parts of themselves.

As I continued to develop my skill in this way of creating and performing devised theatre, I began to share Voice Movement Therapy with performance students and professional performers who all benefitted greatly. In this context, besides the Voice Movement Journey, I find the 10 Vocal Components (see page 19) a particularly useful framework that certainly develops vocal range, but also provides alternatives to habitual vocal patterns and encourages a move away from conformance to the "perfect" performer voice. Working in a systematic way through each of the components, investigating both ends of the continuum (for example, with Free Air, to add a lot of free air to the voice and explore this sound and feeling and then to work one's way to the other extreme and try to remove it completely), discovering ways of personally relating to the various sounds through the body's response and images evoked is incredibly useful to the artist in terms not only of their own vocal development but also in terms of their personal development. However, VMT is a therapy that holds the soul in compassion and *this* makes it uniquely valuable as a container for the performer.

Artists are often trying to give form to their inner turmoil. Approaching devising theatre through VMT is a way to manage and work with things that may be overwhelming when diving beneath the surface. It gives an anchor for self-exploration that is therapeutic and integrated. Performers can more easily hold themselves in the deep underworld exploration that is often required in creating such work, rather than lose themselves in it. Performers often lose themselves in the dark abyss; sometimes they are even encouraged to.

What I have found lacking in performer training is a safe container and ways of working which can safeguard the mental health of such a creator. I've witnessed many young artists dredge up their traumas and take themselves to the brink of a crisis in order to protest something, display intensity, or be seen as being "on the edge." It seems that quite often this is encouraged by peers and institutions as something that is somehow necessary in order to be seen as a successful and even a "real" artist. I've also worked with mature artists who have struggled for years, too scared to investigate and create with the material they really want to express; they've felt it was not safe to venture into the underworld because they might not make it out. Instead of waiting for artists to have a breakdown before we support them, I think we need to change the way we teach, to highlight the necessity of ongoing self-care for longevity within the creative arts.

Immersing yourself in a VMT-informed process of creative development in early adulthood when identity formation is at the fore, puts a performer in a uniquely privileged position. Having time and support to delve deeply into stories and conducting such work in a group for an extended period allows for trust and a sense of safety to develop. It also affords the opportunity to be witnessed by this inner circle. Being witnessed in this context is a powerful transformation catalyst that triggers deeper, more expansive breathing, self-awareness, and emotional connection, and a release–a release of what has been held in the psyche as well as a physical and vocal release. When this happens there is a maturing and expansion of expressive ability and the performer grows.

DISCOVERING THE ROOTS OF VOCAL LIMITATIONS

Sasha, a fourth year performing student, had struggled with the component of Loudness in class explorations, but also in her personal life; her mother was loud and domineering and there was little space in the relationship for Sasha. In a pivotal session for her, we were working in a circle, each student having been offered time to work individually on something of their choosing, with the group as witness to their process. Sasha had chosen to work on Loudness.

In the years before, she had placed strain on her vocal cords, pushing to get greater volume or over-articulating in an attempt to get the audience to hear her. A feeling of a blockage in her throat had challenged Sasha and we had previously spent time on opening this space by working with the Facial Configurations, VMT massage, and gentle soothing resonance. On this day we started with some of these exercises with this aim and we then moved on to developing her grounding and rooting her breath.

Creating a good broad stance, a "warrior stance" with one leg stepped forward in front of the other, Sasha worked to allow her breath to open up and deepen so she could feel its flow deep into the lower abdominal space and the pelvic floor. We worked to open the sound in her torso and throat while maintaining her felt and energetic connection to her lower body and to the ground beneath her feet. Keeping with the image of being a warrior, Sasha supported each breath and nurtured her volume, imagining it to grow and spray out and upwards, filling the studio. She remained mindful of her connection to her lower body and her sense of being grounded and strong. As we worked, Sasha's throat relaxed and she connected to a more deeply relaxed flow of breath. Her voice got louder and louder, fuller and more present than before. After some time she stopped, and lay down on her back. She began to cry, her whole body shuddering, and then a giggle, an expression of great relief. We use the component of Loudness when we are happy and when we are angry, and Sasha realized how the limitation placed on this component by her mother had limited her expression of self in both these emotions over the years. She also realized that she had been afraid of her own strength and that all of this had held her back as a performer.

In a following session, Sasha worked on a song she had written to her mom. Singing it was emotionally difficult. But, reconnecting to her body's memory of the strong warrior, a relaxed throat and the deep-rooted breathing from the previous session, her volume came in powerfully. She could express herself. Her song was touching and a number of the other students were moved to tears as they witnessed Sasha singing her song in full volume. For her, being seen and heard in this way was not only validating but also pivotal to her development as a performer. Being able to connect to her audience from this empowered and honest place gave her a real sense of confidence.

The component of Loudness might be the most important for a performer to master. For Sasha, the expansion she experienced in the component of Loudness was a springboard for her further vocal development. Sasha moved from having the opinion that she couldn't sing to acknowledging that she can and that she actually enjoys it. This process changed the way she created theatre and encouraged her to include songs in her work. Sasha is now a professional theatre performer working internationally. She incorporates the VMT exercises into her daily practice and in her approach to ongoing vocal and performance development.

WORKING WITH A DREAM IMAGE

I use three main ways of entering into the creative process. We can go in through voice—then find the bodily connection to the sound and engage the imagination. We can go in through the body or movement—exploring how the body inspires voice and image. Or, we can go in through the image, exploring what the imagination actively offers in combination with voice and movement. There is a natural fluidity between voice, body and imagination that seems to enable us to lubricate all manner of stuck-ness and offers us an endless number of ways to create with our experiences.

"Douglas" felt stuck. He is an accomplished musician-singer-songwriter who performs both as a solo artist and in collaboration with other musicians. In our first session, Douglas said, "My voice feels separate from me," and, "I want to sing *my* songs." He was searching for a way to embody and claim his voice; years of music study, work as a musician, and many performances had not yet got him to that place. There was a wound that needed to be tended to. In his youth, he had never been encouraged to nurture his musical side. His father regarded music as a frivolous endeavor, a "nice" hobby at best, certainly not a good career choice. As a result, Douglas constantly questioned if he was good enough and, in a way, he swept his authentic voice to the sidelines, further instilling the split he experienced between himself and his voice.

Vocally, Douglas used a lot of Violin when singing. He had a good range from a pitch perspective but there was tension in his neck and throat when singing, especially in the higher notes. When trying to convey emotions in his songs, he would revert to the Violin quality and his habitual head placement. He also used noticeable Glottal Engagement when he started singing. This gave a feeling of abruptness, forcing, disconnection, and of trying too hard. His breathing was not particularly free or expansive; rather, breath capacity and support was harnessed through some physical effort. The majority of his sound was produced in the upper chest or clavicular area and above. His singing was not embodied. He recently shared, "When I sang from a disembodied place, I gave over my power to the audience," and "When disconnected, my voice was out of my control; now it's part of me–things have changed a lot."

In the non-judgmental space of our sessions, there was no such thing as a bad sound; his livelihood and his reputation were not on the line. This gave Douglas permission to experiment with his voice and its embodiment. The Ten Vocal Components, as a language to describe sound in a noncritical way (see page 219), was very useful and the option to amplify or remove each one from the voice gave him inspiration for exploring his voice outside of professional singing or speaking. He could play and rediscover his authentic voice which was in ways different to his performer voice. Ultimately, he developed greater range in singing and in creating songs. As it is in VMT, it was not only about hearing himself differently, but also about feeling into where these sounds were in his body and what physical and imaginal elements arose, and what that meant in relation to where he found himself or what he was working through at the time. The VMT work and his own active psychological process became increasingly and beautifully intertwined, each reflecting on the other.

Entering into the work through active imagination was transformational for Douglas. It helped him to bypass his inner critic and play with what was present in a more embodied way. He often brought dreams or symbols into the studio and this opened space for the exploration and development of subpersonalities which held something powerful for him; this was a completely different way of coming to voice and of allowing songs to emerge that offered a freedom from expectations–personal, parental, and industry-related.

We explored a number of subpersonalities during our sessions. Fazza first emerged in a dream. In the dream, Douglas had pulled over on a deserted highway, a man in a dark blue Italian suit–later named Fazza–walked toward his car and handed him a box through his window. Therein was a single piece of gold, a Lego. Douglas felt strongly that this was what he had been searching for, that the gold Lego symbolized the missing piece and the answer to how to be successful. Over time and by amplifying the dream through voice and movement, Douglas developed the subpersonality of Fazza: a confident, successful, smooth musician whom everybody adored. We played with Fazza's posture and attitude, his image (sometimes working in front of a mirror), his desire for acknowledgment, and we played to discover his voice. Douglas now understood that Fazza was a part of him that needed a voice, a specific expression. Immersing himself in the process, he searched for and purchased the perfect dark blue Italian suit, the right tie and hat, and embodied Fazza.

In working towards integrating Fazza and other subpersonalities, I knew intuitively that Douglas needed to be witnessed; he needed to perform to an audience for this energy to be fully realized. We embarked on a process of devising a voice-led performance that was to function as a rite of passage and which would mark his transition into a new performance of self.

Douglas found focus and clarity as he carefully crafted the performance, deciding on which aspects of his journey he would share and what stories he would tell. He developed costumes, worked on various songs—with different vocal components and musical styles—and ordered these to create a narrative structure and flow. He designed the aesthetics of the performance space mindfully, integrating personal symbols and other images. We invited about twenty guests to the intimate performance space; the guests were all people who would be able to come to the performance with a non-judgmental frame of mind, people who had experienced VMT, who were mindful of such processes, and of the importance of ritual. Some were psychologists, expressive arts therapists, bodywork practitioners, dancers and artists. In the invitation, the witnesses were informed of the purpose of the performance. Candles lighted the pathway to the performance space and witnesses were welcomed and seated in a way that set up the time-space as sacred, as special, as liminal. There was to be no applause (this was hard for performer and audience). At the end, there was a period of silent self-reflection and then some light snacks and drinks to celebrate, also carefully chosen and prepared for their personal symbolism.

For Douglas, it was about having the courage to be present to himself, to claim his ground, and to be seen and heard in performance in a non-judgmental way. It was a performance for himself, not for the audience, not based on what he thought the audience wanted to hear or would think was good, but to express aspects of himself that had not found artistic expression before. This was the initial platform for a deep change in perspective, a coming home from the edge, an embodiment and connection to his voice and a claiming of his ground.

What I witnessed was a developing ability to be generous as a performer while still maintaining his connection to himself. The performance demanded he be present to the moment of performance, to be grounded and connected to his body. He maintained a relaxed open vocal tube and made use of his full vocal range, not just the habitual pitches and patterns. And, he was able to hold more eye contact while singing, something that had been challenging for him before. The relationship between himself and the audience felt connective. We were listening. Having a different experience of the audience allowed him to be with them. As a result, the audience was moved and opened; they appreciated the honesty of what he shared and saw the beauty in his expression and in his process.

Performing is a potent part of the VMT practitioner training process and it can be equally potent for the client who is open to crafting and sharing their process in this way. Douglas's process of integrating his voice, body and imagination through subpersonalities and into performance supported, grounded, and focused him. After the performance, he began taking himself as an artist more seriously, and the fracture that had kept him disconnected from his voice had begun to heal. Douglas told me he had realized that he had about *1200 original songs* on his phone that he had recorded but never shared; his inner critic and the belief that he and they were not good enough had been that restrictive! He shared that these songs were not cutting edge; although, they were simple songs but really beautiful. "They are *my* songs," he said. He referred back to the image of the golden Lego piece and said that over time the meaning of the golden Lego had changed and that now the golden Lego piece symbolized the goldmine of songs that he had been sitting on.

Over the years I have seen that creating autobiographical theatre through a process that prioritizes the emerging voice helps clients to integrate the many and sometimes paradoxical parts of themselves. The rehearsal process gives time to digest, interrogate and reflect on ideas and feelings within the contained therapeutic framework of VMT. This way of working offers a time and space out of the ordinary for the creativity of such an integration to be witnessed by others and thereby be brought into the world outside of the studio. VMT-informed performance opens the space for the sacred act of being present and being witnessed; it is a holy act and a therapeutic experience.

Chapter Six

TOWARDS A LIVING HARMONY: VOICE MOVEMENT THERAPY AS AN INSTRUMENT FOR SOCIAL CHANGE IN SOUTH AFRICA

Gina Holloway Mulder (in conversation with Rev. Boniswa Kamba and Sangoma Nokubonga Mathole)

(The following article incorporates transcribed conversations. As editor, I have tried my best to include as much of the way each of us speaks in describing our own work as possible. Boniswa and Nokubonga are not first language English speakers, so I have occasionally included parentheses to further clarify ideas for the reader.)

INDABA

The years 2020 through 2022 proved to be a multi-layered and complex time for people and countries around the world, a time when the inability of so many of our established political, economic, social and cultural structures to respond adequately to the increased strain caused by the pandemic highlighted the many problems in our systems. There are so many things we are just not getting right and the cracks are showing; we can no longer pretend they are not there and many of us see the dire need for things to change.

I wanted to raise up the South African story within this global narrative and invited two of my fellow South African practitioners of Voice Movement Therapy to a series of conversations. We got together in 2020 via Zoom to discuss what we and our discipline might offer in working towards healthy social change and how we might contribute to bridging the seemingly ever-growing gap between peoples and communities. I believe that we have all been called up to look more deeply at our social fabric and to ask, “What can I do to make things better?” “How can we do this differently?” These questions and our shared passion for and belief in our own work as a powerful transformation catalyst led to our mini-Indaba.

In South Africa, the term *Indaba* refers to big meetings, consultations, or conferences. But it is more than that: Indabas are deep conversations that take a long time and are circular in nature. At indabas we talk about important matters. An indaba offers us the opportunity to look at things differently and from many angles, to hear all sides of the story. The point is to listen and share, to reflect on and take counsel. One is urged to be mindful of oneself and one’s subjective view, to hold the intention of reaching out to the other, and to be open to learning from others. Similar to the creative process, and indeed central to the work of VMT, indabas require us to “trust the process” and to step in with the courage to be lost, while trusting that we will indeed meet one another somewhere along the way, although we never know at the start where that might be. With this in mind, VMT practitioners Boniswa Kamba, Nokubonga Mathole and I began our series of conversations about our country South Africa and how we could share and grow Voice Movement Therapy as a way to nurture social harmony.

Boniswa is Xhosa and the granddaughter of a village chief. She is the founder and executive director of the NGO Voice Movement Therapy Eastern Cape (VMTEC) which takes this work into both rural and city communities. She is a Methodist minister and a counsellor who has worked extensively with families and within the context of Gender-Based Violence. She also works with police departments and in correctional facilities. Boniswa is an elder in her community.

Nokubonga is also Xhosa. She is a Sangoma, a traditional healer continuing a role held by previous women in her family. In addition to being a VMT practitioner, Nokubonga is also trained in Art Advocacy. She works with groups in both the Eastern and the Western Cape and in other areas of the country, focusing on the upliftment and empowerment of impoverished women and children, many of whom have survived domestic violence and/ or are affected by the HIV virus. She also works with youth who suffer with addictions.

I am Gina, an English-speaking South African with a mixed European, British and Middle Eastern heritage. I come with a background in theatre and movement and have a private VMT practice in Durban where I work with individuals and small groups. I have worked in schools for children with special needs, with both professional and student performers, and I lecture at universities. I also work as a business communication coach in companies in

South Africa and abroad.

It was immediately obvious that we were coming from three different perspectives and that the way we each work with VMT is different; we weren't quite sure where to begin. We meandered through a number of circular online meetings asking questions and sharing our work, listening, wondering, and trying to trust that something of value would emerge. Over time, it became clear that something was forming; under the surface some magic was brewing and initiating a ripple effect. This article emerged from these mini-Indabas.

THE REALITY ON THE GROUND

In the book *Art in Action*, Steven Levine advises that we start at home. He writes, "The work of social change begins with trying to understand the world in which people already live. Only then can we see the possibilities of responding to that reality" (Levine, S.).[1]

Although the South Africa we live in today is very different to the country we lived in prior to democracy, we are no closer to the ideal of peace, reconciliation and equality. Our people are facing numerous social and mental health challenges, as well as economic and educational struggles caused by our history and exacerbated by the lack of real leadership in our country, not to mention the acute strain on all systems and relationships caused by the Covid 19 pandemic, the violent politically motivated 2021 riots, the devastating 2022 floods, and incredible inflation as a result of the Ukraine/ Russia war. In some ways, we seem to be stuck in an uncomfortable liminal space between the world of the past and our ideal of a Rainbow Nation. On the ground, South Africans do not feel safe. Physical, economic and food security are fragile at best. Many of us lack a sense of belonging which encourages the escalation of "us versus them" tension. We are struggling to survive in a system that does not support us, that is corrupt and offers false promises, that is deficit-oriented and, on the whole, short-sighted.

When South Africa transitioned into a democracy, we recognized the need for the untold stories of our struggle to be voiced and witnessed by the nation. The Truth and Reconciliation Commission (the TRC) was initiated, and although not a perfect process, it positioned the voice, and in particular the voice of the individual, as an essential vehicle for change.[2] This reflects the essence of VMT: that transformation is possible when we create space for the development and expansion of the expressive embodied voice. Truth and reconciliation are only possible when all our voices are heard; and often, as we have found, words alone are not enough. As VMT practitioners, we can see the promise that our embodied voicework holds for making a meaningful contribution to the reconciliation, healing and future harmony of our communities and our country, from the ground up.

VMT is a Western modality; it cannot simply be inserted into African communities without sensitivity and understanding. Some of the ideas central to VMT–for example: exploring your own embodied voice; voicing yourself, your needs and desires; being assertive–can be regarded as challenging to traditional views, societal structures, established gender roles, and racial etiquette. As South African practitioners, we have been finding ways of introducing VMT as an alternative way of working for both individual and larger changes. In her comments, Nokubonga highlights that this may take time in cultures that may not be so open to sharing their problems in a therapeutic way. An important question to ask, then, is: How do we develop acceptable ways to nurture the individual's voice within a communitarian culture so that the positive changes experienced by individuals can ripple outward into the community? Early in our conversations, Boniswa shared that she believes the first step is the reconciliation of families, saying, "We need to face such challenges on the ground."

WHERE OUR WORK IS NEEDED MOST

Mending Broken Families

Boniswa began sharing VMT within her own community. She was already well respected as a minister and counsellor and this provided a platform of trust on which her work could be built. Since 2012, Boniswa has developed a family-based way of working within communities which creates space for the embodied voice of the individual not only to emerge but also to be supported within the cultural and community context.

There are four pillars to Boniswa's approach:

1. The individual has to be supported by the family and the community at large if real progress is to be made.

2. In individual and group work, Boniswa's focus is on action. She believes that, "Action is what moves us forward." In her sessions, actively engaging people's bodies and minds by doing VMT exercises and creating, in the form of arts and crafts, takes precedence over just sitting and talking and is what leads to the sharing of stories and songs.

3. The individual needs to take ownership of their voice and of the VMT work. Boniswa says, "They cannot wait for us practitioners to come and do it

with them and for them. And they need to share it with others."

4. The process must be sustainable. The individual needs to be able to go into the community and share what they've learned with others, or they should be able to make something (art or craft) out of their process that they can sell to make money. Boniswa believes that "They must be doing something with it for VMT to live on."

In our conversations, Boniswa shared her approach:

> We work in groups. There are groups for girls only, the daughters, and that group is not a big group, it is ten or less at a time. So, there are sessions for girls only and there are sessions for women only; also, there are sessions for boys only and sessions for men only. During these sessions we check each group's real needs and get them to know more about VMT and these exercises of Voice Movement Therapy.
>
> We do the actions [VMT exercises] once or twice a week. Even in the sessions we are doing, we don't keep quiet, we do the "ummms" [the sounds], the positions [Convex/Concave and animal postures], also Massage, Manipulation and Compression to encourage deeper breathing, and when we begin the singing in the midst of those actions—well, it is working. We do not start singing now like we did in the olden days with those Western classical warmups that we did—Doh ray me fa so—we changed that into Loudness, Pitch, Pitch Fluctuation and Harmonic voicing. (See page 18.)
>
> The children: We are bringing children into the light with Voice Movement Therapy. They do dance: African dance and the Western dance, the quickstep. And there is singing—because singing is what is inside, the inner most. And you feel relaxed; even if you are listening to someone else singing, it fills you a bit.
>
> The women: There is this escalation of women's abuse in our country. We share and talk with these ladies who are faced with challenges of this kind; be it rape, be it children being beaten, family splits, violence—you name it, we speak and share these experiences as we go along with our VMT practices. Somebody will feel like something is exploding: "I need to vent it, I need to say it, I need to tell the people what happened to me."

Figure 18. Boniswa Kamba (far right) leading a women's group in a rural community center in Cape Elizabeth, S. Africa in a workshop entitled "Not all closed doors are locked." 2021. Photo: Fuya Mankeye.

Joining the two groups: Then we have sessions for girls and women together so that they are able to interact with one another freely and they are able to share their difficulties with each other; and then, if they can, to share with their mothers. It is especially important for all to be able to express

> themselves safely, to have this sense of safety because people need to feel safe; they want to be safe.
>
> The boys and men: And we also have sessions with the boys' group and the daddies, the men's group. They do the VMT exercises and join in discussing. There are times when they sit and discuss about how they felt when they did the VMT exercises. And then the boys and men come and meet each other half way and they share their ideas and feelings about the challenges at their homes.
>
> Large combined group: And then we do also have the bigger group sessions—these sessions can sometimes include up to 150 participants—where we are able to mix them—girls, women, boys and men of the community—and they do VMT actions and discuss matters of concern and they come with resolutions. When they come back from these VMT sessions they do get together, they start to see things differently and treat each other differently.

Through working with families in small groups based along age and gender lines, Boniswa creates a sense of safety and belonging that opens up creative and embodied opportunities for the voice of the individual to emerge and to be shared and heard. Through VMT principles using song and movement, people's personal narratives, emotions and traumas can be expressed and integrated. These small groups then provide the individual the support they need to voice freely in the next phase where two groups come together. Again, support is created through gender lines. The joining of the community, both male and female groups, nurtures cohesion and provides an opportunity for all individuals to be seen and heard, especially those who would not normally be afforded such an opportunity outside of this kind of process.

Boniswa uses a similar progression with the people she works with within the correctional facilities. There she will work with individuals first and then with small groups of inmates. She works with willing family members, too, but separately at first. Then she creates a space for the family and the inmate to come together. Reaching out to these incarcerated individuals, making them feel safe, and allowing them to express themselves brings fractured families and communities together. Through her work Boniswa tries to create a sense of belonging and an opportunity for people to feel seen and heard, acknowledged and accepted. She believes that reconciliation is only possible if these steps are taken first.

About her work with inmates Boniswa shared:

> I work with specific populations in prison: for example, those with co-occurring substance abuse and other mental disturbances, sex offenders, and older inmates. We work through trauma, hopelessness, inmate identity,

culture and gender-specific issues through the Voice Movement Therapy techniques.

The focus of my work is on socially isolated inmates and those who show interest in the program. Many prisoners do not have anyone to visit them while serving their sentence, even those on trial. They have sometimes lost touch with their families and friends and some of them do not have any family left. I work toward building self-esteem with the inmates who feel weighed down by their experience of traumatic situations, mental disturbances, and the emotional and psychological factors which inhibit and restrict their vocal expression and ability to communicate.

Before involving inmates in my family approach, I facilitate individual therapeutic counselling. I always share different philosophical approaches and theoretical orientations and employ a variety of therapeutics in those sessions. The common factor here is that inmates in a private consultation are free to explore more sensitive issues which they might not be ready to discuss in a group.

Then in a group of four to five inmates, I do exercises that take advantage of the fact that inmates are experienced at playing roles negatively; instead, I direct their skill towards a positive solution, and a healing process is achieved gradually. I am very proud to say Voice Movement Therapy and its role-playing can help offenders perceive their behavior and improve. Lots of their hidden talents come out in these engagements: singing, artistic ability, good behaviors... Reconciliation takes place in many ways.

I'm working with these prisoners there, in the cells, and I make it a point that they see VMT as a tool to break through their traumatizing situations. That word, it's a big word "reconciliation." These people, some of them, did some very bad things that they don't even want to share. VMT is a platform for letting people talk, express, VMT is a tool for opening the mouths of those who have sunk down... Either way, I am meeting with families there, calling upon parents of those who are in prison to do the reconciliation... It is a process. I start by getting everyone to walk around the hall as we talk together, getting them to move and relax a bit... That is my introduction before I get into the gist of the matter. The one who did something bad has something to say, but he can't just come out with it. It is a process.

There is a deeper intention in creating this procedural structure. In anticipating success for this therapeutic process, Boniswa highlights that it is not only about people being seen and heard but also about helping the family and/or community to find new ways of supporting the person who was incarcerated over the coming weeks, months and years. How can we give this person the best chance of success? Boniswa advocates for people who have been through such a process to take ownership of it and to work with others in the community, encouraging them to express themselves and to claim their own voice in creative and embodied ways. Supporting people to become active in the community and to provide a service to others assists in the longevity of the therapeutic outcome.

The idea of being active is central to Boniswa's philosophy: "People must be active in the process—moving, singing, dancing, or creating something with their hands." In her group with elderly ladies, for example, "They make bags or pictures, crochet or knit. While they are doing this, they relax and open up to the therapeutic process; there is safety in the doing, in the creating, and they can then use their voices and share their stories and their troubles."

Incorporating such arts and crafts activity ingeniously connects a familiar activity with something new; it creates a sense of safety, clearing the pathway for further VMT work. Importantly, the items they create during the therapeutic process are then sold to local tourists to provide some small income for these women. Thus, the process of VMT is more sustainable and the work has an economic ripple effect.

Gender-Based Violence and Addiction

Nokubonga's work highlights the healing potential of the creative act and the transformative power of sharing one's story with a group of witnesses. She sees the expressive space created by VMT as one in which people can be emotional and can explore the depths of their traumatic experience. As a healing process, Nokubonga holds that the creative development offered by VMT—specifically the making and singing of songs—is central for her clients' progress and that the transformation of negative experiences into something more positive through creative acts is uplifting.

Nokubonga does a lot of work with women and girls who have experienced rape. She incorporates the elements of Convex and Concave, the Sphere, Breathing, Massage (with permission from the client), (see page 21) and uses the Song as a container for intense emotions. Following are extracts from three case studies Nokubonga shared with us:

> Client A was a 16-year-old girl who had, for years, been repeatedly raped by her biological father, her stepfather, and her grandfather. She had chosen silence, had "decided to endure the stress on her own." But now she felt something was about to burst. She complained about stiff shoulders, and then I asked her if she would prefer a soft healing massage and told her I have to get permission from her to do this. And she said I can continue. As I was doing the massage, I could feel the deep tension which was cracking while I was working with her. The massage lasted for 30 minutes and I had to let her lie for another 30 minutes while I was preparing an exercise for her when she woke up.

> The exercise was about exploring her feelings and trying to encourage her to authentically express herself. I then told the client we are going to do the Sphere work (see page 255) while discovering the playfulness and the deepest thoughts and feelings and I also introduced the idea that she is allowed to vocalize actively when expressing a feeling. I explained everything about Sphere work and the motive behind engaging with it. She took a very big space and claimed boldly that it's hers and she won't allow anyone nearby. She got very angry when I came close and I immediately understood the background of that anger. I encouraged her to continue and then she started shouting with pain, saying "No! No!"
>
> That's when [she realized] that somebody has taken something away from her and that thing belonged to her. As she moved around, I noticed the change in her voice. It was swinging from quiet to loud and she was getting very angry. I said to her to let the anger out, let it out! And she told me some flashes are coming back of what has been happening to her and she cried a very sad cry. I tried to calm her with a warm hug. She was responding dearly to the hug. When I asked her should we continue, she said it's enough for the day. She could see this is taking her somewhere and now she is facing her demons. Witnessing my client going through so much pain was difficult; I could relate to her pain, which helped me to empathize, but I told myself to be strong because if I cry, she won't have hope that this, too, shall pass.

Client B was a 20-year-old woman who was in a brutally abusive relationship. She was "feeling worthless" and lived in fear; her life was being threatened daily. She was in a "very bad state."

> As I tried to work with her, I [invited her to] create a song to express her feelings... She agreed to do so, as she would like to share her experience. She is very brilliant and she is ready to move on with her life. Her song was directly on how could something like this happen to her? What has she done and why is the Lord punishing her in this way? If this is part of her journey, why should it be so painful? The most painful part is when she is asking why no one comes along to rescue her? I asked if she is feeling any pain so we can work on that specific area. She told me the whole body is paining and she suspects it's because she has been a victim for some time now.
>
> I asked the client will it be okay if we slowly do an exercise because I want us to tackle the most affected parts. I then introduced the Convex and the Concave (see page 21). We did it slowly for ten times and after that another ten slowly. She complained about the pelvic area that seemed to be giving a problem when she tilts it to the front and even when she has to bend. That literally meant that she is more damaged around the lower parts. I gave her water and she wanted to speak about the whole pain she endured.

> Through VMT she was really contacting the pain she endured and in this safe situation she was able to express it.

Client C was a 29-year-old woman. She and her two-year-old daughter were the victims of a gang rape that was commissioned by the father of her child. [In South Africa, hiring a person or a gang to rape someone is not uncommon. The normalcy of such shockingly violent behavior further underscores the urgent necessity for changing not only gender attitudes, but the enforcement of laws within communities and the changing of attitudes that this is accepted behavior.]

> In the session, I guided the client in creative songwriting to express her feelings. Witnessing my client was touching, and I recalled what had happened to me. I felt like pausing the session because I, too, was on my own journey because of gang rape. I felt like I also needed to write something about what I have endured and share it. I decided to, and it was done like an assignment. The next session was on hearing one another on what we wrote and we sang it and the lady was so shocked that I went through the same thing. Through us expressing our experiences through the songs, the client felt acknowledged and calmed. [Although it is not common practice to bring one's own traumatic experiences into the session, there are times when a practitioner sharing a part of her story with the client can be beneficial, so long as the practitioner can keep the best interest of the client as her primary focus.]
>
> After that, we did Sphere (see page 21) work in a mirroring way, claiming our space and telling "the men out there" that these are our bodies which belong to us, not them. We tried to create a safe space for ourselves and we embodied our experiences and vocally expressed the way we felt which gave us an opportunity to discover that something had shifted; even though it was small, we could feel emptied...She witnessed me and I witnessed her and we could see we have something in common.
>
> What was obvious through our conversations was that one of the major barriers to accessing therapy within African cultures is the stigma attached to speaking out, especially as a woman or girl against a man. VMT offers a space in which people who have experienced gender-based violence can find some expansion, movement, bodily connection and sound. And when they are ready, they can speak of their trauma and work creatively with it through song, movement, and drawing.

With regard to growing VMT in SA, Nokubonga shares:

> It is going to be difficult because you cannot talk back to your elders. It is

> going to take time to change the mindset of the entire community. We need to have a workshop on changing the mindset. It will take time to get into this gender equality thing. We keep talking about gender equality, but we are not practicing it. When it comes to practicing, it is another story... VMT is where we can have the voices of the voiceless. There is too much misunderstanding. In the olden days they were living like that, but this new generation [of women] is not wanting to think or act like that.

Nokubonga advocates for mass educational drives that focus on shifting attitudes towards gender-based violence. She references a 2016 HIV awareness project called Operation Teta:

> You can open up about what you want and what you don't want. Voicing what we like and what we don't like, facing the facts and dealing with the root of the problem . . . [HIV positive] people were stigmatized and so Operation Teta was implemented to change people's minds. What we noticed was that it worked and people were treating people differently and in a better way than before. It will turn the tables. Yes, and everyone gets a chance to speak.

An important part of Nokubonga's approach is through creative work:

> What I like about VMT, you come with this "Let's do this," and something new comes...poems, songs, stories that are written down. So that thing gives birth to these things on its own… I think that the playfulness in VMT is what is helping us to heal. You will be playing with it and then you will see that the stress is coming out without you noticing it. You will notice afterwards that you are healed.

Figure 19. Nokubonga Mathole working with a client in the village of Kwazakhele, Port Elizabeth, S. Africa, 2023. Photo: Chumani Mathole.

Nokubonga finds the aspect of performance within the group context to be particularly powerful. She helps her participants eventually to be able to stand in front of the group and sing their song or dance their story:

> After working for a while, you come up with a song, a poem...but the moment you see yourself [performing] you know, "I can catch these people's eyes; they are listening to me." It means that there is something important happening and "I do have importance in doing something." Sometimes we let ourselves down, but the moment you get into Voice Movement Therapy, that's where you feel you can lead an entire group on doing this or that. Being able to be on the stage and perform your song is healing. To give youth the task to enact something from their life, you are giving them an opportunity to check in on their mindset about what is happening and what they are feeling, engaging the imagination, educating them in that way. They research themselves and then they come with something. They will not feel left behind.

Nokubonga recently started to work with young addicts and realized that these youngsters need a long time to be able to come out and express themselves. She found that progress was very slow and many children relapsed. She shared:

> I realized that you have to work with them on an individual level before you move to group sessions. VMT is a platform that is giving them a chance to speak out about what really drove them [to addiction]. Through the work they realize that they have left something behind, their dreams and even sometimes a good foundation. With regard to "reconciliation," some of the families, they don't want to take those addicted children back, they've already washed their hands of them. I think VMT can be of great value here. It will take a long time, but these are the children of the future.

On her group work with these youngsters, Nokubonga shares:

> There are those who do not want to speak in front of others. [Sometimes they say that] their parents are not giving them the love that they need. But then you find out that they were given everything, but the child has decided to go his own negative ways. What I do is I ask them to be on the floor and to draw the pictures. I see chaotic pictures; these children seem to be very confused and they don't have direction in life. It is a process and I need to work with them more and more…for many months.
>
> What I see is that they become happy when you ask them to sing or write. I first see the anger, but in the end, when they finish, you can see that there is hope there. But when they come back the next day, you can also see this child is still on the same page that he was on yesterday–and then you ask the problem and they say, "No, I still need some time, but I am trying my best."
>
> There was one exercise I asked them to do in pairs. One person stands in front of the other and they speak. What happened was interesting. The first speaker became angrier as they shared their story, but the other one calmed down. And then the first speaker experienced shame. I then asked them to sing their story. They sang, expressing what they went through and, in the end, you see the child crying...and that is therapy. When [the child cried and the other one realized that] "what I was doing was wrong, so I should get help to come back to life.
>
> When I use the song, I use it for them to express their feelings and then even the body language, somehow it changes. When there is joy, the voice and body language is changing but when there is that stress, then you can feel the voice is moving the other way around–it's getting restricted or cracking. And when it is very emotional, then you can see the client trying to squeeze him or herself as they try to hold themselves together. And that's how I use the song as container. They get to visit the darkest parts of their body from deep down.

Nokubonga introduces songwriting through a timeline structure:

> They write what they felt at the time when the incident happened, and then

> they write about the present and how they feel now, and then we take that and we analyze that. Sometimes they start with the present and then we fill in from the beginning of their journey, from when the incident started, and then we move it along up until we reach that enjoyment of performing and sharing it in the end. In the beginning, they feel tense, but as the song goes right along, you can feel there is a free spirit that is moving in them. You can see that they feel squeezed when they start the song and then as they go slowly with their lyrics, they start to enjoy what is happening. And then, afterwards, we will discuss it. That's how I do it with these clients.

Nokubonga's work with songwriting brings people into the present moment, allowing them to experience themselves in a more positive, expressive, and expanded way. She continues to share:

> Most of the time, the future will come in a poem. For me, poems are a strong thing. In the poem you write what you feel and it will come. That strong energy that comes in the poem, and then putting it into a song and performing, sharing, enacting it for others, is what will give them hope for things changing in the future. I feel they are being equipped to face the future.

Boniswa also values poems and songs as platforms for change and healing. She shared, "The idea of bringing poems [from] within, you know, you talk about the future, people have a vision for long term goals. Within that poem they create some sort of reserve for handling the disappointment if their wishes are not coming [true]." She continues:

> We do singing when we begin our sessions. We normally begin by putting the people in a bigger space and everyone has to walk and at that time they are thinking about themselves and their lives. And as they sing—you know, the "woos" and "woahs" and "mmms"—as they turn around in their walking, they begin to free themselves. The power of the voice will come out whether singing, talking or praising, or doing poems; but you have to wait up until you see the session is moving and the blowing of the voices is beginning to start. You must wait; they will come as they do. Until they come, though, [we must keep] doing the activity. This thing does not just come because you said, "Oh let's sing, let us do singing." Then they will do singing for the sake of singing, but that is not coming from within themselves. Singing that is good, that is coming from themselves, then they are connecting to their innermost.

Nokubonga adds:

> The most important part when you are working in the group is when one

> person [is performing or sharing] and the others in the group are watching. They will get healed through watching the experience of the other client. I find that most interesting, because some of them think that their problems are much bigger than the others and when they hear that person who is on the stage is having heavier troubles, that gives them strength to offload and makes the journey easier for the other client, gaining that trust from someone you have only just met. and feeling that you can speak because this person has more problems than you. So others get healed by somebody's experience, I find that most interesting.

Nokubonga finds this aspect of performance within the group to be particularly powerful. Through her VMT work she helps her participants to eventually be able to stand in front of the group and sing their song or dance their story. Witnessing others gather the courage not only to talk about their trauma, but to create with it and share that creation in performance gives others the courage to do the same. There is great support to be found in such groups.

In some ways Nokubonga's work echoes Boniswa's: they both recognize the success of a therapeutic process which initially works with individuals and then, later on, they find ways of integrating the individual into the larger group. I also use this approach; it seems it is an organic, instinctual way of working with people.

In the Workplace

I, Gina, have been lucky to work with people from many different ethnic groups and cultures in South Africa and abroad. What this has shown me is that Voice Movement Therapy successfully bridges the cultural and language divide, since tones and qualities of voice and movement are the bedrock on which all communication between people is built. In addition, its non-judgmental philosophy and the neutral terms we use, combined with the specificity of both the vocal and the non-vocal components which are action-based rather than opinion-based, offer some common ground that can be used as a starting place for all kinds of connections and social change. VMT is very successful in bringing diverse groups together and, although I love working with children and youth, I am going to focus here on an area not often addressed in our discipline: work in the field of corporate communication training.

Within the South African context, there are a number of things that prevent people from having and using their voice effectively in the workplace. One challenge is that most places of work use English, and for many people English is not their first language. This creates a barrier to communication, not simply from a language perspective, but from physical and psychological perspectives, as well, any one of which can affect our manner of speaking and body language. Since communication is a felt physical experience, any training which does not address communication from an embodied perspective will, I believe, have limited success. Another challenge is that companies generally adopt a Western approach to leading, and people who cannot step up, share their ideas, and claim their voice and place in the company—within groups/teams and with superiors—get left behind. Although companies highlight teamwork, if you as an individual are not able to voice yourself successfully within groups and/or to your manager, you will inevitably have less career success than someone who can. However, people often don't feel safe to express themselves at work since their job and livelihood might be jeopardized by what they say. In South Africa, where the unemployment rate is the highest in the world, currently sitting at 46.6% (as at December 2022), people cannot risk losing their job.

Over the years I've had many one-on-one clients who have come to me because they've noticed that their career development was being hindered by their inability to voice themselves fully and clearly. Sometimes there are articulation challenges that need to be addressed (although I don't believe in accent neutralization), but more often it is a psychological and therapeutic journey such clients need to embark on. One of the things I do with business clients is to bring deeper awareness to the moment of communication. I help them to realize that charged moments, silence, or uneasiness in relation to a specific colleague or when speaking in public, have physical, breathing, vocal, and emotional elements and are very often related to habitual patterns initially adopted during earlier communication experiences. We explore the skewed beliefs about themselves or others and their sense of self in the world and within the company. When people discover these layers of self-expression and grasp that they can learn to breathe, ground themselves and sound confident and assertive through vocal qualities, we make real progress towards upskilling them. It is empowering because, initially, most people don't realize that they have a choice in how they present themselves vocally and may communicate in an unconscious way. Once conscious of this fact, clients are better able to sculpt their interactions with others purposefully and more effectively.

I conducted a series of group workshops with a big national bank in South Africa as part of a "change management" process. I worked with the Customer Contact Centre staff. This is a unique context from a business perspective because these people need to be able to communicate clearly with customers, team members and superiors in a highly stressed environment (stressed for the staff but also for clients who call in, since they are discussing financial matters). Call centers have notoriously high staff turnover rates. The pay is generally not great, one often gets verbally abused by people calling in, and the work environment is not unlike a chicken run: employees work long hours with very few bathroom breaks and have an exceptionally high daily call target with computerized systems that immediately push calls within a few seconds of the last one. Most people work in this environment because they simply do not have other employment options. The physical, mental, and emotional toll on the person is significant. My task was essentially to implement a Voice Movement Therapy-informed program that could help these people keep some connection with their bodymind and voice in this context and also improve their general communication skills.

The three-day workshop always begins with a discussion about the relationship between the metaphorical and acoustic voice and then I ask the participants to draw their relationship with their voice. These images are always interesting to see. There is often the expression of being too soft in volume, or feeling unheard, feeling small or isolated, feeling blocked or choked. Some people like their voices and draw them in a positive light. We take a few minutes for the participants to share their drawings and any reflections they may have with the group. Then we go inward and work with breath, focusing on getting participants to become more aware of the contraction and expansion of their breath and opening up their body for a more expansive breathing experience.

One of the exercises I use is the VMT Spiral of Maximum Stretch, which really opens up the chest, the sides and the back of the torso (see page 22). This is based on the spherical work that comes from the natural action of breathing. We also work with some simple resonance exercises; the focus here is to bring awareness to the breath, body and voice, and the relationship between the three. Using their hands, participants feel their bodies expand and contract as they activate their areas of expansion, increasing their resonance and the carrying quality of their voice. We also work on rooting the breath and voice, connecting the whole body in the production of sound. We pay attention to sitting posture and how different postures impact breathing and voicing, and affect their overall sense of self. I introduce the participants to the Vocal Tube and invite them to experience the feeling of lengthening and dilating the Tube and to hear the different vocal qualities of Flute, Clarinet and Saxophone (see page 20).

During the second day, we do a short recap of Day One and get right into some more breathing work, deepening and expanding the breath further through a Spinal Twist Breathing exercise. We also work with various basic vocal warm-up exercises, connecting with resonance and playing around with Pitch. Most of Day Two is about the Vocal Components. I take a very physical and playful approach to this exploration, bringing in the imagination as much as possible rather than promoting a focus on achieving the "good voice." We work through exercises to further the understanding of the Timbres. We pretend to be grand opera singers to play with vibrato and pretend to nervously cross a tight rope bridge hung over a high ravine to access Pitch Fluctuation. We imagine that we are monsters to explore Disruption, and donkeys to feel into the registers of Modal and Falsetto (see page 21). Through this unconventional, creative and playful approach to communication training, I have been able to dissolve all manner of tension and resistance. Participants relax and become more connected to their voice and realize they have a broad vocal range from which to speak.

We then take these Voice Movement explorations into a discussion about how the sounds–these Vocal Components–make us feel, both when we make them and when they come from others. We unpack this from a spoken rather than sung word and communication perspective, shedding light on how the sound of a voice communicates feeling and intention and that this is a large part of the communication process. We explore these reflections in pairs and small groups through role-play and further develop awareness of self (bodymind and voice) and other as we do so. This process sheds light on many aspects of a person's life–besides their phone-based job–and the participants gain a different understanding of themselves and of how others relate and/or respond to them. They begin to see that there are alternative and possibly better, more effective ways of communicating, both verbally and physically. This also demonstrates that we all have a choice in how we communicate with others. Thus, communication becomes more conscious and more empowering for the participants.

After a warmup of breathing, voicing and moving, Day Three of the workshop is mostly spent working with the Sphere to develop awareness of personal space, self in space, and self in relation to other in space (see page 21). We also explore how one's experience of the Sphere affects verbal and non-verbal communication. This part of the workshop develops from exploration of each individual's Sphere, to working in pairs, and then to small group reflections on the day's process and each person' experience of it. Participants are then asked to make a second drawing which expresses their new relationship to their voice. These drawings and reflections are then brought into the larger group and we share reflections on the whole three-day process, along with the "before" and "after" drawings. Each participant is given a chance to present to the group. Often there is a noticeable difference in a person's sense of presence and in their voice. Vocal transformations can happen quickly!

Vocal health is something which is also part of the program. These people are effectively professional voice users who most often get no voice training whatsoever and vocal fatigue and damage are evident in some cases. As part of the workshop, I provide a vocal health practice program for the participants to take home and continue with on their own. This includes many of the breathing, physical and vocal exercises we did at the workshop. There is also a "quick recovery" guide for them to follow if they are treated badly by a client and need to re-set themselves before they connect with the next caller. Self-care is highlighted throughout and participants are upskilled in this regard, too.

To end the workshop process, we all join together in improvised song and dance, using a shared leadership approach in which each person comes forward individually to have their chance to be in the center of the circle and lead the group. Sometimes the women will sing one part and the men another; it is a joyous, inclusive, and inspiring way to end. Participants always leave feeling more positive and more motivated than when they arrived. They feel acknowledged and resourced and that they have an important role to play in the company. Participants report having more empathy for each other and begin to treat each other differently. They also relate differently to the clients they deal with and are better able to manage their stress levels.

Figure 20. A group of employees explores their voices in a corporate workshop led by Gina Holloway Mulder. Midrand, Gauteng, S. Africa. 2018. Photo: Gina Holloway Mulder.

One of the challenges we face as South African VMT practitioners is finding ways of sharing our work that are financially viable for us and financially possible for the client; most people cannot afford to pay for therapy or personal development workshops. If we could get more companies on board with such training programs, I believe that both the companies and the individuals would benefit, and that these benefits would ripple out into society. Implementing VMT in places of work could have a significant impact on the lives of South Africans.

STEPS TOWARD CHANGE

Our mini-Indaba provided some valuable insights about how VMT is already moving us towards social harmony. It is clear that if we feel safe we can find common ground, when we find common ground we can start growing together, and when we grow together there is sustainability and longevity.

VMT Creates a Safe Space for Self-Expression

Such a space contains and embraces; it invites people in to feel a sense of equality and belonging. If we are dreaming about social transformation in South Africa, the first thing we need to do is create safe spaces for relational connection, for only then will individuals be able to find and use their voice to be assertive about what they need, want and don't want. When people feel safe, included, acknowledged and held, they can express themselves and take action to join with others.

Steps We Can Take

VMT helps us to establish a common ground from which we can begin to grow together.

1. Disharmony is often a result of people and groups experiencing themselves as completely different from others. The "Us" and "Them" dynamic is all too common in our world today, and merely highlighting the racial, cultural, economic, and political divide, which is what our policies and our customs do, hasn't gotten us anywhere closer to being able to live in harmony with each other. VMT gives us an opportunity to strip back the things that separate us and allows us a more neutral space where we can come together to explore the human experience. The 10 Components of Pitch, Pitch Fluctuation, Timbre, Glottal Engagement, Volume, Disruption, Register and Vowel (see page 18), which potentially exist in all voices, can bind us together and give us opportunities to find common sounds and feelings.

Breathing together and sensing each other in space gives us a tabula rasa from which to start finding our new songs, solos, duets, rhythms, potent chorus lines and harmonies. In unison, we realize that we are more similar than different. The joy of feeling sound, one's own vibrational resonance and that of the other person, and hearing voices coming together beautifully brings us closer together and into harmony with each other. Furthermore, singing together requires a deep listening. Success depends on developing a sensitivity to the expressions of another person. It is only when we are attuned to ourselves and to others in the moment that we will be able to find harmony. In this positive state, we can open our hearts and minds to how things could be. It is only through feeling differently about each other that we can really start acting differently. When we have found this kind of common ground, we can begin to heal and build something new together.

2. Working from within the individual and then progressing to the group promises sustainability. This way of working seems to emerge organically through the VMT process and proves to have a great impact. Interestingly, Dance Movement Therapist Norma Canner, whose way of working greatly influenced the VMT Foundational Training after its reincorporation in the year 2000, also worked in this way. The progression, or process of expansion, starts from within the client's body and ripples outwards from the individual, to the dyad (a meaningful pair), to the small group, and then to the larger group. This way of working with individuals and then progressing to group work has a positive impact because it mirrors the developmental process. As infants, we initially connect with and look for safety within the relationship with our primary caregiver, often our mother. We then develop a connection with our father, and then siblings, who form the first small group. The process then ripples outwards to include extended family members, peer groups, school, religious community, and continues on to include the larger community, the city or town, the nation, and sometimes beyond. A client who is supported in this way of progressing no longer feels isolated and unsafe, but rather, empowered and valued as a member of the community and the greater society.

There is another level to consider if our work is to have a broader impact. It's all very well working from within specific communities; however, if we are imagining how VMT could have a national and sustainable impact on peace, we need to find opportunities for our work in places where people from different cultures, subcultures, communities, and income levels already come together. Although there is progress in this regard, for the most part South Africans keep to themselves, to their own communities and cultures. If we are to create bridges that lead to social change and greater national harmony, then we need to sing to each other and together. Working within schools, companies and organizations, which in SA, by law, have to be culturally diverse, would be greatly beneficial.

A RAINBOW NATION NEEDS SONGBIRDS

The concept of the Truth and Reconciliation Commission, the TRC, which was conceived of and first applied in South Africa at the end of apartheid and the formation of a new and more representative government, has since been implemented in a number of other countries as a way to open space for people to come forward safely to share their stories and experiences of the atrocities of war, persecution, and human rights violations. The power of the TRC cannot be underestimated in its ability to allow people their voice and to provide witness to these previously unheard stories. I feel, however, that something more is required. The following, said by Anne Brownell to me in a private conversation, suggests what we three editors think might be of use:

> The original meaning of the word therapy is "to wait upon, to attend." As with the TRC, we must attend to each other's individual voices, our stories, but then we must move beyond talk; we must sing and dance together, enacting our truths for each other in a common sharing.

There have been many projects and organizations that have aimed to address aspects of reconciliation within South Africa. The majority have neglected to include the body and the voice in any profound way. Within the creative arts, focused initiatives in theatre, dance, music, art projects, and choirs have made a great impact. But, if we as a nation are traumatized—and I believe we are—what we need is therapy. Voice Movement Therapy has something unique and powerful to contribute. Trauma and conflict affect our body and impact the way we move and don't move, how we hold ourselves, and how we connect or disconnect from our feelings. Trauma disrupts our expression of self and affects our voice. Therefore, a process of healing needs to create space for freedom of expression and the liberation of the embodied voice.

Furthermore, since trauma is experienced in relationship, we need to offer opportunities to mend them and find new ways of relating. If any process is to change the fabric of South African society, it must include aspects of both voice and embodiment in relationship. Reconciliation processes and projects that do not work within the sphere of embodiment and envoicement with the intention of mending this aspect of relationship between self and other through physicalized action and enactment will have limited success. We know that voicework is profoundly unifying and that it opens safe space for us to share our vulnerabilities. VMT facilitates a specific kind of deep communication and allows us to have uncomfortable conversations in a new way. We South Africans have been stuck in the same verbal telling of the story; VMT provides a non-language-based framework for truth-telling and reconciliation, a *human language* through which we can find a new voice with which to tell our unique stories.

Governments do very little to support the individual in their personal transformation and yet expect change in the greater society. Identity evolves from the individual's experiences of their body and sense of self in the world. This is what needs to shift! *Without change in the habitual patterns of self-expression, there will be no shift. Words are simply not enough.* We cannot talk our way into peace, nor into reconciliation. It demands more: more engagement, more imagination, more courage, more ownership of our own behavior. If we as practitioners can provide a safe container for such a creative and dynamically embodied process, a place where all manner of self-expression and story *can* find voice, where the soul can sing and dance and be witnessed, where relationships can be forged through truth and being with that which is uncomfortable, then we may have a pathway for greater social harmony.

Perhaps reconciliation is a word trapped in the past. In a way, it implies that things should go back to how they were before. I think we need a new forward-facing framework. How do we pick up the pieces, listen to each of our unique stories, and mosaic a beautiful picture with them? How do we begin to sing and live in harmony with each other? I think it is not reconciliation that we are longing for; it is *harmony*.

Figure 21. Boniswa Kamba leads a small group in her singing and walking exercise at the IAVMT Conference, Oudtshoorn Western Cape, South Africa, 2011. From L to R, Carol Grimes, Ben van Rensburg, Boniswa Kamba, and Gina Holloway Mulder. Photo: Deirdre Brownell.

NOTES

1. Stephen K and Ellen G Levine, *Art In Action: Expressive Arts Therapy and Social Change.* London, UK. Jessica Kingsley Publisher. 2011, p. 28.

CONCLUSION

GOING FORWARD: GROWING AND GROUNDING IN UNCERTAIN TIMES

Anne Brownell, Deirdre Brownell and Gina Holloway Mulder

In this final chapter, we wish to speak to the future of VMT and address some areas in which we think, and hope, it will grow. Personal investigation, socio-political striving, scientific application... What makes VMT relevant to individuals and groups today? How can it be of value, for example, in environmental movements such as ecotherapy? How can our work be extended more widely into school and youth programs as well as businesses? How does it relate to neurological and vibrational theory: for example, working vocally to calm individuals with PTSD and others struggling with anxiety? Most importantly, how can this work help individuals and groups find and claim their voice to fight for human rights, including the rights of women, people with disabilities, individuals with non-traditional gender identities, indigenous peoples, and others struggling with various kinds of differences, especially socio-economic inequality? How, in this increasingly polarized age of "us" and "them," can we learn to engage our whole body, not just our head, and dare to sing and move together in ways that will help us re-engage with each other with *our whole selves*, to find the commonalities that will enable us to communicate more clearly and effectively so that we may live in that sought-for balance between the rights of the individual and the well-being of the community?

First, we must ask ourselves, what do the various Practitioners of Voice Movement Therapy represented here, and all other Professional and Qualifying Members of this discipline, have in common? What unifies our work?

Here are four basic principles:

1. Everything we need can be heard in the voice, and the Vocal Components help us to do that;

2. Just as there are no "bad" sounds produced by the voice unless they are physically damaging, so there is nothing, so "unspeakable" that it cannot be dealt with, as non-judgmentally as humanly possible, within the double container of a "safe space" established and held by a VMT practitioner, whether a therapist or therapeutically aware teacher, and the structure of self-composed song;

3. It is necessary to engage the whole body in physical action in order to confront difficulties and disagreements in an effective and lasting way;

4. Lastly, to return to the very beginning of Chapter One, all of us need, at our moment of greatest affect—even if we do not know or fear its source—to keep singing so that we may truly express our feelings and thus be able not only to release the muscular body armoring that holds them in, but loosen up our emotional "stuckness" as well. When we can do that, we can begin to engage in a new way with those with whom we differ.

Practitioners of Voice Movement Therapy passionately believe that, even in this age of overwhelming partisanship, we can, by taking the risk to engage our whole self through different modalities such as music, movement, enactment, and imagery—all the expressive arts—and, with regard to our own particular work, to sing and move together in a way that goes "beyond words" to find common ground.

Gina: Reflections on the Search for Soul

In the preceding chapter, I endeavored, with two of my Xhosa colleagues, to share our vision for our country South Africa and how we see VMT as an instrument of progress. There is no doubt that we are living in uncertain times. To some, it may feel like the world is falling apart and that life is becoming increasingly fragmented and de-humanized. As I watch the people around me, I see the impact that the past few turbulent years have had on them and their relationships. It seems to me that humanity is facing a diabolical mental health crisis that permeates every layer of society and does not leave untouched any geographical or socio-political context.

Alfred Wolfsohn described his experience of war and PTSD as a "loss of soul" and recognized that it was the suffering soul that was seeking expression in the students who came to him for help. Today, as well, it is the soul we need to tend to.

The journey to find and heal the soul requires us to venture vulnerably into the dark inner depths of ourselves, with the intention of having a meaningful encounter with our shadow that will result in an improved understanding of it and our acceptance of this part of ourselves. Self-awareness is our developing ability for such profound and uncomfortable self-reflection; healing is what happens in the soul as a result of such an encounter. VMT offers a container for this journey. We need such safe spaces and programs that allow free expression and give us time to understand ourselves anew and therapeutic relationships that support us in our re-configuring and manifesting the lives we truly want.

The ancient Greek adage, "Know thyself," surfaces, and what we seem to need now, more than ever, is to find ways of knowing and relating to our physical, emotional and soulful self. The stories and case studies that we have shared bear testimony to the fact that allowing the embodied voice to rise up in us to be released into the world and heard by others is a way to know ourselves and a way of tending to the soul's suffering. A part of me imagines that VMT could save the world; of course, that is a fantasy, but I do believe it can make a significant difference to the lives of people who dare to enter such a process to find their voice and heal.

VMT practitioners across the globe are sharing this work and carving out new ways of opening the space for different groups of people. There is scope for VMT to be useful in a great number of contexts. I am excited about further research into how the process of VMT may impact on neurobiology. It is my understanding that a certain level of repatterning and rewiring can happen in the brain which leads to clients having a new or different sense of themselves in the world. As discussed in Chapters One and Three, VMT can contribute to this process by uniting thought and feeling through the voice. I also see great potential for VMT as an arts-based research methodology that can facilitate uncomfortable conversations and inspire meaningful ones within companies, schools and other organizations. I have seen the potential for this work to be integrated into business and leadership programs and think such programs could make a positive impact in this context, especially if it could affect government programs.

Deirdre: My Vision, My Purpose

DREAMSCAPE: An Adjunct Program for Elementary, Middle and High School Students with Hidden Learning Disabilities

A *dreamscape* is an open canvas on which to paint your future. What I've always wanted to do is to start a program locally to help people with hidden learning disabilities–such as dyslexia, dyspraxia, and other sensory processing and executive function disorders–to develop their sense of self-worth by claiming their voice, and then to expand this program nationwide to other schools and states. It would have the following aims:

1) Help people to take back, literally to re-embody their voice to strengthen their self-concept and overcome the stigma of having a hidden disability that makes them appear to be less capable than they are. This involves

enabling them through voice, movement, imagery and enactment to be able, effectively and with conviction, to declare their own truth in order to counter the way they have often been misdiagnosed and misunderstood as stupid or lazy. Working creatively in song and story with issues encountered in their environment—in school and at home—and being given the time and space to express their feelings and ideas, to declare their wants and needs in order to give them room to breathe and open up space to communicate more effectively, can build self-esteem and assurance;

2) Provide individualized educational help through creative academic tutoring combined with the Orton Gillingham method and other techniques to reinforce and increase their communicative skills, both written and oral;

3) Work within the frame of a focused understanding of how moving and vocalizing as pursued through Voice Movement Therapy engages both sides of the brain—the linear and the spatial—to bring to light unconscious issues in a way that enables literal meaning to come together with feelings and attitudes in one vocal expression. As has been said, language can be thought of as having two channels: the words we say to convey the cognitive meaning; and the tones of voice, the subtext, in which we express ourselves and convey how we feel about what we are saying. Working through song and vocalization amplifies discrepancies between these channels and provides a new kind of experience so that they can become congruent.

4) In addition, I hope to provide in-service trainings for teachers and other educators, and groups for parents, to make the experience of having a hidden learning disability more understandable and accessible to them.

I would have benefitted greatly from Voice Movement Therapy at the time of my own initial testing which was designed in such a way that, no matter how well I did, it continued until I eventually failed. No matter that the purpose was to determine my highest level of performance in a number of areas, it still felt like failure. This is the way that psychometric testing generally works and it reinforces the negative self-concept of the person being tested. From our point of view, we have been set up to fail, since no explanation is given to us that the point is, actually, to determine the level and extent of disability so that it can be remediated. It is meant to be helpful, not shameful, but that is not how it is usually experienced.

What made me feel unsure and unsafe was that other students often bullied me because I was different, and because I felt inadequate, I couldn't really express what I wanted to say. My tutor, however, figured out HOW I learned and everything that happened in that room during those times enabled me to learn and become more accomplished.

Nothing breeds success like success and nothing fosters success like understanding, one's own and that of other people. I benefitted from ideas and innovations leading up to the "Americans with Disabilities Act" passed when I was in college and got wonderful tutoring from a gifted and inspired Learning Disabilities teacher and excellent instruction from an equally gifted Adaptive Physical Education instructor. I also got a lot of reinforcement along the way from family and friends. However, shame was still a daily companion. As someone whose parents had been told when I was eight years old that I was "not college material," I received first my BA. in Rehabilitation and Conditioning, then my MA in Psychology, and then went on to earn my Ph.D. in Psychology. This kind of success, in whatever field they choose, is what I want for others whom I hope to reach out to and help before they have to endure the shame so many have experienced because of having a hidden learning difference.

Anne: Singing Together

Aside from the use of the physical self to make body percussion, the voice is the only instrument wherein both player and played upon are contained within the same organic form. Located between the head and the heart, it is able, through the words we say and the way we say them, to unite both thought and feeling to express our particular individual selves and to communicate with others. As both a producer and a source of vibrational energy and pulse, encompassing a large range of pitches and a great deal of tonal variety, it can help us connect both oneself to oneself and to other individuals and groups, as well.

Through the act of moving and sounding together in a way that establishes a framework safe enough to encourage exploration and investigation, we can further create a state of entrainment whereby people, through their own tonal and rhythmic activity, come together on an actual physiological level. This has the ability to help us feel and become more aware of what unites rather than what divides us, and how, as human beings, we are more alike than different. It can also, through quiet meditative song, enable us to tune in to the vibrations of our mistreated Earth, the ground that underlies and supports us.

Through its basic principle of action, of taking disagreement and conflict and other forms of disruption or dis-ease "to the floor"–in the privacy of the studio, in workshops and larger groups, perhaps in more public arenas–Voice Movement Therapy aims through an expressive, exploratory and ultimately harmony-seeking process, to resolve incongruities both within the self and between groups. This is a principle held in common with all the Expressive Arts Therapies and the Creative Arts from which they spring.

A teacher I once had at Bennington College, a poet named Ben Bellitt, said, "What great religions and great literature have in common is the ability to contain conflicts within a structure." The Expressive or Creative Arts

Therapies have that capacity, as well. Their aim is to be not reductive but inclusive, helping us to rescue from the shadows neglected or unconscious parts of ourselves that may have great value, in order to integrate them into our being so that they may become not a hindrance, but a help, to us and perhaps to others, too. Voice Movement Therapy has its own principles and practices, its "psychology of song" which can be actualized in its own sphere or adjunctively with other disciplines. In this book, we have endeavored to convey to you a sense of what it is and how it works, through the examples and in the words of some of its practitioners. Before you go, I would ask you to consider all the voices it contains, the ones engaging and the ones being engaged. Wait a moment . . . then imagine us all singing. Together.

Figure 22. VMT Training group and teachers, Marion, Music Hall, Marion, MA, in 2020 just before pandemic closing. March 2020. Photo: Yeyette St. Louis.

GLOSSARY

A GROUP OF VMT-SPECIFIC AND VMT-RELATED TERMS AND THEIR USAGE

Terms Particular to Voice Movement Therapy (VMT)

Voice Movement Therapy (VMT): An expressive or creative arts therapy founded by Paul Newham in the early 1990s based on the extended voicework of Alfred Wolfsohn and Roy Hart and influenced by: Jungian psychology, particularly the practice of Active Imagination and the concepts of Anima and Animus, the Shadow and the principle of Enantiodromia; the body-oriented psychotherapies of Wilhem Reich and Alexander Lowen; and the practice of otolaryngologist Paul Moses in diagnosing physical and psychological conditions by the sounds of the voice.

Voice Movement Therapy Registered Professional Practitioner (VMT-R): To be registered by the International Association for Voice Movement Therapy (IAVMT), a person must have completed a full 2-year approved training, with a supervised internship of 3 individual clients for 20 sessions each and a group of not less than 3 people, for 8 sessions each, plus a short thesis.

Voice Movement Journey: Jung's concept of *Active Imagination* offers the imaginative engagement of images, narratives, and/or personified entities as a bridge between the ego and the unconscious mind. VMT's use of the Voice Movement Journey opens a vista to perceive what is already present by embodying the felt image and bringing it to life through voice and movement.

Core Principles Particular to VMT

(See Chapter One for detailed information)

Vocal Components

1. **Metaphor of the continuous, flexible vocal tube**
2. **The Ten Vocal Components:** Pitch, Pitch Fluctuation, Loudness, Nasality (also known as Forward Pharyngeal Resonance and Bird), Free Air, Glottal Attack or Engagement, Disruption, Articulation, Timbre, and Register.

Non-Vocal Components

Concave/Concave spectrum
The Sphere
The Human /Primate interface
The Four Animals (also known as the Postural Developmental or Animal Cycle)
Movement, Massage, and Compression while the client is moving and sounding.

The Bridge: Viewed generally, and particularly in classical music, as the place where the voice breaks in the transition between Registers, it is seen in VMT as a bridge to both increased pitch range and to the unconscious. Where classical music seeks the *passagio*, the smooth, unbroken passage in transitioning from one vocal Register to another, these "gear changes" (often referred to in this way because they are each produced differently by the vocal mechanism), VMT uses the disruption of sound to probe deeper into the emotions and the unconscious mind, including body memory, through a broader expression of types and qualities of sound.

The Spectrum of Convex and Concave, that all sound and movement are on a spectrum between least and most, can be seen as a practical application of *enantiodromia*, the idea that something when pushed to its extreme turns into its opposite: for example, "I laughed until I cried."

The Sphere, imagined kinesthetically as one's reach space with all parts of the body; psychologically as a kind of portable womb; and energetically and emotionally viewed as "my space" in terms of how large or small it feels at any given moment. Related to the use of the circle as an organizing factor in many disciplines, the difference in VMT is that the sphere is 3-dimensional and derives from the subtle movements of the body when it breathes.

Terms Related to VMT Principles and Practices

Active Imagination: This Jungian concept offers the imaginative engagement of images, narratives, and/or personified entities as a bridge between the ego and the unconscious mind. VMT's use of the Voice Movement Journey (see above) opens a vista to perceive what is already present by embodying the felt image and bringing it to life in voice and movement.

Armouring: The muscular act of holding back emotions is, from a vocal point of view, the most common cause for blockage of the free flow of sound This term and usage originated, in relation to the whole body, from the work of Wilhelm Reich who is generally thought of as the first body psychotherapist.

Catharsis: Freud's concept of the achievement of this state requires that the telling of a traumatic event be imbued with the energy and emotion of the original occurrence if it is to have any curative effect. Paul Newham's psychology of singing takes this notion to its ultimate extreme because: 1) the act of singing amplifies elements of speech (such as dynamics, slowness or speed of execution, range, quality of tone) which makes vocal problems, distinguished as "disconnects" or lack of congruence between what is being said and how it is said, more obvious and available to be worked with, and 2) the purpose of singing is to convey emotion by the feeling tones with which the words are conveyed which means that it is already aligned with Freud's purpose of connecting affect with action.

Enantiodromia: The theory that anything pushed to its extreme will turn into its opposite, for example, "I laughed until I cried."

Entrainment: With regard to Voice Movement Therapy, when one sounds and moves together with one or more people for an extended time, they will come into sync rhythmically and often their heartbeat will adjust to a group rate. This is a major component of *somatic counter-transference* in which the therapist's body as well as their mind gives them knowledge of the emotional state of their client in a physiological way.

The principle of *fascination* is the conception, as first described by Siegfried Bernfeld, that humans, especially children, respond to the sounds and movements of other people by trying to imitate them, for example: a grandmother rounds her mouth at a baby and says "Oh" and the baby first shapes the mouth and then, over time and with repetition, vocalizes that sound. This is not unlike the observation by Paul Moses that audiences and listeners in general will react to what they hear in a singer's or speaker's voice unconsciously, for example: A tenor is singing beautifully but reaches a note where his voice tightens up and the audience will start instinctively to clear its collective throat or cough; or a person will say, "I'm glad to see you," while the tonal message received by the listener is saying, "I can't stand the sight of you." In VMT, the act of making contact with the client through vocalizing in a similar manner can both put the client at ease and give the practitioner an insight into physical and emotional problems the client is having because the practitioner is getting a sense of how they feel in one's own body.

Streaming, the release of energy through the whole body (a Reichian term), is what needs to happen to achieve the free or "unchained" voice.

Subpersonalities: is a concept popularized by John Rowan's book of that name and preceded by Jung's idea of archetypes and other people's notions that the self consists of many separate and distinct parts which may emerge at different times. It can is useful in VMT because by exploring the many different voices that go with these parts or characters, and what their function is in a particular person's life, the individual can enact them fully.

Voice reveals character: The notion that a person's character can be determined by listening to their voice was observed by Alexander Lowen and studied deeply by otolaryngologist Paul Moses who diagnosed vocal conditions by listening to the sounds of a person's voice before observing vocal structures by looking at them.

Vox Humana, originated by Wolfsohn and developed further by Hart, is based on Wolfsohn's battleground experiences of hearing the voice *in extremis*, with a full range of types and qualities of sounds not limited by notions of vocal categories such as tenor and bass. This was further influenced by the Jungian notions of Anima and Animus as applied to the voice, i.e., that the components or qualities of sound in an individual's voice are not limited by an arbitrary division into male and female but contains both, the male having a feminine side or characteristics and the female having a masculine side or characteristics. It is interesting to note that when a person is screaming in agony, it is often hard to know whether that person is male or female just by listening.

Other Terms Used in This Book That May Be Unfamiliar

Adaptive Identity (also false or "as if" self): This is an individual creation by a person attempting to adapt to their life situation or an unreceptive environment in order to survive and to be able to function with others who may perceive that person differently than they perceive themself. For example, someone with dyslexia, often accused of being lazy or stupid, may choose the former, for at least that is voluntary.

Body Mapping: the process of creating body maps using drawing, painting or other art-based techniques to visually represent aspects of people's lives, their bodies, and the world they live in. Body mapping, as generally practiced, originated in South Africa as a therapeutic tool for women living with HIV.

Body-mind Split and Bodymind: The philosophical view, established by Rene Descartes in the 1600s, that the mental and physical parts of us are different, and a more current approach in which they are seen as a single integrated whole. In VMT work, the notion of a split is considered useful in two areas: 1.) dealing with dissociation in instances of trauma (for example, physical or sexual abuse, or responding to emergency situations even while incurring bodily pain and harm) when, in order to survive, the mind ignores what is happening to the body, and 2.) in speaking or singing, when the words a person is using to describe what they are thinking or feeling is not congruent with the tones of voice in which they are being uttered.

Cerebellar Ataxia: A condition in which the nerves of the cerebellum which regulate balance and swallowing and other automatic bodily functions degenerate. As the disease progresses, the person loses the ability to move in a balanced way, to talk, walk, speak intelligibly, or swallow, becoming increasingly dysfunctional.

Cri du chat (sp5-syndrome): A congenital defect in which the person is born with a long, narrow body, long face, low-slung ears, and extremely tight muscles, making it difficult to both walk and talk. It is sometimes accompanied by retardation, but not always, the deficits observed in the person being not only a difficulty in controlling their body, but also great difficulty in communicating because of the rigidity of the facial, chest and abdominal muscles.

Dyslexia: A difficulty distinguishing and manipulating symbols for both reading and writing.

Devised Theatre, often referred to as collaborative creation: A process in which the performance score originates from the collaborative improvisatory work of two or more people. The improvising in this devising process happens mostly in its creation, as it usually has at least a partially fixed form by the time it is presented.

Dissociation: The separation of something meant to be a whole into two distinct parts. In dissociative disorders, this refers to a disconnection between one's sensory experience, sense of self, or personal history.

Dyspraxia: A condition of the central nervous system that often makes people tactily defensive, with difficulty locating themselves in space, and extremely mood as well as body-sensitive.

Echo-location: The ability to navigate in the physical world by bouncing sound off objects to know where they are and what they might be; for example: bats and whales navigate by echolocation.

Hidden Learning Disabilities: Whereas a learning disability associated with more profound special needs refers to a difficulty in learning or understanding things or in managing everyday activities and becomes apparent very quickly, usually due to a limited cognitive capacity, a hidden disability is not readily apparent. For example, although a person with dyslexia may express themselves extremely well verbally, and have an average to very high I.Q., they may have an extremely difficult time learning to read and write; or a person with executive function deficit will be hindered in their ability to process information efficiently which may affect their ability to manage their own thoughts, emotions, or activities.

Imaginal Psychology: As taught and practiced by Aftab Omer in his graduate program at Meridian University, Petaluma, CA, its purpose is to enable the student or client to find their real self as opposed to the adaptive identity they may have been forced to create due to their life circumstances or environment, in order to find their "soul's passion" or purpose in life. In *Reimagining Psychology* and *The Soul's Code*, James Hillman was intent on re-imagining and redefining psychology as a soul-based quest deriving from Jung's use of image, archetypes, dreams and other imaginative forms to investigate the unconscious mind.

Indaba: a form of meeting in S. Africa where people come together with as open a mind and heart as they can manage and no pre-conceived idea of where they want to go, but a willingness to explore, to hear everyone, and to trust that, at some point, they will meet and discover a common purpose.

Non-governmental Organization (NGO): This is different from a private charity in that is linked to the government and derives some benefit from it while being relatively independent and non-partisan,

Non-suicidal Self-injury (NSSI): The *Statistical and Diagnostic Manual of Mental Disorders (DSM-5)* defines it as the deliberate, self-inflicted destruction of body tissue without suicidal intent and includes behaviors such as cutting, burning, biting, and scratching one's skin, which begins with the overwhelming impulse to injure oneself, an increasing build-up of tension before the act, and a feeling of release/relief at its completion but then begins again.

Orton-Gillingham: A structured approach to gaining literacy, especially for people with dyslexia and other hidden learning disabilities, which breaks reading and writing, especially spelling, down into smaller skills involving letters and sounds, and then builds on these skills over time.

Ostinato: A continually repeated musical phrase or rhythm.

Pacinian Corpuscles: Encapsulated ending of a sensory nerve that acts as a receptor for pressure and vibration.

Passaggio: The smooth, unbroken passage in transitioning from one vocal Register to another to create a beautiful seamless sound.

Sangoma: A traditional medicine woman in Xhosa culture.

Shamanism: A shaman is both a teacher and a medicine man, and in many cultures an inspired priest with a particular way of relating to nature and to human nature for the benefit of the tribe or group.

Shadow: According to C.G. Jung, that part of one's psyche that contains all manner of capacities and potential that if simply denied, not recognized and owned, can lead to the impoverishment of one's personality and energy and also to the loss of a bridge of connectedness to others.

Tardive Dyskinesia: Involuntary movements, especially but not entirely limited to the mouth and jaw, which can be caused by alcoholism, psychotropic medications and certain anti-nausea medications, which block dopamine receptors in the brain.

Triple Goddess: In many mythologies, this tripartite goddess contains within herself the 3 main faces of womankind: the Maiden, the Young Woman, and the Old Woman: or Crone.

Vagus Nerve, also known as the vagal nerves: The main nerves of your parasympathetic nervous system. This system controls specific body functions such as digestion, heart rate, and immune system. These functions are involuntary, meaning you can't consciously control them.

Vocal Folds: a different term for vocal cords.

Xhosa: A South African tribe or indigenous group. Nelson Mandela was Xhosa.

CONTRIBUTORS

SEBASTIANA BLACK, Dip. BACP, MSCT, VMT-R (UK, Czechia), is an integrative arts counis an integrative arts counsellor, a Mindful Self-Compassion teacher, and a singer-songwriter. She facilitates workshops and retreats in Norwich and the Czech Republic, works with drama and dance movement therapy students at the Universities of East Anglia and Derby, and conducts a private practice. She finds that vocal expression in an attentive, non-judgmental atmosphere encourages clients to give voice to and transform trauma, increasing self-regulation, creativity and wisdom. Sebastiana also co-facilitates Mindfulness and Nature retreats with her partner Rob, nourishing a deeper intimacy with the natural world. She sang in the award-winning short film *Malka*, loves bringing world music to audiences with her cèilidh and concert band *Zaramo*, and has recorded two albums including original songs with her duet, *Fire Doves. expressivevoicevmt@gmail.com*

ANNE BROWNELL, MA, RSA, VMT-R (USA), is Executive Director of the Norma G. Canner Foundation for VMT, a not-for-profit school conducting full trainings, short courses and projects in the USA and abroad. After working with pioneer dance therapist Norma Canner and noted clinician and author Penny Lewis, Anne's search for the vocal component for a movement-oriented therapy led her to be the first American to train in London with founder Paul Newham, teach and supervise with him in England and America, and in 2001 establish her own training program in the United States and then in South Africa. Her video, *VMT Virtually? Working through a Pandemic* (YouTube) illustrates how she and her training group and teachers continued to work on-line till Oct. 2021when they reconvened in person for a month-long intensive module to complete this program. Anne has been a consultant for schools with children experiencing developmental and language delays, taught the first for-credit graduate course in VMT in the USA, conducts a private practice, and presents at conferences at home and abroad. Prior experience includes working in Early Intervention, supervising graduate students in Dance Therapy on the therapeutic use of the voice, and conducting music and movement groups for previously homeless and substance abused people with HIV and AIDS. She is a founding member of the IAVMT and has served as scriptwriter and executive producer on several films by her son Ian Brownell about the Expressive Therapies, notably *A Time to Dance: The Life and Work of Norma Canner and Going to the Source: A Study of Group Process in the Natural World.* Her CD, *A Journey in Song,* illustrates a range of possibilities inherent in a single human voice and she delights in performing songs in different genres. She and her daughter Deirdre recently moved to Wareham, MA where they are starting a practice with individuals with hidden learning disabilities and others seeking personal growth and inspiration through the voice. *vmtusa@aol.com*

DEIRDRE BROWNELL, MA, PhD, VMT-R (USA), is a singer as well as a scholar and believes that music has a language all its own that everyone can understand somatically and spiritually, if not cognitively. She began assisting in Step One Early Intervention at age 12, and since she was too young to be paid, the staff (especially the PT and SLP) taught her, instead. She has a BA in Reconditioning and Fitness, and a Master's and PhD in Psychology from Meridian University in California where she received a strong grounding in Imaginal Psychology. After training in South Africa, she interned there at a school for children with cognitive and physical delays. Her dissertation is about healing the loss of the embodied voice in people with hidden learning differences. Deirdre is dedicated to working with anyone struggling with a difference from the norm which sets them apart and causes them to feel misunderstood and "voiceless." She loves to sing and has recorded one album, *Evolution. dbdc125731@aol.com*

GERTRUIDA DOWSE, BA (hons), SW, Dipl. Play-Therapy and Marriage Counselling and Preparation, VMT-R, is both a Life and Wellness Coach in Oudtshoorn, South Africa, offering both online and actual therapy sessions for individuals, couples and groups, and a formal Mediator and works with clients to confront and reconcile differences, using VMT to help them become more aware of their own feelings in order to understand the other person better and find a meeting point for cooperation. Gertruida is a former director and trainer of FAMSA Karoo, an affiliate for ICAS, LifeAssist Metropolitan, and a network provider for Universal Care, focusing on Employment Wellness programs and trainings and supporting professionals to cope with stress, anger and life demands. Outside the office, Gertruida loves to work in her garden and walk in the fields. She particularly enjoys entertaining others with her husband Steven in their cozy home. *gerdvmt@gmail.com*

ANNA GRABNER, MA, VMT-R, is a singer and psychologist who combines creative and therapeutic work through VMT. After training in South Africa in 2012, she moved to Portugal where she offers individual sessions and groups, in-person and on-line, and facilitates retreats and workshops indoors and in nature. Her fascination for vocal improvisation has led her to participate in and facilitate acapella groups where people can connect through simple meditative song, and to collaborate with massage and music therapists offering Healing Sound Massage. Since becoming a mother, she has accompanied women in exploring their maternal voice in relation to their changing body to help them feel more empowered for labour and postpartum recovery. She also co-organizes sisterhood circles, inviting women to reflect on self-care and share and express themselves through song and dance. *anna@yourvoicemoves.com*

CAROL GRIMES, VMT-R, is a British singer, songwriter, poet, blogger, teacher, and author of a memoir, *The Singer's Tale.* Beginning as a busker on the streets, she came to public attention when she joined the band *Delivery* and recorded an album with them before departing on a solo career and creating an extremely large discography. After performing and recording in the UK, USA, Sweden, Jura and Poland, she became angry at the injustice, cruelty and poverty she witnessed around her and became an activist. The first musician to step up for Rock Against Racism, she sang also for striking miners, the fire service, and refugee centers. For many years, she conducted the *Sing for Joy Choir* for people with Parkinson's and other neurological conditions. She toured with Orlando Gough's *The Shout* for 12 years; has performed at the Royal Albert Hall as well as Ronnie Scott's and many other well-known jazz clubs; conducted workshops for teens with behavior disorders for the Prince's Trust; taught rock, pop, soul, blues and jazz at the City Lit in Central London; and loves to write. *carol@carolgrimes.com*

EVA HAIDL, VMT-R (Austria), is a singer, songwriter and musician who studied Jazz at the University of Performing Arts in Graz as well as at the Guildhall School for Music and Drama in London. Eva's search for authenticity as a singer and voice teacher led her to the VMT training in America in 2004 and to work with patients at the Jules Thorn Mental Health Day Care Centre in London in her practice year, becoming a certified VMT practitioner in 2007. She was invited by Anne Brownell and Christine Isherwood to be the first apprentice teacher on the VMT training, then located in Martha's Vineyard, MA, and served for three years as a director of the IAVMT. In her private practice as a teacher of singing, she encourages personal expression through the voice, Eva has been working with beginners and professional singers of all ages for over 15 years. For the past 6 years she has focused extensively on leading group workshops in VMT and Gospel and World Music in Austria, Germany and Italy, and was a senior teacher for the Max Reinhardt Seminar at the Drama Department of the Vienna Music University. *eva@voicemovement.at*

MELANIE HARROLD, VMT-R, Certified Body Psychotherapist (UK), worked as a professional singer/songwriter, recording artist, band member, and touring musician for twenty years and currently performs and tours with the group, Daphne's Flight. For the last ten years she has been teaching singing while engaged in extensive experiential research into the connections between vocal expression, movement and psychotherapeutic process. She trained in Voice Movement Therapy in 1993 with founder Paul Newham and has been a regular guest teacher on subsequent trainings with Anne Brownell in the US and S. Africa, teaching also at the Apollo School in Beijing, China. As well as practicing as a Body Psychotherapist, she teaches singing to large groups, works with individuals from her home, and leads therapeutically based voice workshops in the UK and abroad, teaching voice and movement with The National Youth Theatre and The Circus Space, and has run a twice-weekly singing class at the Horniman Museum in London. She is a Founding director of the IAVMT. *kathryn_melanie@hotmail.com*

CHRISTINE ISHERWOOD, MA, VMT-R, REAT, USA/UK singer/songwriter, directs and teaches the Voice Movement Therapy Training Program, works with individual clients, conducts workshops and trainings internationally, and supervises VMT students and practitioners. She has been engaged in teaching VMT internationally for more than twenty years in the UK, USA, Europe, Asia, and Australia. She trained and then taught with founder of VMT Paul Newham in London in the mid-1990s. In partnership with Anne Brownell, she co-taught the Norma Canner Foundation Training for many years and is now its director. She also founded the first VMT Training Program in Beijing, China under the auspices of Apollo Education and Consulting. Prior to VMT, she earned a degree in Cultural Studies at the University of East London, UK, a Diploma as an Assertiveness Training Teacher with the Redwood Women's Training Organization, did a two-year training in Humanistic and Transpersonal Psychotherapy, and studied therapeutic healing with noted eclectic healers. She has over thirty years' experience working with street homeless people in Central London; as a mental health counsellor in the fields of addiction, domestic abuse, sexuality and gender; as a group facilitator and trainer; and as a VMT practitioner with those seeking to transform themselves through the voice. A founding director of the IAVMT, her MA is in Clinical Mental Health Counselling and she holds a Certificate in Traumatic Stress Studies. Christine has written and performed in political musicals, toured the UK and Europe with theatre groups and bands, and recorded as a pop singer. She has lectured and taught at Liverpool Institute for the Performing Arts (LIPA); the Western Australian Academy for Performing Arts (WAAPA); and has been adjunct faculty at the Creative Integrative Expressive Arts Therapy Training Program (CREATE),

Toronto, Canada. Christine continues to commit herself to an intensive exploration of VMT and the voice, to learn and to write. She currently lives in Boston, MA. *singingthepsyche@vmtuk.com*

BONISWA KAMBA, Rev., VMT-R (Port Elizabeth, South Africa), is a mother of three grown daughters and two sons. As a Reverend, Boniswa currently ministers at Ntabakandoda Circuit at Kwa-Komani District in the Eastern Cape under the leadership of UMCOSA (the United Methodist Church of Southern Africa). She is a qualified counsellor and trainer who has worked for 13 years in the diocese of the Port Elizabeth Anglican Church, helping people to develop life skills and providing therapeutic counselling to traumatized women and children. Between 2009 and 2012, Boniswa worked with WAWA (Women Against Woman Abuse) providing counselling to victims of gender-based violence and human trafficking, and in 2014 began working with small groups and individuals focusing on developing and strengthening family bonds. Boniswa trained in VMT in Oudtshoorn South Africa, qualifying as a registered professional practitioner in 2013. She is dedicated to the work of VMT and has established the registered not-for-profit organization Voice Movement Therapy Eastern Cape (VMTEC) endorsed by the National Department of Social Development. Boniswa was invited to Parliament to present a statement on the challenges faced by communities in the Eastern Cape and was instrumental in submitting the Women Empowerment and Gender Equality Bill, incorporating several key VMT principles. Boni also works with the Department of Transport, facilitating VMT-based workshops on depression, stress and anger in the workplace, and volunteers at the Educational Support Services Trust in collaboration with the Health Department, promoting good health within communities, with a focus on children pre-birth to 19 years, also using VMT principles. *bonikamba@gmail.com*

IRENE KESSLER, MA, PhD (FL, USA, born in NYC), was an opera singer for many years, performing minor roles at the New York City Opera, the Metropolitan Opera, and Teatro Principale in Barcelona, Spain. Becoming increasingly interested in the use of voice in therapy, she earned her MA, moved to Boca Raton, FL and became an eating disorders specialist. Completing her PhD in 1997 while qualifying in VMT with Paul Newham and Anne Brownell in Somerville, MA, she went on to work at the Radar Institute and the Renfrew Center. In practice for over 30 years, she also sang in a local quartet that performed opera, operetta and Broadway tunes, continuing to sing until her death a few years ago.

ANNE MAARMAN, VMT-R, Born in Northern S. Africa, she has lived most of her life in George. Pastoral Counselor and former nurse, she focuses on helping stroke patients and those recovering from long Covid, using VMT principles and practices. Through singing, massage and breathing together, she helps patients to fight their way back to health through the long emotional and spiritual as well as physical process of coming out of a coma or other significant state of illness to find themselves again. Anne works alongside other therapists to provide safety to her clients and support to their families, assisting them through the depression that comes with experiencing a stroke or other protracted and profound illness. Aside from her work as a pastor and a VMT practitioner with both individuals and groups, Anne is a highly sought motivational speaker. *annerossvmtsa@gmail.com*

SOPHIE MARTIN, MA, VMT-R (Australia), has worked as a Voice Movement Therapy Practitioner since completing her qualification in 2010. She holds a Master's in Creative Arts focusing on the healing of trauma through voice and theatre. Her passion and belief in the power of the voice to transform and heal has taken her to work in many places with people living "on the edge" in terms of physical and/or emotional survival: a major slum in Nairobi, a detention camp on Nauru, under-served aboriginal communities in Darwin, and young people who self-harm in Sydney, writing the first study using VMT in hospital with a particular population which was then published in a psychological journal. From remote communities to major cities, Sophie has worked to empower people by helping them find their actual physical as well as their metaphorical voice. Sophie lives in Perth and holds workshops and individual sessions online and in person. In 2020, she became the mother of her first baby girl which made her passionate about working with other mothers and children on attachment and gentle parenting through voice and song. *sophie@vmtoceania.com*

NOKUBONGA CORDELIA MATHOLE, VMT-R (Port Elizabeth, South Africa), completed her experiential training in Oudtshoorn, S. Africa in 2012 and qualified as a professional practitioner soon after. Her background includes advanced administrative skills in asset-based citizen-led development, soccer cinema screening programs, and program development and communication with funders. Training in VMT was a new departure from her business work and led to her involvement in action-based programs on Gender Based Violence (GBV) and its connection to HIV/Aids in young people. Nokubonga has also established her own NGO, VMT South Africa (VMTSA), and works individually and with groups. A mother of 4 children, she has recently moved back from the small town of Peddie to Port Elizabeth where she is extending her NGO services, focusing her VMT work on GBV and HIV/Aids. As a domestic violence survivor herself, she actively encourages storytelling and songwriting. She is passionate about women who have incurred emotional problems from great suffering and is eager to engage them in the transitional process of gaining greater control of their lives. *ncmathole@gmail.com*

GINA HOLLOWAY MULDER, MA, BADA (hons.), PGDA, MAP, VMT-R (Durban, S. Africa), has been facilitating personal and corporate communication, self-cultivation, creativity and performance development through voice and movement work since 1999, incorporating Voice Movement Therapy into her practice since 2007. She trained in VMT in the USA and was the first South African to qualify as a professional practitioner. Gina practices at her private studio in the Springside Nature Reserve located in Kwa Zulu Natal, offering individual, couples, and group sessions and workshops, and 5-7 day private retreats to local and international clients. Through Voice 360, she develops VMT-informed training programs and interventions for individuals and teams at different organizational levels. With a background in physical theatre and a passion for choreography, she focuses her creative work on integrating voice, body, and psyche for devised interactive theatre. She is committed to growing the practice of VMT in South Africa and globally, and has run multiple workshops in therapeutic, academic, and corporate contexts in both South Africa and Malaysia. She has lectured in VMT, including at South African universities. Gina is passionate about the relationship between recent neurological discoveries and the work of VMT and is interested in researching and writing about that connection. *gina@voicemovementtherapy.co.za*

JULIA NORTON (San Francisco Bay Area, California) is a singer, actor, and voice coach with over 25 years' experience teaching people how to enjoy a free and healthy voice. Born in the UK, she has been singing her whole life and teaching groups to sing since she was 18. Always compelled to understand more about the emotional story behind a singer's experience, she discovered Voice Movement Therapy in 1998 before qualifying as a registered practitioner and moving to San Francisco in 2000. Since then, she has composed music for theatre and circus, directed, and produced an award-winning album, *Lullaby Island*, performed jazz and musical theatre, and trained as a voice actor. She was a teaching artist for the San Francisco Opera Guild and Summer Conservatory and has presented at conferences around the world, teaching therapists, dancers, and expressive artists how to use their voices to free their emotions and creative talents, and was a former director of the International Association for Voice Movement Therapy. In 2018 she won a Voice Arts Award for her role in Disney's Star Wars game *Jedi Challenges* and launched her popular podcast "Dark and Twisty Tales," available on iTunes. She currently divides her time between teaching, acting, singing and "getting up to stuff" with her family and noisy terrier. Julia is passionate about helping people discover a free, connected, and healthy voice. *voicework@julianorton.com*

VERONICA PHILLIPS, BACP, VMT-R (London, UK), has a background in teaching dance, drama, and special needs. She trained in VMT with founder Paul Newham in 1998-2000 and then in integrative, psychodynamic psychotherapy. Combining the two, Veronica's work can emphasize moving fully into the expressive, creative self-development path of VMT or into more analytically attuned relational psychotherapy, her focus emerging from the client's wishes and needs and the two disciplines meeting in attention to breath and body. Veronica is also a trained Supervisor through CSTD (Centre for Supervision and Team Development). Her work with VMT, both individual and group, invites anyone to seek out, explore, and express their unique, authentic self and develop true autonomy. Workshops include Singing for the Timid and Terrified and Stories for Self-Exploration and Transformation, influenced by subtle energy work and shamanic practices. Integrated into her work is a sound knowledge and personal experience of emotional/developmental trauma, as well as the experience of and empathy with the shock, destabilization and deep grief of sudden trauma. Much of her understanding is based on a clear awareness of attachment needs, and generational and ancestral constellation work. She served on the board of IAVMT for many years. *veronicavmt@hotmail.co.uk*

MALI SASTRI, VMT-R (USA) singer-songwriter and band leader, is a Registered Voice Movement Therapy practitioner based in Boston, MA. She trained with founder Paul Newham, Anne Brownell and Christine Isherwood in London, UK from 1999–2001. For the past eleven years, Mali has worked with individuals and groups, primarily in the Boston area, and since 2012 has been part of the music education program at Tunefoolery, a Boston non-profit for musicians in mental health recovery. Mali's work rides the edge between artistic and therapeutic practice, with an emphasis on breath and the song-as-container. Performing often with her band *Jaggery*, she is a singer, songwriter, composer, performer, and artist/practitioner—a forever student and lover of voice. *mali@jaggery.org*

STARREVELD, TRACY, VMT-R, is a UK-based certified proofreader and copyeditor. She trained in VMT on Martha's Vineyard in 2002 and did her internship at an elementary school in Vermont, including working imaginatively and effectively with a young child with selective mutism. Always fascinated by people's stories and with a background in creative performance and personal growth, in addition to working as a practitioner. Having qualified with Chapterhouse Publishing, she specializes in supporting creatives, coaches, therapists, bodyworkers, teachers and health practitioners to express themselves through written content. For web copy, social media posts, newsletters, blogs or e-books, she helps her clients tell their own unique stories through concise and compelling copy that communicates exactly who they are and what they do. She continues to express herself through audible blog stories, mainly anecdotal pieces focused on personal growth and well-being. *info@starreveld.com*

BEN VAN RENSBURG, VMTR, Certified Addictions Counsellor (Cape Town, S. Africa), found VMT and felt it was made for him. Starting to use aspects of it in his work at a residential addictions clinic where it was soon incorporated into the regular program in two weekly groups, as well as in his work with individual patients, he also assisted on the second VMT Training in South Africa and established and maintained his own practice. His untimely death in his early 40s left a big hole, as he was greatly loved by all who knew him.

LERINA VAN RENSBURG, SDCSA, VMT-R, Postgraduate Education Certificate (Unisa), Level 6 Teachers Licentiate and Vocal and Theory Gr. 8 (Rockschool), Vocal Gr. 8 (Trinity), Music Theory Gr. 6 (Trinity), Performance Certificates in Folk Singing and Vocals (JAM), Digital Music Production (Emendy), Short Course in Management and Marketing for the Music Industry (Pretoria, S. Africa) has been entertaining audiences from a young age. Her teaching experience ranges from London-based schools such as CHIMS (Courtney House Instrumental Music School) and heading up the Music Department of Pretoria-East Primary. In 2005, Lerina founded Vibrience Music Notes where she has not only been teaching Vocals and Guitar but also steering the music academy into a flourishing business. In 2016, she launched a second music school, Ovie-Vibz, with 14 teachers in its employ and still growing. Lerina's teaching philosophy is based on exploring voice and enabling every student to have the freedom to express themselves through their voice and to experience it it fully. In 2022 Lerina designed and built a hall near Pretoria primarily for VMT trainings. The next Norma Canner Foundation Training will take place in 2024 at the VoiceBox where she will not only administrate, but assist on the Training. *lerina@thevoicebox.co.za*

TRISH WATTS, Dip. M.Ed, VMT-R, singer/songwriter (Australia), believes passionately that "Every life can SING!" She was pelted into her own life by the singing of the village church choir & instilled with a dream that singing is a way of life and a medicine for all. Trish trained with the Norma Canner Foundation Training, Martha's Vineyard, MA, USA and has a private practice in Sydney, Australia. Her love of travel and different cultures led her to facilitate VMT workshops and courses in India, Cambodia & New Zealand and, closer to home, to offer vocal programs to Afghani and Iranian women as a volunteer for STARTTS (Service for the Treatment and Rehabilitation of Torture & Trauma Survivors) in Sydney. Trish co-founded Willow Publishing & is a successful songwriter and recording artist with over 10 CD collections of original work. She has a Diploma in Music Education and is an accredited Singing & Piano teacher with the NSW Conservatorium of Music. Directing acapella choirs is part of her life-blood. Choirs include *Colla Voce*, a vocal multi-cultural ensemble; the *Sydney and Cambodian Threshold Choirs* (singers who sing beside bedsides in palliative care and recovery); & the *Music Arts School Community Choir of Phnom Penh*. She sang with the woman's *Crocus Quartet* and *Café of the Gate of Salvation Gospel Choir*. For the past 40 years, Trish has worked as a freelance artist, workshop & retreat facilitator, affording her the freedom of a creative path. She has a strong grounding in sacred, spirited communal song. Her winding path has taken her around Australia and overseas to the UK, Europe, USA, India, South Africa, New Zealand. More recently, Trish lived in Phnom Penh, 2015-17 & co-founded Cambodia Sings, a not-for-profit organization to "rekindle the love of singing for all Cambodians." She is a trained InterPlay facilitator (an improvisation-based community arts practice), and co-founded InterPlay Australia over 25 years ago. Anchored in the bedrock of play, her VMT work combines its essence with a deeply spiritual sensibility. *trish@vmtoceania.com*

HELEN WHITE, CPRP, VMT-R, has been a mental health professional for over twenty years, working primarily with people with major mental illness. Helen's passion for psychiatric rehabilitation led her to begin her training in Voice Movement Therapy in 2008. She has witnessed VMT's ability to empower a person through their voice, resulting in greater self-confidence and self-esteem. Helen is a Certified Psychiatric Rehabilitation Practitioner using VMT in her clinical practice. She has presented her expressive arts initiative, Voice Studio – group work that she has done with persons with psychiatric disability – at several psychiatric rehabilitation conferences. In her private life, Helen enjoys voice coaching, and singing and dancing in her community, as well as working with individual VMT clients. She lives in Ottawa, Canada, and has two daughters and four grandchildren. *recoverydiscovery@vmt.ca*

NAME INDEX

A

Alta du Toit School, 114-116, 122
Artaud, Antonin, 10, 201

B

Brook, Peter, 10, 201

C

Canner, Norma, xvi, xvii, 24, 29-31, 267
Carlington Assertive Community Treatment Program (ACT), Ottawa, CA, 79, 81-82
Chodorow, Joan, 11, 172, 177

D

Damasio, Antonio, 13, 30-31
Descartes, Rene, 13
Dychtwald, Ken, 13, 30

F

Freeman, William C., 113, 128, 129, 134-135
Freud, Sigmund, 5

G

Gilligan, Carol, 106
Grotowski, Jerzy, 10, 201

H

Hart, Roy, xvi, xx, 6, 9-10, 30-32, 201
Healing Hand Project, 46
Hidden Voices of Cambodia, 34, 36, 43
Hillman, James, 13, 282

J

Jung, Carl, 7, 29, 31, 169

K

Khmer, 37, 39, 40-42, 44-45
Kibera slum, 47

L

Lewis, Penny Bernstein, 11
Liger leadership Academy, 40, 42-3
Lowen, Alexander, 4, 12, 29, 31, 212, 219

M

Max Reinhardt Seminar, 227
McMillan, Barclay, 79
McNiff, Shaun, 13, 29
Meanwood Park Hospital, 62
Mondil, Kiri, 42
Moses, Paul, 16, 31

N

Nauru, xii, 34, 45, 50-3
Newham, Paul, xv, xvi, xx, 3, 10, 29, 30, 75, 79, 83, 90, 139, 173, 176-7, 201, 203, 213, 216, 277, 279, 285, 288-289, 292

O

Omer, Aftab, 25, 30, 282

P

Pardo, Enrique, 10
Paxton, Steve, 11
Pyramid of Arts, Leeds, UK, 62

R

Reich, Wilhelm, 11, 212

S

Serenity Prayer (orig. Prayer of St. Francis), 99
Sing for Joy Choir, 68, 146-248
Singing Cure (The), xvi, 3, 10, 13, 15-6, 30-32, 75

T

Temple, Nina, 146-147
Threshold Choir, 36, 39, 40, 166
Theatre without Words, 10, 15
Triple Goddess, 194, 197
Tripoliti, Elina, 147

W

Wolfsohn, Alfred, xv, xx, 4, 155, 201, 216, 272, 277

X

Xhosa, 247, 272, 282-283

SUBJECT INDEX

A

Active Imagination, 7, 26, 28, 87,169, 182, 193, 194, 199, 225, 243
adaptive identity (*see also* false or "as if" self), 25, 111-112
ADHD, 28, 124
alexithymia, 92
arpeggio, 195
alternating strabismus, 108
Anima and Animus, 7
Animal Postures (Postural Cycle), 22-23
Armouring (character), 12
auditory processing disorder, 108
ataxia, cerebellar, 131

B

Bel Canto, 5, 11
Bioenergetics, 12, 212
blending (in singing), 20-21, 95, 164
body mapping, 96
body memory, 111
bodymind (and body-mind split), 13, 30, 151, 182, 236, 263-264, 281
break (in singing), 20, 164, 204
bridge (in VMT) - *see* Break, 14, 20, 25

C

catharsis, role of voice in, 14, 207
congruence (of thought and feeling) as applied to VMT, 13, 34, 155
congruent, 6, 13, 274
contact improvisation, 11
core principles of VMT, vocal and non-vocal, 13, 17, 24, 28-29, 191, 195
cri du chat (*see also* 5P- syndrome), 114, 119

D

devised theatre, 203, 236-237, 240
dissociation, 13
dyslexia, 25, 28, 108-109, 273
dyspraxia, 28, 108, 273

E

echolocation, 281
Enantiodromia, 6
entrainment, 275
esophagus, 18, 216
extended voicework, xx

H

Hidden Learning Disabilities, 273-274

I

iliopsoas muscles, 212
Imaginal Psychology, 25, 111-112
Indaba, 246-248, 266

L

Larynx, 18, 27, 210-211, 214, 216

M

M.E. (known in US as chronic fatigue syndrome, CFS), 147
metaphor of continuous flexible vocal tube (also extended vocal tube), 18, 28, 187, 202
mind-body split (*see* bodymind), 13, 30, 151, 182, 236, 263-264, 281

N

non-suicidal self-injury (NSSI), 90-91, 94
Non-Vocal Components, 21, 46, 96, 144, 153, 163, 261

O

Ostinato, 167
Otolaryngologist, 16

P

Pacinian corpuscles, 14, 30
Passagio (in singing), 20
parasympathetic nervous system, 212
Parkinson's Disease (PD), 68, 113, 146, 148-149
performance art, 236
personal song, 26, 34, 153
pharynx, 18, 216
physical theatre, 236-237

S

Sangoma, 246-247
selective mutism, 113, 134, 137
Shadow, 4, 7-8, 15-17, 23, 38, 61, 96, 99, 153, 155, 159, 162, 171-177, 192, 202, 205-206, 236
Shamanic, 153, 190, 193, 196, 282
soma, 13
somatic countertransference, 126
Streaming, 12
Subpersonality, 110-111, 137, 154-155, 157, 159, 161, 174, 237-238, 244

T

talking cure, 15
tardive dyskinesia, 132

V

vagus nerve, 30, 216, 187
vibrato, 19, 216, 264
Vocal Components, 19, 26, 28, 40, 92, 153, 155, 159-160, 163, 165, 187, 196, 203, 208, 221, 224, 226, 233-234, 240, 243-244, 261, 263-264
vocal folds (cords), 27, 187, 210, 214
Voice Movement Journey (*see* Glossary)
vox humana (*see* Glossary)